Encyclopedia of Reptiles and Amphibians

By John F. Breen

Distributed in the U.S.A. by T.F.H. Publications, Inc., 211 West Sylvania Avenue, P.O. Box 27, Neptune City, N.J. 07753; in England by T.F.H. (Gt. Britain) Ltd., 13 Nutley Lane, Reigate, Surrey; in Canada to the book store and library trade by Clarke, Irwin & Company, Clarwin House, 791 St. Clair Avenue West, Toronto 10, Ontario; in Canada to the pet trade by Rolf C. Hagen Ltd., 3225 Sartelon Street, Montreal 382, Quebec; in Southeast Asia by Y.W. Ong, 9 Lorong 36 Geylang, Singapore 14; in Australia and the south Pacific by Pet Imports Pty. Ltd., P.O. Box 149, Brookvale 2100, N.S.W., Australia. Published by T.F.H. Publications, Inc. Ltd., The British Crown Colony of Hong Kong.

Frontispiece:
African treefrog, *Hyperolius* sp., a member of the large African and Asian family Rhacophoridae, related to the ranids. Photo by Van Raam.

ISBN 0-8766-220-3

TO

MARY E. DONOVAN

Contents

FAMILY IGUANIDAE
Knight Anole . . . Iguanas . . . Basilisks . . . Miscellaneous
Iguanids
FAMILY CHAMAELEONIDAE
FAMILY CORDYLIDAE
FAMILY TEIIDAE
FAMILY LACERTIDAE
FAMILY GERRHOSAURIDAE
FAMILY SCINCIDAE
FAMILY ANGUIDAE
FAMILY VARANIDAE
FAMILY AMPHISBAENIDAE
THE TUATARA

Preface

In the past two decades the interest in reptiles and amphibians has increased tremendously. The literature relating to the natural history and care of these fascinating creatures has hardly kept pace with the quest for knowledge. In 1967 alone, according to U.S. Fish and Wildlife Service figures, the United States imported 405,134 reptiles and 137,697 amphibians. Additional millions of individuals of native species were bought and sold. Specific information on the various individual reptile and amphibian species has been scattered, and in the past it has often been necessary to consult many books and pamphlets in order to acquire some piece of basic information. Clearly, there existed the need to bring under one cover a complete account of the many reptiles and amphibians that are commonly available.

The primary function of this book is to give the reader the necessary knowledge for the keeping of reptiles and amphibians alive and in good health in captivity. Secondarily, it is a general survey of the herptiles of the world that should prove useful to those who do not keep live specimens but nevertheless have a desire to learn more about them.

I would like to take this opportunity to thank the many workers in the field of herpetology who have gladly shared their experiences with me. Thanks are due S. N. F. Sanford and Alice Kendall for their valuable counseling. A special note of thanks to Glen G. Gowen, a keen young herpetologist who has assisted in many ways. Finally, I want to thank my mother, who withstood the growing pains of an aspiring herpetologist, and my wife, who many times set aside personal interests to further the present study.

John F. Breen

CLASSIFICATION OF THE
LIVING REPTILES AND AMPHIBIANS

according to Mertens, 1960.

AMPHIBIA
Caudata; Newts and Salamanders

1. Hynobiidae.
2. Cryptobranchidae.
3. Ambystomatidae.
4. Salamandridae.
5. Plethodontidae.
6. Amphiumidae
7. Proteidae.
8. Sirenidae.

Salientia; Frogs and Toads

1. Ascaphidae.
2. Discoglossidae.
3. Pipidae.
4. Pelobatidae.
5. Leptodactylidae.
6. Bufonidae.
7. Rhinophrynidae.
8. Brachycephalidae.
9. Hylidae.
10. Ranidae.
11. Rhacophoridae.
12. Microhylidae.

Gymnophiona; Caecilians
1. Caeciliidae.

REPTILIA
Testudines; Turtles and Tortoises

1. Cheloniidae.
2. Dermochelyidae.
3. Chelydridae.
4. Kinosternidae.
5. Platysternidae.
6. Dermatemydidae.
7. Emydidae.
8. Testudinidae.
9. Carettochelyidae.
10. Trionychidae.
11. Pelomedusidae.
12. Chelidae.

Crocodylia; Alligators and Crocodiles

1. Alligatoridae.
2. Crocodylidae.
3. Gavialidae.

Rhynchocephalia; Tuataras

1. Sphenodontidae.

Sauria; Lizards

1. Gekkonidae.
2. Pygopodidae.
3. Agamidae.
4. Chamaeleonidae.
5. Iguanidae.
6. Xantusiidae.
7. Cordylidae.
8. Teiidae.
9. Lacertidae.
10. Scincidae.
11. Dibamidae.
12. Anguidae.
13. Anniellidae.
14. Xenosauridae.
15. Helodermatidae.
16. Varanidae.
17. Lanthanotidae.
18. Amphisbaenidae.

Serpentes; Snakes

1. Typhlopidae.
2. Leptotyphlopidae.
3. Aniliidae.
4. Uropeltidae.
5. Xenopeltidae.
6. Boidae.
7. Acrochordidae.
8. Colubridae.
9. Elapidae.
10. Hydrophiidae.
11. Viperidae.
12. Crotalidae.

Turtles Common and Rare

TURTLES IN GENERAL

The herptile neophyte may occasionally mistake a salamander for a lizard, a legless lizard for a snake, or even an aquatic snake for an eel. But there is no possibility of mistaking a turtle or tortoise for anything else we know. All turtles and tortoises possess a shell of sorts. It may be very rudimentary, as in the ocean-dwelling leatherback, or quite highly developed, as in our common box turtles, but it is always present and serves to unite all the diverse species into the order Chelonia. Turtles and tortoises of all kinds are commonly referred to collectively as chelonians. The name "terrapin" is sometimes encountered in our reading, but it has little scientific significance and if used at all should perhaps be confined to the diamondbacks—salt- or brackish-water species of the genus *Malaclemys*.

Of all the herptiles, turtles are the ones most commonly under observation in the home. When I was about six years old, an aunt returning from a trip to a distant city presented me with two baby turtles as souvenirs of her trip. I knew little about reptiles at the time, but the quaint little creatures captivated me at once, and I spent most of my after-school hours watching them. Considering what little I knew of their requirements, it seems remarkable to me that they survived for many months. Soon after their arrival, other baby turtles were purchased locally from time to time. I could not differentiate one species from another, but I would try to pick out individuals having different markings. Thus was initiated a lifelong interest in reptiles and amphibians. Many herpetologists, both amateur and professional, will no doubt be able to recall a similar initiation into their field of study.

13

Students of animal behavior regard chelonians, especially the land-dwelling forms (the tortoises), as the most intelligent of reptiles. Tortoises seem more intelligent than their aquatic relatives, and those turtles that leave the water frequently to dwell on land seem more intelligent than the strictly aquatic types. None of our so-called intelligence tests is fool-proof, but in such common laboratory test problems as finding their way out of a maze, tortoises have fared as well as rats. We must always be mindful that instinctual behavior can be confused with intelligence. As an example, we place a turtle and a tortoise on a table or elevated platform and leave the room. Very often, when we return, we find that the turtle will have managed to fall off the table while the tortoise has warily inspected the drop to the floor and has decided to stay put. Before we rush to the conclusion that the tortoise is the more intelligent of the two, we must remember that in the natural state the turtle suns on rocks and logs and is accustomed to dropping safely from a height into the water below while the tortoise does not do so. A tortoise does not appear very intelligent in a watery environment, and here the results of any test we might devise would weigh heavily in the turtle's favor. A true test of intelligence would involve two reptiles of the same species, age, sex and conditioning, but this would only tell us what we already know—that in every species of vertebrate animals, including human beings, some individuals are brighter than others!

Turtles and tortoises, for the most part, adapt readily to conditions of captivity. As a result of this, they frequently breed in confinement. In most species the sexes may be separated quite readily by the difference in tail length and thickness. The male has the longer, thicker tail. In addition, males often have a concave lower shell. Also, there may be differences in color between the sexes. Courtship performances may be quite elaborate; the mating itself may take place in the water or on land, depending on the species. The normal hatching time runs from two to three months, but in some cases the baby turtle may spend the winter within the egg and come out in the spring. If a female of one of the aquatic types deposits her eggs in the water because she cannot find a suitable nesting site on land, the eggs will quickly drown and become useless for hatching purposes. If deposited on land in a location lacking adequate moisture, they will spoil by drying out. Sometimes eggs will be trampled or broken by the turtles if not taken out of the enclosure at once. In

A box turtle hatchling.

Notice the large umbilicus on the hatchling below. Photos by R. J. Church.

Hermann's tortoise, *Testudo hermanni*, depositing an egg in her nest.
Photo by O. Stemmler.

any given batch of eggs from the same female, some may be fertile while some are not. A female may lay fertile eggs from a mating which took place quite some time back. It is not unusual for a female to lay fertile eggs when she has had no contact with a male for two years. Eggs are best hatched in a sterile environment. A gallon jug having a wide mouth is good for a small number of eggs. The cover may be perforated to admit some air, and paper towels may be used as the hatching medium. Under natural conditions the eggs may adhere to each other, but under artificial incubation they are best separated. Damp paper towels may be crumpled and placed under and above the eggs to provide a duplication of the soil in which the eggs would naturally develop. A temperature range of 65 to 80° F. is desirable during the incubation period, and a slight night-to-day temperature fluctuation is considered by some to be beneficial. Alternate methods for the successful incubation of turtles' eggs are available; any method that controls the critical factors of heat and humidity is likely to be successful.

Chelonians have become adapted to many kinds of environments. Some never leave the water, whereas others never go near it. The majority of the 250-odd species of chelonians reside in the vicinity of a body of water but spend much of their time sunning out of the water. In captivity, the different species present quite distinct problems in their care, and chelonians of various families cannot be indiscriminately mixed with any degree of success unless a large outdoor enclosure is available. In general, turtles and tortoises are peaceful animals, although males of some species may fiercely combat each other during the breeding season. We do not know how prevalent this fighting is among chelonians in the wild state, but it has been repeatedly observed among such different captive species as the common snapping turtle, *Chelydra s. serpentina*, and eastern box turtle, *Terrapene c. carolina*.

Baby turtles are sold by the hundreds of thousands each year, and this has been going on for decades. They are the most popular of the herptiles bought for the home vivarium. Some are captured wild, but many are raised under semi-natural conditions on the so-called turtle farms of the southeastern United States. Of late, these farms have been forced to meet exacting standards of cleanliness, and this has resulted in a low production of baby turtles. As a result, certain very common foreign turtles have come to take the place of native American turtles in pet shops and department stores. At the present time, the South American slider, *Pseudemys scripta callirostris*, is the foreign turtle most frequently seen in the tanks of dealers.

The red-ear turtle, *Pseudemys scripta elegans,* is the most popular American turtle. Photo by R. J. Church.

Some species of baby turtles are easy to raise and quite undemanding, but others are very delicate and will tax the skill of their keeper to the fullest. Once the critical first year in the turtle's life has passed, it seems much better equipped to cope with the limitations imposed upon it by conditions of captivity.

Some baby turtles are very rarely met with in the wild state, possibly because of their extreme secretiveness during this stage of their lives. Baby box turtles are seldom found, baby wood turtles are real rarities, and even baby spotted turtles are not often collected, even where most common. Juveniles often present problems in identification, though nothing like the ones posed by larval frogs and salamanders. Once in a while one may buy or find a baby turtle that does not fit the description of any known species. I have such a specimen in my collection at the present time. It has traveled many miles to the offices of turtle specialists in an attempt to find a name— all without result. One can only guess that it is either an extreme aberrant of some known species or a hybrid resulting from the interbreeding of different species. It is an extremely beautiful little creature, now in its third year. It has been greatly outstripped in growth by the other turtles with which it is being raised, and I can only conjecture that its slow growth is in some way connected with its uncertain parentage. Such are the rarities which the turtle hobbyist seeks out. Occasionally a two-headed turtle is found, and amazingly, may pass through a number of hands before it is finally recognized. Often such a freak will have internal abnormalities prejudicial to its continued existence, though a few have been kept alive for several years. The most recent example to come to my attention was a hatchling southern painted turtle, *Chrysemys picta dorsalis*. It changed hands several times at a profit to each previous owner, in terms of dollars. This particular species is not an easy one to bring out of babyhood, and I would consider the several months that the two-headed individual survived to be about the average for a more normal specimen under anything but the most exceptional care.

Turtles and tortoises are perhaps the longest-lived of all back-boned animals. A properly-cared-for specimen may well outlive several owners. No really short-lived species is known, and representatives of some species have been known to live a hundred years or more. Because of their long natural life and their general hardiness when out of the baby stage, the turtles that a herptile hobbyist

Baby box turtles (above) are very different in appearance from their parents, but the stinkpot, *Sternotherus odoratus* (below), is simply a miniature version of its elders. Photos by R. J. Church.

One advantage of baby turtles in the apartment is their ability to thrive in small, simple containers. Photo by R. J. Church.

acquires are likely to become permanent fixtures in any general collection of reptiles and amphibians. One may still walk into a pet store and purchase a baby turtle for less than a dollar, but anything that is at all uncommon on the turtle market will command a good price.

Because nearly all species of turtles are declining in numbers, some seeming almost at the point of disappearing in the wild state, it is most heartening to learn of the successful propagation of the rarer kinds in captivity. Even such unlikely places as New York apartments have become successful breeding plants for our rarest turtles. Luckily, a baby turtle given good care will mature rapidly and may become capable of reproduction before the end of its third year. The interest in chelonians has continued unabated for very many years and has today reached its highest state of sophistication.

Turtles are the oldest of our living reptiles; on the basis of fossil records, the basic chelonian stock has been practically unchanged for at least 200,000,000 years. The turtle of today looks very much the same as it did long ago. In the line of evolution the tortoises or land-dwelling forms were derived from those which live mostly in or near water. All turtles, even the marine types, lay eggs and must come ashore to do so; thus, no turtle species could survive very long without a beach or land area in which to deposit its eggs, nor could any turtle exist long in a place which has permanently frozen soil.

Like all other reptiles, chelonians reach the height of their abundance in the warmer regions of the world. The life history of many species is very incompletely known, and even their classification remains the subject of argument by taxonomists. Some taxonomists place all our turtles and tortoises in the order Testudinata, rather than Chelonia. Whatever their scientific designation, the turtles and tortoises, in their limited number of something over 200 species, form a conveniently circumscribed group for study in captivity. It is possible for a private collector to assemble a reasonably complete gathering of the world's chelonians, at least as regards the representation of the major families.

All sea turtles, even the gigantic leatherback, *Dermochelys coriacea*, must come ashore to lay their eggs. Photo by Malay Information Service.

SNAPPING TURTLES

If the snapping turtle, *Chelydra serpentina*, were a rarity, it would be much-sought-after by zoos and private individuals. Because it is common and familiar to nearly everyone, however, few stop to consider what a really curious turtle the snapper is. With its huge head, ungainly build, outsized tail, and vicious disposition, it presents a memorable picture when stranded out of its watery home. Snapping turtles are thoroughly aquatic animals, seldom voluntarily leaving the water except to deposit their eggs, which may number about 25. The eggs are round in shape and have been likened to ping-pong balls. They normally require about three months to hatch, but there have been cases in which the babies have spent the winter within

Common snapping turtle, *Chelydra serpentina*. Photo by R. J. Church.

their eggs and emerged during the spring. Babies measure a little over an inch in shell length and adapt themselves readily to an aquarium arrangement with a few inches of water and a couple of rocks. The snapper is neither a swift nor graceful swimmer—it is primarily a bottom-walking species—and will make use of the rocks to protrude its head occasionally to obtain air and survey its surroundings. It is said that snappers eat vegetable matter, but I have never seen one—and I have kept many—that did not prefer a diet of meat and fish. If kept on a well-balanced diet, the snapper does not require sunlight or any substitute for it. Fairly cool water, 65 to 70 degrees, seems to suit it best; it is one of the hardiest turtles in captivity.

The alligator snapping turtle, *Macrochelys temmincki*, is one of the largest fresh-water turtles in existence. A fully grown specimen may have a shell length of over two feet and reach a weight in excess of 200 pounds. Both the common and the alligator snappers are ready biters when out of water and are able to inflict considerable damage with their strong jaws. The alligator snapper is not as agile as the common snapper and shows little of the aggressiveness of that species. Either species may be safely handled by its long tail, held well away from one's body. No very large snapper should be lifted by the tail, however, because any damage to the tail vertebrae is likely to prove fatal ultimately. Large snapping turtles of either species are very predaceous creatures, and no other animal is safe in an enclosure with them. At the same time, baby snappers may have their very long tails injured or even bitten off by aquatic turtles of other kinds. Both kinds of snappers become quite tame in an aquarium and will grow rapidly if cared for properly. Whole or chopped raw fish is the best food for the alligator snapper; the shell quickly softens if the animal does not receive an adequate intake of calcium. Though shy by nature, alligator snappers in aquariums will learn to compete with other turtles for proferred bits of food. The ideal arrangement for a snapper is, however, an aquarium or outdoor pool of its own. The two species of snapping turtles resemble each other in appearance, but each is quite distinct and there is no interbreeding in areas where their ranges overlap. Together they make up the family Chelydridae and range from Canada to northern South America.

PLATELESS RIVER TURTLE

Whenever I visit the reptile house of the Bronx Zoo (New York Zoological Gardens) in New York, my first stop is in front of the large tank housing a single specimen of the plateless river turtle, *Carettochelys insculpta*. The front limbs of this strange turtle are developed for use as paddles, like those of the marine turtles, while its shell is covered with a layer of skin instead of horny plates. As the droll creature flippers lazily from one end of its tank to the other I pause to wonder how many herpetologists have, or will have, the opportunity to see a living specimen of this rare New Guinean turtle. Its range is limited to the southern part of the island, and there is very little in the literature of herpetology to tell us much about it. It is said to favor the brackish water of its island home.

Big-headed turtle, *Platysternon megacephalum*. Photo by G. Marcuse.

BIG-HEADED TURTLE

Another turtle oddity is being imported in some numbers. This is the big-headed turtle of southeastern Asia, *Platysternon mega-cephalum*. Superficially resembling our snapping turtles, the present species is in a family all by itself. It frequents mountain streams that are cool and in captivity does best in water between 65 and 70 degrees. Meat and fish form the bulk of its diet. It is a good climber and leaves the water frequently to sun itself on overhanging branches. Many of the specimens reaching this country are between six and seven inches in shell-length and have a tail about as long as the shell. Some examples are quite willing to bite when handled. Not much has been learned of this turtle's habits; it is said to deposit only two eggs at a time and captives occasionally emit a kitten-like mew. Two sub-species have been named: *megacephalum* from China, the rarer form, and *peguense* from Burma, Thailand, and Vietnam.

MEXICAN RIVER TURTLE

Some of the herptiles which are regarded as being very rare are, in fact, quite common in the areas where they are found but are seldom exported. The Mexican river turtle, *Dermatemys mawi*, may fall into this category. Having no close relatives, it currently enjoys sole occupancy of the family Dermatemyidae. A coastal river turtle, this species may feel at home in slightly brackish water. In southern Mexico it is sold in the market places and is also eaten by the natives of British Honduras and Guatemala. Very few specimens appear on the price lists of herptile dealers.

MUSK AND MUD TURTLES

The family Kinosternidae embraces a group of aquatic turtles known as musk and mud turtles. The common musk turtle, *Sterno-therus odoratus*, is well known in the eastern United States, where in many places it is the commonest reptile. It is one of our smallest turtles, and an adult will seldom measure more than four inches in carapace length. In color, the musk turtle well matches the muddy ponds, ditches, and generally stagnant water that it inhabits, the

Mexican river turtle, *Dermatemys mawi*. Photo by J. Alan Holman.

only relief from its drab brown being the two light stripes on the head and neck. Mainly carnivorous, musk turtles forage by night and day and will devour nearly anything in the way of animal matter that they may find. They come out of the water to bask only rarely and under aquarium conditions will do well without any means of leaving the water. I have kept musk turtles in shoreless aquariums for periods of up to four years. I know of no hardier turtle, nor of any whose appetite is easier to please. Musk turtles seem very resistant to the illnesses which occasionally plague the semi-aquatic and terrestrial chelonians, and sunlight is not a requisite in their care. When first caught, a musk turtle will try to bite and will exude a musky secretion; it is surprisingly difficult to hold one without being bitten, for a musk turtle has a short tail, quite unlike the snappers', and the shell is often slippery and algae-covered. The half-dozen or fewer hard-shelled eggs of this species are often deposited in a seemingly careless situation, sometimes not even covered with soil or leaves.

Mud turtles, genus *Kinosternon* and related forms, are closely allied to the musk turtles, differing from them in having lower shells which are hinged to the extent which permits some species to close up as completely as a box turtle. Generally, mud turtles frequent shallow water; only rarely may an individual be found wandering about on land outside the egg-laying times. Olive, brown, and black are the predominate colors of the numerous species of the genus which, in one form or another, ranges throughout North and Central America and northern South America. Under captive conditions mud turtles are active and seem always on the look-out for food. An adult or baby will thrive in a straight-sided aquarium without means of leaving the water, but the depth of the water should be adjusted to the size of the individual so that it may obtain air at the surface without swimming. Babies, as well as adults, are voracious feeders on meat and fish and if mixed with other baby turtles are likely to obtain much of the food supply. While it is possible and often pleasing to mix various species of chelonians in the same cage, in my opinion the individuals should at least be of the same family. The mud turtle is a rugged animal and can be expected to live many years under captive conditions. Some twenty species and subspecies of mud turtles are recognized, and only a real turtle expert could identify all of the known forms without recourse to formal keys and technical descriptions.

Big-headed mud turtle, *Claudius angustatus.* Photo by J. Alan Holman.

Two genera of the family Kinosternidae are seldom seen in captivity, although they are common in the market places of the cities of southern Mexico, where they are sold for human consumption. These are *Claudius* and *Staurotypus*. The big-headed mud turtle, *Claudius angustatus*, has a greatly reduced lower shell which is not movable to any extent. The guau turtle, *Staurotypus triporcatus*, is a really huge member of the musk and mud turtle family, attaining a shell length of at least fifteen inches. Its disposition is fully as irascible as our diminutive musk turtle's, and its huge size renders it an adversary to be reckoned with at close quarters. A third species, *Staurotypus salvini*, of southern Mexico, is sometimes called the crucilla turtle. All three species could well be termed giant musk turtles; their habits appear very similar to those of our more familiar types.

EMYDID TURTLES

The largest group of turtles, in terms of number of species, is the Emydidae. This family contains most of the pet trade turtles and those for biological laboratory study. Some of the most beautiful

Blanding's turtle, *Emydoidea blandingi.* Photo by Dr. Herbert R. Axelrod.

turtles in the world are members of this family. Because of their diversification of coloring and habits there is little monotony in a study of the group, of which there are over 130 species and subspecies. An account of all of the emydid turtles is much beyond the scope of a book of this type. Besides, there are very many about which very little is known. Importations from Asia are supplying us with species which have been little known heretofore and, hopefully, observations of private collectors, as well as aquarium and zoo staff members, will supply us with good published accounts and pictures of the less familiar emydid turtles.

The painted turtles, *Chrysemys picta,* are beautiful, alert, quick-diving denizens of practically all sizable bodies of water in the eastern United States. In its four subspecies, *Chrysemys picta* presents a most attractive blending of black or olive, red, and yellow stripings and blotches. The most familiar of the painted turtles to the pet trade is the southern painted turtle, *Chrysemys picta dorsalis,* which comes from Louisiana and bordering states. In this form, the brilliant orange-yellow stripe running the length of the black upper shell is characteristic and is carried into adulthood. Grown painted turtles do well in captivity, but the babies are delicate little creatures, requiring a great deal of sunlight and a nourishing diet high in calcium and vitamin content and presented to them in finely ground form. They do not compete well with the more robust babies of other species of turtles and are best kept segregated for rearing purposes. All painted turtles, whether young or adult, are much given to sun-basking and must be provided with a suitable land area for this purpose. The males are readily distinguishable by their possession of long claws on the forefeet.

Blanding's turtle, *Emydoidea blandingi*, most common in the states bordering the Great Lakes, is a moderately large species which may measure eight inches or more in shell length when fully grown. It is an omnivorous creature but in captivity, at least, seems to prefer a meat diet. The Blanding's turtles that I have owned have all become amazingly tame; if they have any drawback as members of a turtle collection, it is in the tremendous appetite they display. The males seem ready to mate at all seasons, and perhaps the species is one which might be raised in quantities under favorable conditions. A bright yellow chin and throat impart a relief to the otherwise sober coloration. Blanding's is one of the emydid turtles whose babies are seldom found.

The European pond turtle, *Emys orbicularis*, is considered a close relative of Blanding's turtle and, like the latter, can eat either in or out of water. It lives well in captivity and becomes tame. Because of their large adult size, both the European pond turtle and Blanding's should have a good-sized water area in which to exercise. Pond turtles are said to over-winter in their eggs and emerge in the spring. Both species prefer to hibernate under water, buried in mud, but in neither is this rest period essential for longevity.

"Terrapin" is a name that is commonly applied to those fresh and brackish-water turtles that are of some importance economically because of the palatability of their flesh. In the present writing, we will confine the name to the diamondback terrapin, *Malaclemys terrapin*, a resident of eastern United States coastal marshes and other tidal waters from Massachusetts to Florida, then west to the Gulf coast of Texas and Mexico. The diamondbacks are confined to salt and brackish water in the natural state, and there is a difference of opinion among turtle keepers as to whether the salt content of their water is an important factor in maintaining them in captivity. My own opinion is that it is very necessary to provide brackish water for these handsome terrapins if they are to be kept over a long period; this is especially important if the other conditions of their environment are less than ideal. At least a tablespoonful of ordinary salt to a gallon of water provides the salinity these turtles require to prevent skin troubles from arising. Among the diamondbacks, of which there are seven subspecies currently recognized, the female attains a shell length nearly double that of her mate. The species has acquired its name from the distinctively sculptured shell, each plate of which is raised in concentric rings. A really beautiful turtle is Florida's west coast variety, the ornate diamondback terrapin, *Malaclemys terrapin macrospilota*. These turtles will learn to accept food items quite different from anything they might find in their native marshes, but an occasional feeding of molluscs is desirable.

The map and sawback turtles, genus *Graptemys*, are an interesting complex of nine currently recognized species confined to North America. Like the diamondbacks, to which they are closely related, the turtles of this genus show great disparity in size between the sexes, the female being much the larger. As a group, they are deepwater, diving turtles, and the adults are wary and very difficult to net. Some of the species have pronounced serrations along the keels of their carapaces and from this may be recognized at a distance. Sunning turtles all, they require in captivity a recognition of their individual needs and will fail to thrive unless these are met. The adult females of some species develop enormous heads and jaws, presumably to cope with the hard-shelled molluscs to which they seem partial. The Mississippi map turtle, *Graptemys kohni*, is the

Sabine map turtle, *Graptemys pseudogeographica sabinensis*, Louisiana-Texas border. Photo by J. G. Walls.

Spanish turtle, *Mauremys leprosa.* This turtle is often included in the genus *Clemmys.* Photo by G. Marcuse.

European pond turtle, *Emys orbicularis.* Photo by G. Marcuse.

species most often sold in pet stores. Generally considered delicate, the young can be raised successfully on chopped raw fish supplemented with lettuce leaves. Among the more beautiful members of the genus are the ringed sawback turtle, *Graptemys oculifera,* and the yellow-blotched sawback turtle, *Graptemys flavimaculata.* The map and sawback turtles do not enter the brackish water frequented by diamondbacks.

The spotted turtle, *Clemmys guttata,* is familiar to most residents of the eastern United States. Their small adult size of about four inches and the bold yellow speckling of their carapaces lead to their ready identification. Small, shallow bodies of water are a frequent abode, and often the turtles may be caught by hand in large numbers. Turtles which are abundant in the spring and early summer may disappear when the weather becomes hot, and it is believed that the species may aestivate. Baby spotted turtles are not common in collections; like many other baby turtles they are highly secretive until well grown. The sexes of the spotted turtle may be distinguished at once by anyone who has had much experience with the species. The male's head is less ornately adorned than the female's, his plastron is decidedly concave, and his tail is longer and thicker. There is not much difference in size between the sexes. Like all other members of the genus *Clemmys,* the spotted turtle makes a good adjustment to confinement and becomes very tame. A diet of meat and fish is preferred.

Many writers about reptiles have commented on the desirability of the wood turtle, *Clemmys insculpta,* for collections. Lacking the brilliant markings of some emydid turtles, the wood turtle is, nevertheless, a quietly handsome member of the family. Its shell is roughened, each scute set apart from the others, and its fleshy parts are adorned with brick red or, more rarely, yellow. Wood turtles are able to live on land or in the water and are practically omnivorous. The best arrangement for them is a large land area and a spacious pool to satisfy their occasional inclination to enter the water. Berries of several kinds, strawberries in particular, are relished by captives. Unfortunately, this desirable turtle does not appear on the price lists of dealers as frequently as it once did. Turtle collectors and collections are on the increase, and I do not know whether this has played a significant role in the lessening numbers of wood turtles.

Alligator snapping turtle, *Macrochelys temminckii*. Photo by Dr. Herbert R. Axelrod.

Common snapping turtle, *Chelydra serpentina*. Photo by Dr. Herbert R. Axelrod.

Spotted turtle, *Clemmys guttata.* Photo by. R. J. Church.

Clemmys nigricans, northern China. Photo by G. Marcuse.

The bog turtle, *Clemmys muhlenbergi*, once fairly common in favorable localities, has become so rare and sporadic in occurrence that it is possible that some readers may never see a live one. We do have the encouraging information that a few are being bred and raised in captivity, and it seems possible at present that such colonies may exist long after the species has vanished from its native haunts. I have a single adult male from Chatham, New Jersey in my collection. He was captured in the typical meadow stream habitat of the species, and I would judge from his appearance that he is quite old. In the six years he has been with me he has remained very timid, in distinct contrast to the other *Clemmys* turtles I have. He will leave the water and scamper toward my hand to take food, but he always pauses while still a few inches away, seemingly unable to work up the courage to take the proferred morsels from my fingers. When I withdraw my hand, leaving the food behind, the pieces of meat are grasped and taken into the water for swallowing—he will never eat anything while out of the water. When handled, as during the periodic cleaning of his shell, he will remain withdrawn in his shell indefinitely. Any kind of rock in his pool seems to terrorize him, and he will ceaselessly seek escape while it is present. The requirement of a dry area has been solved by gently sloping the aquarium by propping one end on a block of wood. This set-up provides a water depth of about two inches and a dry area covering one-third of the container. Most nights are spent out of water. Over the years, my specimen has been kept in good health on a diet of lean raw beef chopped into small pieces and supplemented frequently with a few mealworms or a nightcrawler. To discourage the possibility of fungus development, a small amount of vinegar is added to the water occasionally, after cleaning. In keeping with his distinction as a rarity and to minimize his chances of contracting a disease, he is kept isolated from other turtles. He receives no sunlight, except that filtered through ordinary window glass, and this seems to be not an essential requirement for the successful maintenance of most adult turtles.

The west coast pond turtle, *Clemmys marmorata*, in its two subspecies, ranges from British Columbia southward to northern Baja, California, and may reach a carapace length of over seven inches. It is very aquatic in its habits and sometimes enters brackish water; large colonies may sometimes be found confined to small areas.

Plateless river turtle, *Carettochelys insculpta*. Photo by P. C. H. Pritchard.

Mexican river turtle, *Dermatemys mawi*. Photo by P. C. H. Pritchard.

Common musk turtle, *Sternotherus odoratus*. Photo by P. C. H. Pritchard.

Eastern mud turtle, *Kinosternon subrubrum subrubrum,* eastern United States. Photo by P. C. H. Pritchard.

Pseudemys is the genus which supplies so many of the small turtles used for the pet trade and in research. Its various species and subspecies have a wide distribution in the western hemisphere, and most are very attractive turtles and eminently suitable members of the private collection. The red-eared turtle is the one seen most often in the aquariums of pet dealers where, unfortunately, their care is often not of the very best. There seems to be a prevailing idea that these small creatures can best be kept in good health, while awaiting buyers, in dry or nearly dry tanks. This is not so. True, when a large number of turtles are confined, they present less of a cleaning problem in the absence of water. But under such conditions these small turtles do not feed and the mortality resultant from desiccation and starvation must surely offset whatever small advantage accrues from not having to feed them and provide a change of water daily. All of the pseudemid turtles are sun-loving creatures and are at their best in an aquarium which provides a large, rounded rock or dry shore for sunning or at least drying out occasionally. Feeding habits within the genus are varied—some species seem omnivorous and quite willing to eat most anything, while others exhibit a preference for either vegetable matter or meat. From personal experience I can attest that the growth of these babies can be phenomenally rapid under favorable conditions in captivity. A hatchling the size of a quarter may in a couple of years become the size of a small saucer.

The red-bellied turtles, *Pseudemys nelsoni* and *Pseudemys rubriventris*, with their coral plastrons, are bright and hardy members of the family. The adult females may reach a length of nearly fifteen inches; the males are smaller and have the long foreclaws which distinguish the males of many emydid species. Red-bellies have a curious distribution, consisting of at least four distinct populations, the most perplexing of which is the isolated colony in Plymouth County, Massachusetts. One expects to find large basking turtles in some places, but their presence in New England is surprising and they seem, somehow, out of place.

In our southern states the cooters and sliders, *Pseudemys floridana* and *Pseudemys concinna*, are common and very familiar animals. There is a bewildering array of variation among them, and even the student who specializes in the study of turtles will find it difficult to attach with certainty a subspecific designation to some individuals of the group. Mostly, they reach a large adult size and do well in captivity. Babies enter the pet trade, to some extent, and enjoy a varied diet. These turtles, in their two species and some eight subspecies, intermingle freely in the wild state, and this habit is carried over into captivity. The subject of hybridization is a fascinating one, and in the literature one finds records and photographs of the curious creatures that have resulted from the union of two quite different animals. Experiments of this kind have been taking place for some time; the San Diego Zoo, which has produced a wealth of information about reptiles through the activities of the reptile men connected in one way or another with it, has succeeded in hybridizing rattlesnakes—animals which normally do not adjust to captivity to the extent of breeding, even within their own species! What brings all this to mind is the attempt on the part of some of my male sliders to court a much larger yellow-spotted Amazon turtle, *Podocnemis unifilis*, female that is temporarily caged with them. This turtle and the sliders are so far removed from each other on the turtles' phylogenetic tree that they have been placed in different suborders. With our ever-increasing knowledge of how to make herptiles feel at home in captivity and with the maturing of artificial insemination experiments, who can say what future investigation along these lines may reveal?

The red-eared turtle, *Pseudemys scripta elegans*, has long been the reptile most widely kept as a pet in the United States, even though reduced numbers are causing it to be supplanted, to a degree, by the very common South American slider. Red-eared turtles are the first reptiles acquired by many reptile admirers, and their pretty colors and good disposition combine to make a favorable introduction to the world of reptiles. A close relative of the red-eared turtle is the yellow-bellied turtle, *Pseudemys scripta scripta*, of the southeastern United States.

Northern South America is the home of a common and beautiful turtle that is imported in large numbers. The South American slider, *Pseudemys scripta callirostris*, delicate of form and coloring, is a tropical turtle and is best kept at a temperature of not less than 78–80 degrees.

The chicken turtle, *Deirochelys reticularia*, is, for a turtle, a graceful and streamlined inhabitant of that region—the southeastern United States—which is the home of so many species found nowhere else.

Guau turtle, *Staurotypus triporcatus.* Photo by P. C. H. Pritchard.

Western painted turtle, *Chrysemys picta belli.* Photo by Dr. Herbert R. Axelrod.

Southern painted turtle, *Chrysemys picta dorsalis*. Photo by Dr. Herbert R. Axelrod.

Blanding's turtle, *Emydoidea blandingi*. Photo by Dr. Herbert R. Axelrod.

The extremely long neck of this species is reminiscent of the Australian and South American snake-necked turtles, but actually chicken turtles are not closely related to the snakenecks. An inhabitant of ponds and other quiet waters, the chicken turtle is mainly carnivorous. I would call the species a difficult one to raise from babyhood but quite hardy as an adult of four to six inches. The olive-brown carapace is finely lined with yellow—reticulated—whence the species has received its specific name.

Conspicuous and unique in the turtle fauna of the United States and Mexico is the box turtle in its several species. The eastern box turtle, *Terrapene carolina carolina*, may be taken as representative of the species. The highly domed carapace and the hinged plastron will at once serve to distinguish this turtle from other chelonians of the areas it inhabits, as will its habitually terrestrial mode of living. All of the box turtles have brown or blackish shells, adorned in some cases with yellow radiating lines. Males of the eastern species are among the handsomest turtles of the North American continent; they often have bright red eyes and seem to attain a larger average size than their mates, sometimes reaching a carapace length of six inches.

Box turtles are long-lived reptiles. With whatever skepticism we may view published records of longevity in turtles, there seems little doubt that box turtles may, on rare occasions, live a century. Sometimes very old-looking individuals may be found, but they are not common; to my way of thinking, this fact lends considerable credibility to the tales of longevity we read about. Box turtles resemble the true tortoises in their way of life, but are more closely related to the aquatic and semi-aquatic species mentioned in the foregoing paragraphs. After a rain they may be found wandering about in abundance in some places; in hot, dry weather they go into seclusion. Specimens in captivity do best under dry conditions, with periodic soakings in water. In a well-regulated household a bathtub may not be considered the ideal place for turtles, but I know of one specimen that has for years been doing well in such a situation. She is thoroughly soaked with a bathspray each day and about once a week allowed to wallow about in water of two-inch depth. It is at such times that she seems to drink. Her diet consists almost solely of hamburger, and she is not interested in less than the best grade. No amount of teasing will cause her to close her lower shell. She was picked up

Comparison of the single hinge of a box turtle (above) and the double hinge of a mud turtle (below). Photos by G. Marcuse.

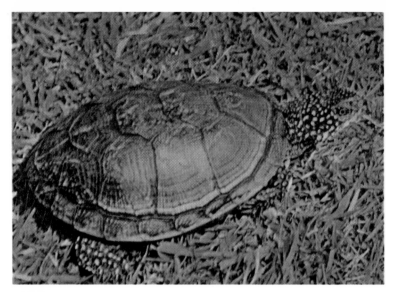

European pond turtle, *Emys orbicularis*. Photo by P. C. H. Pritchard.

Diamondback terrapin, *Malaclemys terrapin*. Photo by Dr. Herbert R. Axelrod.

/Florida diamondback terrapin, *Malaclemys terrapin macrospilota.*
Photo by P. C. H. Pritchard.

Mississippi map turtle, *Graptemys kohni.* Photo by Dr. Herbert R.
Axelrod.

wandering along a busy street of a large city, apparently an escaped pet, since from the very first she has displayed no timidity.

Baby box turtles are not found with any degree of frequency. They require more moisture than their elders and more attention to their dietary requirements. Often they feed readily and voraciously and prefer a meat diet. I have kept many juvenile box turtles of different subspecies and cannot recall of any that would partake of vegetable or fruit offerings. The baby Gulf Coast box turtle, *Terrapene carolina major*, is sometimes represented by an individual or two in the large batches of turtles which originate in Louisiana. It has distinctly aquatic proclivities and, in general, is a more difficult animal to raise than the young of the Florida box turtle, *Terrapene carolina bauri*, and the ornate box turtle, *Terrapene ornata*. The last two do well as babies and will often live, but they show hardly any growth if their diet is lacking in the essential vitamins and minerals. Adult box turtles can be called omnivorous, and the types of food they accept would form a long list. Whole or chopped earthworms are greedily accepted by most individuals, but box turtles display a great deal of individuality. Nearly all adults make a quick and good adjustment to cage life, but rarely one is found that day after day and month after month will do little besides seek escape. Such individuals feed sparingly, which reflects itself in a rapid loss of weight. There is little point in keeping such an animal.

Florida box turtle, *Terrapene carolina bauri*. Photo by Dr. Herbert R. Axelrod.

Fat-necked turtle, *Siebenrockiella crassicollis*, Southeast Asia. Photo by M. F. Roberts.

Box turtles can be tethered out-of-doors by means of a small hole drilled in the posterior margins of their carapaces. This should be done only in places where they will be free from attack by dogs or other predaceous animals. Water should be available constantly, as should a means of getting out of the sun. If more than one turtle is kept, they should be separated to avoid entanglement of their restraining lines. In a fenced yard they may be allowed to roam freely and will seldom make an attempt to dig out. However, despite their clumsy build, they can and do climb; if the fence is low it should be fitted with an overhang to prevent this means of escape. In general, box turtles can be expected to do well in captivity and often become the favorites of a collection.

Mexico is a vast area, and inhabiting its varied terrain are many creatures of great zoological interest. Four, possibly more, box turtle species are found here but, like so many Mexican reptiles, they seldom reach zoos or private collections, so we know little of their habits.

Of the various Asiatic species of emydid turtles, the batagur turtle, *Batagur baska*, is one of the largest, having a shell length of two feet or more. This very common chelonian is herbivorous and, as can be imagined, consumes great amounts of plants, its saw-edged jaws

Yellow-blotched sawback, *Graptemys flavimaculata*. Photo by P. C. H. Pritchard.

Spotted turtle, *Clemmys guttata*. Photo by P. C. H. Pritchard.

Bog turtle, *Clemmys muhlenbergi*. Photo by P. C. H. Pritchard.

Wood turtle, *Clemmys insculpta*. Photo by P. C. H. Pritchard.

Reeves' turtle, *Chinemys reevesi*. Photo by G. Marcuse.

enabling it to make clean cuts with a minimum of effort. Good eating, it is hunted locally, and its eggs are collected in large numbers for human consumption. The batagur is not one of the really handsome emydids, but males of the species are said to assume a nuptial dress, something not common among turtles. The batagur frequents brackish water, and captives will benefit from the addition of salt to their water. Batagur turtles deposit large numbers of eggs on the beach at a point beyond tidal influence. The oval eggs are three inches in length and require over two months to hatch. The adults are wary reptiles, fast runners and strong swimmers. The usual method of capture is by means of a trap. Neither babies nor adults are commonly exported.

The three-striped batagur turtle, *Callagur borneoensis*, also an Asiatic species, though commonly regarded as a fresh-water species, is actually a frequenter of coastal waters and is a plant-eater.

Reeves' turtle, *Chinemys reevesi*, is a member of a genus containing three species. A common and small species of China and Japan, Reeves' turtle is a dull-brownish little animal that is not often more than four inches in shell length. Hardy and long-lived, they spend most of their time under water, where they will voraciously eat meat, worms, and fish. I once acquired a number of hatchlings and will always remember them for their continual fighting with each other. They were well fed, so their squabbles were not prompted by hunger. Little harm resulted from their disharmony.

The Spanish turtle, *Mauremys leprosa*, and the Caspian turtle, *Mauremys caspica*, are commonly imported. The Spanish turtle often arrives with its shell in a deplorable condition, said to be caused by the seasonal drying-up and stagnating of the ponds it inhabits. As a species it does well in captivity, as does the Caspian turtle. Many kinds of turtles, especially those of the tropics, have had their shells devastated by erosion by the time they are collected. The etiology of these conditions is probably varied. Some respond well to treatment while others are resistant. I do not think it is wise to introduce a turtle with a bad shell to one's collection; in the case of valuable exotic specimens that cannot be seen before purchase, it is worth the price of a telephone call to the dealer to ascertain their true condition before they are shipped.

The Asiatic box turtles of the genus *Cuora* have recently become popular among herptile keepers. The Malayan box turtle, *Cuora amboinensis*, is the species most often available. It rather closely resembles our native box turtles. Like them, it has the ability to close the lobes of the plastron. *Cuora trifasciata* (three-lined box turtle) is, to me, an exquisitely beautiful turtle whose delicate shadings of color show off to great advantage under good lighting. There is nothing gaudy about it, yet the contrasts of brown, yellow, and red and the dark band on its head impart an out-of-the-ordinary appearance. The care of captives is not difficult; perhaps the best arrangement is one which provides equal land and water areas, with the water depth proportioned to the sizes of the turtles. Like other turtles native to the warmer regions of the world, the members of this genus should never be subjected to low temperatures. I would regard 75 to 80 degrees an ideal temperature range. It is fortunate that we are today able to procure from reptile dealers at a relatively low price so many kinds of reptiles which not long ago could be obtained only with considerable difficulty and after lengthy correspondence. The Asiatic box turtles fall into this category. Although the older books on reptiles hardly mention them, no doubt our knowledge of the *Cuora* species and others will keep pace with the influx of live material.

Red-bellied turtle, *Pseudemys nelsoni.* Photo by P. C. H. Pritchard.

West coast pond turtle, *Clemmys marmorata.* Photo by C. M. Bogert.

Cooter, *Pseudemys floridana*. Photo by Dr. Herbert R. Axelrod.

Slider, *Pseudemys concinna*. Photo by P. C. H. Pritchard.

Three-lined box turtle, *Cuora trifasciatus*, above; Malayan box turtle, *Cuora amboinensis*, below. Photos by G. Marcuse.

Confronted by so many desirable reptiles offered by dealers, the collector must exert will power to keep a private collection within reasonable bounds. Each additional specimen will mean additional work, and work is pleasurable to a point only. Certainly the care and feeding of any private collection should never be allowed to become burdensome. Most herptiles will live for a long time if properly cared for, and one of the purposes of this book is to enable a beginner to lay out a plan for a collection. He may wish to specialize in one kind of reptile or another or to have a collection that represents a cross-section of the reptile and amphibian worlds. Whatever the choice, it is important to impose limitations on the numbers of individuals and not purchase any herptile simply because it is available at the moment. There is fun in waiting, and although the particular species you want may take time to obtain, its value will be enhanced when you finally obtain it.

Thurj's turtle, *Hardella thurji*, is a large, thoroughly aquatic species from India and Pakistan. The shell of a fully grown female may be 20 inches in length. It feeds mostly on plants and is best kept at a temperature not lower than 75 degrees. The temple turtle, *Hieremys annandalei*, is similar in size and habits and is likewise Asiatic in origin.

The roofed turtles, genus *Kachuga*, are represented by six species, some quite attractive in their color and markings. Their shells are prominently keeled along the top and, viewed from the front, are rather tent-like in conformation. Roofed turtles do not appear to be built for swimming, but I would call them diving turtles. They are thoroughly at home in an aquarium that provides only a small island for leaving the water. As captives they feed incessantly upon lettuce leaves and other green matter; they do not show any interest in meat.

Southeast Asia provides us with the snail-eating turtle, *Malayemys subtrijuga*, a species closely resembling our native musk turtles in gross appearance. Turtles of this species do best in fairly shallow water that does not force them to swim to the surface to take air. Captives will seldom leave the water, and it is questionable whether a landing-place lends anything to their comfort. This rather somber little turtle may feed largely upon molluscs in its native habitat, but my records show that the ones I have had have readily accepted pieces of raw beef as a substitute for their natural diet. Snail-eating turtles are a common species, and a single shipment arriving in the United States may contain several hundred specimens.

Yellow-bellied turtle, *Pseudemys scripta scripta.* Photo by P. C. H. Pritchard.

Red-eared turtle, *Pseudemys scripta elegans.* Photo by Dr. Herbert R. Axelrod.

South American slider, *Pseudemys scripta callirostris*. Photo by Dr. Herbert R. Axelrod.

Chicken turtle, *Deirochelys reticularia*. Photo by P. C. H. Pritchard.

Kachuga smithi, Pakistan and northern India. Photo by G. Marcuse.

Thurg's turtle, *Hardella thurgi*. Photo by G. Marcuse.

Snail-eating turtle, *Malayemys subtrijuga*. Photo by G. Marcuse.

Gulf coast box turtle, *Terrapene carolina major*. Photo by P. C. H. Pritchard.

Eastern box turtle, *Terrepene carolina carolina*. Photo by M. F. Roberts.

Florida box turtle, *Terrapene carolina bauri*. Photo by Dr. Herbert R. Axelrod.

Three-toed box turtle, *Terrapene carolina triunguis*, Mississippi to Texas. Photo by P. C. H. Pritchard.

Three-keeled turtle, *Geoemyda trijuga.* Adult above, juvenile below. Photos by G. Marcuse.

The flat-shelled turtle, *Notochelys platynota*, is a vegetarian, feeding mostly on berries and greens. It comes on the turtle market once in a while and is native to Vietnam, Burma, Sumatra, and Borneo.

Turtles of the genus *Geoemyda* are found in the tropical Americas and Asia. Some are semi-aquatic, while others dwell mostly on land. There is great diversification in appearance among the related forms, a few possessing a bizarre shell development in their early years. They are not the easiest of turtles to pinpoint as to species and subspecies and, like other difficult groups, are occasionally misidentified. A clue to the habits of any turtle may be had by noting whether the hind feet are webbed and, if they are, how extensively. Most, if not all, chelonians have good olfactory powers; the more terrestrial *Geoemyda* species seem to have their sense of smell especially well developed. Their keen investigation of other turtles and foreign objects gives an impression of intelligence.

Geoemyda grandis, Southeast Asia. Photo by M. F. Roberts.

Caspian turtle, *Mauremys caspica.* Photo by P. C. H. Pritchard.

Reeves' turtle, *Chinemys reevesi.* Photo by Dr. Herbert R. Axelrod.

Spanish turtle, *Mauremys leprosa.* Photo by G. Marcuse.

Malayan box turtle, *Cuora amboinensis.* Photo by P. C. H. Pritchard.

Rough turtle, *Geoemyda punctularia*. Photo by R. J. Church.

All *Geoemyda* species should have both land and water areas in their cages. Individuals will soon show their preference, and the proportions of dry and wet areas may be adjusted accordingly. Some commonly imported turtles of this group are the furrowed land turtle, *Geoemyda areolata*, the rough turtle, *Geoemyda punctularia*, and the three-keeled turtle, *Geoemyda trijuga*. All *Geoemyda* species should be kept warm. In most of their forms they represent a sort of transition from aquatic to terrestrial habits, and turtles of this type seem admirably adapted to confinement. An example is our North American wood turtle, *Clemmys insculpta*.

II

Other Turtles and the Tortoises

SOFT-SHELLED TURTLES

The numerous soft-shelled turtles form a thoroughly aquatic family: the Trionychidae. With their flexible, leathery shells and elongated snouts, no one acquainted with turtles is likely to mistake these curious animals for anything else. Some writers have called these turtles the most aquatic of freshwater species, but I would hesitate to apply this designation to them. In the wild state, they may once in a while be seen basking on a floating log or sandy beach. Such species as our common snapper seem much more independent of land, though not the efficient swimmers the soft-shells are. Soft-shelled turtles, especially juveniles, become tame enough to greedily snatch food from one's fingers. The adults are sometimes morose and resent familiarity by biting viciously when handled. It is difficult to avoid the serpentine thrusts of their heads, and the best way to handle a large specimen is by the rear of the carapace. The eastern spiny soft-shelled turtle, *Trionyx spiniferus spiniferus*, is fairly typical of the group. It is a difficult turtle to catch with a net. For an animal whose entire structure is modified to suit the needs of an aquatic existence, its ability to run quickly on land is amazing.

Soft-shells should not be allowed to crawl on hard or rough surfaces, because they lack the bony armor of other turtles and may easily injure their tender plastrons. I consider it neither necessary nor desirable to provide their aquariums with landing places. Best suited to their needs is an aquarium with several inches of very fine sand on the bottom. The sand should be covered with water to a

Three-banded box turtle, *Cuora trifasciata*. Photo by P. C. H. Pritchard.

Thurg's turtle, *Hardella thurgi*. Photo by G. Marcuse.

Snail-eating turtle, *Malayemys subtrijuga.* Photo by Dr. Herbert R. Axelrod.

Roofed turtle, *Kachuga smithi,* India and Pakistan. Photo by S. Minton.

Spiny soft-shell turtle, *Trionyx spiniferus*. Photo by Dr. Herbert R. Axelrod.

depth not too great to prevent the turtles from extending their long necks to the surface without leaving their hiding places under the sand. It should not be inferred from this that soft-shells remain habitually buried in an aquarium. Tame ones are quite vivacious and spend much time exploring the confines of their home. Soft-shells should not be mixed with other, less fragile types of turtles, for they are easily injured by bites and scratches from other turtles. The soft, proboscis-like extension of their snouts can easily be amputated in a dispute over a morsel of food. Kept alone, with a minimum of handling, soft-shells do well. The babies of some species are adorned with attractive markings; young Florida soft-shelled turtles, *Trionyx ferox*, are especially attractive. Some species, like the giant soft-shelled turtle of southeast Asia, *Pelochelys bibroni*, grow to a shell-length of over three feet. Soft-shells are primarily carnivorous; none of the number of species that I have kept would show any interest in lettuce or other vegetable matter. North America, Asia, and Africa all have indigenous soft-shelled turtles.

SEA TURTLES

The true sea turtles have been placed in two families. The lone member of the first family is the huge leatherback turtle, *Dermochelys coriacea*, of the family Dermochelyidae. Attaining a shell-length of over five feet and weight approaching a ton, the leatherback has rarely been kept in captivity. Like other marine turtles, the leatherback has huge flippers instead of the usual turtle forelimbs. This may be the heaviest of our living reptiles, and a verbal description hardly does justice to the immensity of a fully adult living specimen. Imagine a turtle whose flippers may span 12 feet! The lack of a horny, plated shell is one of the more obvious features that separate this turtle from other sea turtles which are, outwardly, of similar form and habits. Babies, measuring three inches at hatching, are brightly spotted and covered with small scales. As the reptile grows, the scales are lost and replaced with the leathery skin of the adult, dark brown or black in color. The dissection of leatherbacks discloses omnivorous feeding habits.

The family Cheloniidae includes our more familiar sea turtles like the loggerhead, *Caretta caretta*, hawksbill, *Eretmochelys imbricata*, ridleys, *Lepidochelys* species, and green turtles, *Chelonia mydas*. Sea

Pacific ridley turtle, *Lepidochelys olivacea*. Photo by P. C. H. Pritchard.

Rough turtle, *Geoemyda punctularia*. Photo by Dr. Herbert R. Axelrod.

Furrowed land turtle, *Geoemyda areolata*. Photo by P. C. H. Pritchard.

Florida soft-shelled turtle, *Trionyx ferox*. Photo by P. C. H. Pritchard.

Three-keeled turtle, *Geoemyda trijuga*. Photo by P. C. H. Pritchard.

turtles are among those marine animals that adapt readily to a synthetic oceanic medium if it even grossly approaches their natural water in its principal salts content. Aquarists who keep marine fishes have long been familiar with the packaged chemical compounds which, when dissolved in fresh water, create an approximation of natural ocean water. These complicated compounds are very necessary in the keeping of most fish species, but hardly so in regard to marine turtles, which have survived over long periods in ordinary tap water to which enough table salt has been added to lend a brackish taste. Natural sea water can be used for sea turtles, but in some ways the artificial product is better, lacking, as it does, the many microorganisms which die off and start to alter the nature of sea water when it is placed in an aquarium.

Baby sea turtles are often encountered in large numbers when they have broken out of their shells and are crawling toward the shallow waters that will harbor them in their infancy. A single specimen may be confined in a five-gallon aquarium but can be expected to grow rapidly and will soon require a much larger aquarium. Clean and sterile conditions are desirable, as with the keeping of all reptiles, and this can be best accomplished if the turtle is fed in a basin or other container separate from the dwelling unit. This method of feeding will not allow decaying food particles to foul the water of the turtles' permanent homes. Since only the adults come out on land, and they only for egg-laying, it is not necessary to provide any land area in the aquarium housing small sea turtles. In the early stages of their lives, when first hatched, ocean turtles will thrive in shallow water only a few inches deep. This, unfortunately, does not show off to any great extent their graceful swimming motions which are so attractive in deeper water. Food will consist of fish, molluscs, and water plants mostly; experimentation will quickly show what is preferred. Though rarely available commercially, baby sea turtles may be acquired through purchase or exchange with a collector who has the opportunity to catch them near their nesting sites.

SIDE-NECKED TURTLES

If this book were to make an attempt to present information about reptiles in the strict order of their taxonomic classification, the side-necked turtles of the families Chelidae and Pelomedusidae would have to be put into a section by themselves. All of the turtles we have

Helmeted turtle, *Pelomedusa subrufa*. Photo by P. C. H. Pritchard.

so far discussed draw their heads into their shells by a vertical bending process. With the present group, however, the neck is bent under the shell sideways. This difference in the way the neck is bent is considered a very fundamental one, so much so that the side-necks have been put into a separate suborder. All side-necks are fresh-water turtles; some are thoroughly aquatic, others less so, but there are no marine or strictly terrestrial species among them.

The matamata turtle, *Chelys fimbriata*, is a sidenecked species and one of the most bizarre reptiles in the world. Its grotesquely flattened head terminates in a projecting snout and is covered with filamentous protuberances which may be an aid in detecting the aquatic creatures upon which it feeds. The mouth is very large and the jaws are fleshy, rather than hard and sharp. When it feeds, the matamata simply opens its mouth and sucks in the fish or other small animal that unwarily approaches too close. The shell is odd in that each shield is. elevated to a point. In fact, there is little about the matamata that is not curious. Compared with other turtles, its features seem an accentuation and combination of the more unusual features of other genera of chelonians.

Leatherback turtle, *Dermochelys coriacea*. Photo by P. C. H. Pritchard.

Loggerhead turtle, *Caretta caretta*. Photo by D. Faulkner.

Atlantic ridley, *Lepidochelys kempi*. Photo by P. C. H. Pritchard.

Hawksbill turtle, *Eretmochelys imbricata*. Photo by P. C. H. Pritchard.

An inhabitant of South American waters, the matamata is frequently exported and finds its way into the aquariums of turtle fanciers. For an exotic animal of such outstanding interest, the price of this turtle is not high. It may reach a shell length of a foot and a half, but a large specimen can be confined in a relatively small aquarium because it is not an active turtle. As a boy, I would frequently visit a large public aquarium and, to me, the most fascinating of the varied displays was a small aquarium of perhaps twenty gallons capacity which housed a matamata. I do not know whether this specimen established a longevity record, but I do know that this particular specimen occupied its modest home for at least ten years. It never strayed from its favorite corner. Matamata turtles are sensitive to light and do best under subdued lighting. The water-depth should depend on the size of the animal and should allow it to obtain air while resting on the bottom. A docile species, it is neither able nor inclined to bite with any effectiveness. Its water should be maintained at a temperature of between 78 and 85 degrees.

Central South America has several turtles that are noted for their extreme length of neck. One of these is the Argentine snake-necked turtle, *Hydromedusa tectifera*. These interesting members of the turtle clan have a head and neck that is as long as their shell. Quite timid when first caught, they remain so for some time but eventually lose their shyness and become very tame, feeding readily on meat and fish. They should have some means of leaving the water, though they are highly aquatic and excellent swimmers. The common toad-headed turtle, *Batrachemys nasuta*, is rather nondescript in appearance except for its head, which is very broad in matured examples. It is carnivorous and spends most of its time in the water.

The flat-headed side-necked turtle, *Platemys platycephala*, is one of the more attractive of the side-necked turtles, pleasing in its muted browns and yellows. A specimen with an eight-inch shell is fully grown. This, too, is a fish-eater.

The reptile fauna of Australia and New Guinea is fully as interesting as the many fascinating birds and mammals which inhabit these land masses. The common snake-necked turtle, *Chelodina longicollis*, has long been a familiar animal to keepers of vivaria. Five other species of *Chelodina* are recognized, and some grow to a large size. The broad-shelled snake-necked turtle, *Chelodina expansa*, may measure two feet in carapace length. The species kept in captivity

Platemys platycephala, Brazil. Photo by M. F. Roberts.

have proven very satisfactory and long-lived, subsisting indefinitely on a diet of meat and fish, rarely taking vegetable matter. They should be maintained at a temperature of 75 to 85 degrees. Their light-colored eyes give them a rather curious expression.

Related to the snake-necks are the side-necks of the genera *Elseya*, *Emydura*, and *Pseudemydura*. The red-bellied is one of the prettier and smaller members of the New Guinea side-necks. Its scientific name is *Emydura albertisii*.

Africa and Madagascar, as well as South America, give us a variety of turtles grouped within the family Pelomedusidae. All are rather plain-looking, their browns and blacks relieved, in some species, with splashes of color about the head. The helmeted turtle, *Pelomedusa subrufa*, and common African mud turtle, *Pelusios subniger*, appear often on dealers' lists. I have kept these hardy turtles for years in shoreless aquariums, and it is likely that in their natural state they do not often leave the water.

Matamata, *Chelys fimbriata.* Photo by Dr. Herbert R. Axelrod.

Green turtle, *Chelonia mydas.* Photo by P. C. H. Pritchard.

Argentine snake-necked turtle, *Hydromedusa tectifer.* Photo by P. C. H. Pritchard.

Toad-headed turtle, *Batrachemys nasuta.* Photo by P. C. H. Pritchard.

By no means so exclusively aquatic is the yellow-spotted Amazon turtle, *Podocnemis unifilis*, of South America. Until recently, babies of this species were imported in great numbers. With proper care, they live well and grow rapidly. Specimens in my collection have been omnivorous, eating with equal relish such varied items as canned dog food, bits of raw beef, chopped whole fish, and lettuce and other greens. They seem to have more intelligence than the semi-aquatic emydid turtles. Sun-lovers, they will frequently usurp the available land-area of their aquarium and bite other turtles which attempt to dislodge them. Likewise, they will gain possession of rocks or other sunning places by harmlessly nipping other basking turtles. Very sensitive to chilling, these turtles should be kept at a temperature of about 75 degrees, and this must not be allowed to drop at night. Like many other tropical reptiles, *P. unifilis* can be killed by a single chilling. The six-tubercled greaved turtle, *Podocnemis sextuberculata*, is another species frequently imported. It does well if kept warm. It does not often leave the water and is mainly, if not wholly, carnivorous. The arrau turtle, *Podocnemis expansa*, is the largest of the genus; its shell may measure over two feet. It is an important food animal in northern South America.

TORTOISES

The true tortoises of the family Testudinidae are the favorite group of many amateur and professional herpetologists. They range in size from diminutive forms to the gigantic tortoises of the islands of the Aldabra and Galapagos groups. Some are somberly hued, while others must be classed among the most beautiful of the world's reptiles. Over sixty species and subspecies have been named, but of this number about one-fourth are the aforementioned giants which can rarely be procured or seen outside zoos. Tortoises are highly responsive reptiles and have long been regarded as the most intelligent of reptiles, but we cannot be sure whether this is true. Mostly creatures of warm and dry places, few will long survive captivity if kept in dampness or allowed to become chilled. They are the most docile of the reptile groups in their general demeanor and can seldom be induced to bite. Of the continents, only Australia is without tortoises. Africa has the greatest number of species. If we examine the hind foot of a tortoise we see that it is without webs; these reptiles are completely adapted to a terrestrial existence, and

Yellow-spotted Amazon, *Podocnemis unifilis.* Photo by R. J. Church.

Toad-headed turtle, *Batrachemys nasuta.* Photo by G. Marcuse.

Flat-headed turtle, *Platemys platycephala*. Photo by Dr. Herbert R. Axelrod.

Common snake-neck, *Chelodina longicollis*. Photo by G. Marcuse.

Broad-shelled snake-neck, *Chelodina expansa.* Photo by C. M. Bogert.

Emydura kreffti, Australia. Photo by C. M. Bogert.

Texas tortoise, *Gopherus berlandieri*. Photo by R. J. Church.

Bowsprit tortoise, *Chersina angulata*, South Africa. Photo by R. J. Church.

most kinds will not voluntarily enter water. Most subsist on vegetable matter, although a few will take meat from time to time. All should have fresh drinking water available in a low-walled container which cannot be easily tipped.

Four kinds of tortoises are found in North America. The gopher tortoise, *Gopherus polyphemus*, is familiar to residents of the southeastern United States. Gopher tortoises' long burrows, with a mound of sand at the entrance, are in evidence wherever the terrain is suitable. The Texas tortoise, *Gopherus berlandieri*, takes the place of the gopher in that state, while further west the desert tortoise, *Gopherus agassizi*, prevails. The Mexican giant gopher tortoise, *Gopherus flavomarginatus*, is found in the northern part of that country and has recently come on the animal market in some numbers. These tortoises may require some moisture in the early stages of their development, but the adults thrive best in a warm and dry environment. Vegetables and fruits make up the bulk of their diet.

The genus *Testudo* is made up of five species which are further divided into a number of subspecies. All are very much alike in outward appearance and habits, but the tortoise specialist nevertheless takes special delight in identifying them right down to subspecies.

Hermann's tortoise, *Testudo hermanni*. Photo by R. J. Church.

African mud turtle, *Pelusios subniger*. Photo by Dr. Herbert R. Axelrod.

Yellow-spotted Amazon, *Podocnemis unifilis*. Photo by Dr. Herbert R. Axelrod.

Gopher tortoise, *Gopherus polyphemus.* Photo by P. C. H. Pritchard.

Texas tortoise, *Gopherus berlandieri.* Photo by P. C. H. Pritchard.

Two of the most commonly kept kinds are Hermann's tortoise, *Testudo hermanni*, and the spur-thighed tortoise, *Testudo graeca*. Imported specimens commonly measure about six inches, and specimens of this size are frequently kept outdoors, in an enclosed yard or garden. Succulent fruits and vegetables are their choice of foods, and a specimen in good condition will consume a surprisingly large amount. If in perfect health, they may be permitted to hibernate, but any tortoise which is not of normal weight and vigor is not likely to survive such a period of rest. Certainly hibernation is not essential to their well-being, and if kept warm most specimens show little inclination to dig in for the winter. Though land animals in every sense of the word, Hermann's tortoise and the spur-thighed tortoise will enter a shallow container of water and seemingly benefit from such a bath. It cannot be emphasized too strongly, however, that these reptiles are extremely sensitive and are not able to withstand chilling, especially if it is combined with dampness. They are quick to contract respiratory disorders, a common manifestation of which is a wheezing cough.

One of the most beautiful members of the tortoise family is the Indian starred tortoise, *Geochelone elegans*. Of moderate size, this species has each shield of its shell raised in a concentrically ridged cone. Radiating lines of bright yellow symmetrically arranged on a field of black present a striking picture of this Asiatic species. Closely related and hardly less handsome is the leopard tortoise, *Geochelone pardalis*, of Africa, which sometimes will weigh eighty pounds when fully grown. Lately this species has become familiar, as large numbers are imported and sold to private collectors and zoos. There are two varieties, the commoner being the eastern leopard tortoise, *Geochelone pardalis babcocki*. In contrast to most tortoises, one South American kind is noted for its partiality to a humid forest environment. The South American forest tortoise and the red-foot tortoise, *Geochelone denticulata* and *Geochelone carbonaria*, are very much alike and were long considered a single species. Commonly imported, they are among the least expensive of exotic chelonians and do not demand the arid conditions upon which so many kinds of tortoises are dependent. They should be kept warm, 75 to 85 degrees, and fed abundantly on soft fruits and vegetables.

The real giants among the tortoises are, curiously, confined to small islands—the Galapagos Islands off western Ecuador and the

Seychelles Islands and Aldabra Islands off the east coast of Africa. Two species of giant tortoises are recognized, one from the Galapagos, *Geochelone elephantopus*, and one from the Aldabra group, *Geochelone gigantea*. Both species have subspecies. In the case of *G. elephantopus*, there are very many subspecies—each island having, it seems, a distinct form of tortoise. Giant tortoises have been known to exceed a shell length of four feet and a weight of 400 pounds. Despite the tight restrictions governing their export, quite a few Galapagos tortoises somehow get out of the islands. Grey or black in color, they would be even more startling to behold if they matched in gaudiness some of their smaller relatives. The giant tortoises live well over a hundred years and may even exceed two hundred. They grow quickly at first, then much more slowly. They are being propagated in small numbers in the United States.

The pancake tortoise, *Malacochersus tornieri*, is a frequent arrival from East Africa. This agile reptile has a very soft and flexible shell which enables it to squeeze into rock crevices in time of danger. An adult will have a shell about six inches long and only an inch high, presenting a very flattened appearance. In breeding habits the species is unusual in depositing only a single egg in July or August, the baby emerging in the fall. In captivity, pancake tortoises can be made to feel at ease by the provision of a hiding place to imitate the narrow rock crevices of their natural habitat. Whether a box or some other arrangement is made, it should have a roof only slightly higher than the tortoises' shells.

Among the more commonly imported African tortoises are the hinged tortoises, *Kinixys erosa*, *K. homeana*, and *K. belliana*. These are curious in the structure of their carapaces, being able to bring the rear portion down to meet the lower shell, affording the animal good protection from predatory creatures. Some dwell in damp places and are said to pursue and devour aquatic animals as well as the vegetables and fruits which form, at least in captivity, their more usual diet. Other, more obscure forms of African tortoises are those of the genera *Psammobates* and *Homopus*. The former genus has several small, rather bizarre little species that are confined to South Africa and are not commonly imported. They are among the smallest of the tortoise group. Madagascar has the spider tortoise, *Pyxis arachnoides*, perhaps the smallest tortoise.

Giant gopher tortoise, *Gopherus flavomarginatus.* Photo by P. C. H. Pritchard.

Desert tortoise, *Gopherus agassizi.* Photo by C. M. Bogert.

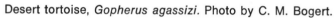

Hermann's tortoise, *Testudo hermanni.* Photo by P. C. H. Pritchard.

Indian starred tortoise, *Geochelone elegans.* Photo by P. C. H. Pritchard.

Hinged tortoise, *Kinixys homeana*. Photo by G. Marcuse.

TURTLE CARE

The care of turtles can be as simple or as complicated as one wishes to make it. Beginning turtle keepers are advised to start with inexpensive, easily procured types and, when the successful care of these has been mastered, graduate to the exotic or rarer kinds of native turtles. It should be understood that while baby turtles are very appealing, their care presents more problems than that of their more adaptable adults. Because they will readily consume many kinds of foods that are deficient in the vitamins and minerals which are essential to growth and health, many baby turtles in captivity appear to be doing well for a short time, only to fall eventually into a state of poor health which can be reversed only with great difficulty, if at all. It would be senseless and needlessly repetitive to list under the heading of each species all the foods that that particular kind of turtle can be fed.

Generally speaking, aquatic turtles are largely carnivorous, semi-aquatic types both carnivorous and herbivorous, and the tortoises largely herbivorous. This is not an infallible way of defining feeding habits, but it will apply in a general way. I have found it easy to bring babies of the aquatic types out of their critical period of infancy with finely chopped whole fish of the various kinds sold as bait for fresh and salt-water anglers. These bait fish seem to contain all the really essential ingredients for the promotion of normal growth, and may be varied with chopped worms, freeze-dried and live tubifex worms, enchytrae, crushed snails, and other small aquatic animals. The packaged ant-egg products sold so widely as food for baby turtles are all but useless in the care of baby turtles and should have no place in their diet. If a baby turtle is well nourished, an occasional feeding of finely ground lean raw beef seems to do little harm, and a few of the really hardy types of small turtles can even be maintained indefinitely on a diet of this sort, although they will seldom show normal growth. Vionate and bone meal, mixed in small amounts with a chopped beef diet, will help prevent vitamin deficiency conditions. Canned dog foods of the better grades are well fortified with vitamins and minerals and can be used with success when the infancy stage has been outgrown. From the standpoint of the keeper, it certainly is a convenient food to feed sub-adult and grown turtles.

Baby turtles such as the chicken, painted, and European pond turtles are difficult to raise and must be provided with food closely approximating that which they would find in the wild state. Freeze-dried and live tubifex worms, varied with ground pond snails, form a good starting diet for hatchlings. Marine turtles, babies especially, will do well on chopped fish and molluscs. In the early stage of my reptile-keeping, I maintained a baby snapping turtle on a diet of nothing but finely cut raw beef. It was about two inches long when I obtained it and after a year still appeared in excellent condition, with no shell-softening, but neither had it shown any noticeable growth during this time. I now realize that if it had been given more nourishing food it would have shown much growth. The snapper is a notably hardy turtle, and I doubt whether many other turtles could be successfully maintained over a long period of time on such a deficient

Forest tortoise, *Geochelone denticulata*. Photo by P. C. H. Pritchard.

Leopard tortoise, *Geochelone pardalis*. Photo by Dr. Herbert R. Axelrod.

Red-footed tortoise, *Geochelone carbonaria*. Photo by H. Schultz.

Galapagos giant tortoise, *Geochelone elephantopus*. Photo by P. C. H. Pritchard.

diet. A similar experiment with a baby alligator snapper terminated with great shell-softening and early demise. In connection with this experience with the baby alligator snapper, it will be of interest to note that it is the only turtle in my experience which will develop the symptoms of vitamin deficiency, such as soft-shell, and yet continue to grow several inches before succumbing. The thoroughly aquatic baby turtles will generally ignore lettuce leaves or other vegetable matter; the semi-aquatic, basking types of the family Emydidae will often avidly devour such matter thrown into their water. The terrestrial emydids such as the wood, box, and Blanding's turtles can and do eat on land, but their babies are best fed in very shallow water. Only a very few kinds of adult turtles resemble the true tortoises in being able to eat on land.

Poor nutrition early in life can lead to dwarfing. This two-inch turtle is a three-year-old diamondback. Photo by R. J. Church.

In the case of turtles beyond their third year, much less attention needs to be given to diet. While babies are best kept on a daily small feeding, most adults will do well on a liberal meal twice a week. The bone-hardening process seems to be completed during the first years of a turtle's life, and I cannot recall a case of shell-softening in an adult turtle, though other debilities can develop through improper feeding. For the reasons given above, it is obvious that a half-grown or adult turtle is easier to care for than a juvenile. I consider the box turtle an ideal species to begin with—but only if well grown.

Baby tortoises are, if anything, even more difficult to raise than their aquatic and semi-aquatic relatives. For the most part herbivorous, it is essential that the crushed fruits and vegetables given them be well mixed with powdered vitamins and calcium. They should have drinking water available at all times, for creatures of small bulk will desiccate much more rapidly than larger ones. Some of the fruits and vegetables which may be offered tortoises are lettuce, bananas, pears, berries, and chopped carrots; hard-boiled eggs with crushed shells and canned dog food may be offered. Some baby tortoises will take earthworms. Their drinking water should contain copper—a penny will do—and a piece of slowly dissolving calcium block in the water will be of benefit, too. These should be placed in the swimming-water of baby aquatic and semi-aquatic turtles, also. Caring for baby turtles and tortoises requires something of the gardener's "green thumb." Some persons have had remarkable success in raising them but in such cases a great deal of patience has played a major role. Collectors with little time for the sympathetic care required by most baby chelonians will find half-grown or adult specimens more accommodating in their requirements.

The matter of providing correct air and water temperatures for turtles and tortoises is a very important one, as it is for nearly all other reptiles. Some writers attempt to describe what they consider optimum temperatures for various chelonians. Such information seems somewhat overdone; all turtles and tortoises are warmth-loving animals, with the possible exception of the Asiatic big-headed turtle and certain very aquatic native species. I consider a temperature range of 78 to 83 degrees quite satisfactory for the great majority of turtles and tortoises. Tropical tortoises, particularly, are apt to fall into serious trouble if the air temperature falls below 70 degrees. With these, even cold drinking water may prove detrimental. At 90

Hinged tortoise, *Kinixys belliana.* Photo by Dr. Herbert R. Axelrod.

Aldabra giant tortoise, *Geochelone gigantea.* Photo by P. C. H. Pritchard.

Parrot-beaked tortoise, *Homopus areolatus*. Photo by M. F. Roberts.

False gavial, *Tomistoma schlegeli.* Photo by H. Hansen, Aquarium Berlin.

degrees many turtles show evidence of distress. This is especially true of those species which may normally aestivate in the wild state during hot weather, and of the aquatic species which may enter deeper water at such times. At the upper limit of the desirable temperature range, there is increased activity and a need for larger and more frequent feedings.

Tied in closely with the subject of feeding captive turtles is the matter of cleanliness. It is rather startling to read, as I have recently, in a supposedly erudite publication, that cleanliness is not important in keeping chelonians. Anyone who has kept large numbers of turtles and tortoises will know the detrimental effects that a sustained state of fouled water can have. I consider it a good idea to feed aquatic and semi-aquatic turtles in a container other than their permanent home. Few keepers of turtles have the facilities for installing the complicated plumbing which will permit large aquariums to be easily drained and refilled with fresh water. The excreta of turtles has far

Example of a well-planned but simple aquarium for water turtles. Photo by R. J. Chuch.

Terrariums for tortoises need not be complicated to be attractive. Photo by R. J. Church.

less of a polluting effect on their water than decaying bits of fish or meat. The plastic basins sold in department and variety stores are light and easy to handle, and may be bought cheaply. They are ideal feeding places for turtles of small to medium size. Water used in these basins should be near the temperature of the permanent home. Incidentally, when large numbers of baby turtles are being reared, these plastic containers can be utilized as nurseries. The cleanliness of the turtles themselves should be given some thought. Algae are often found on the shells of wild turtles, often to the degree of completely obscuring their shell markings. I do not think that captives should be compelled to have their beauty so concealed, and I use ordinary household vinegar and a soft cloth to periodically clean the shells of my turtles. A brush would be more effective, but experience has shown that even a soft-bristled brush will greatly agitate turtles, sensitive as they are to any tactile stimuli of their shells.

The pH factor in water has undergone considerable study by aquarists who keep and breed fishes. They have found that it may be critically important in the propagation of certain fish species. The

Young caiman, *Caiman yacare.* Photo by H. Hansen, Aquarium Berlin.

Gavial, *Gavialis gangeticus.* Photo by K. Alexander.

Spectacled caiman, *Caiman crocodilus*. Photo by M. F. Roberts.

Desert iguana, *Dipsosaurus dorsalis*. Photo by J. K. Langhammer.

matter is little understood as it relates to turtle husbandry, but we do know that fungus infections can often be cleared up when there is a drastic reduction in the alkalinity of the water. Monobasic sodium phosphate can be added to water to bring it to the desired pH. Vinegar can be added to achieve the same result. Kits for the simple testing of pH content can be bought in most pet shops. A slightly acid water may be best for most turtles—a reading of pH 6.6 or 6.8. With continued experiments in the breeding of chelonians in captivity, it would not be surprising to find that pH is a factor of some consequence.

Sunlight is very important to most turtles and tortoises and is essential in the raising of some species. The ordinary high-walled aquarium will filter out most of the beneficial rays, as will ordinary window glass. For this reason, low-sided aquariums are best for turtles. These can be placed in open windows, preferably with a southern exposure; so placed, they will allow the inmates a natural sunbath. Of course, this can be done only in warm weather. During our northern winters, turtles which have hatched in the fall can be brought through the difficult months with the use of one of the many sun lamps on the market. These lamps vary considerably in the intensity of their ultraviolet ray output and lacking, as we do, specific information pertaining to the effect of long exposure of turtles and tortoises under these lamps, it is best to limit their use to the time specified for humans. Such directions accompany these lamps, some of which may be purchased for as little as ten dollars.

Most turtles will feed readily in confinement, although some are excessively shy when first caught and may refuse to eat the first week or two. If a turtle is being kept under good conditions and refuses to eat over a long period, there can be any one of several distinct causes. First of all, the food itself may be at fault. Most turtles' feeding habits are not specialized to the extent that they will accept no substitute for the food they are accustomed to taking in the wild state. I have, however, noted that certain of the mollusc-devouring species which develop enormous heads in the adult stage will often refuse any substitute for their natural fare. This condition may prevail in adults of certain map turtles and musk turtles. Snail-eating turtles of the genus *Malayemys* are said to feed on little else, but in an aquarium they will readily accept a substitute diet. A turtle which naturally hibernates in cold weather may be disinclined to partake of food during this period, but this is not usual; such a specimen will continue to feed, at least sparingly, as a rule. A turtle in really poor health will not eat, and a variety of conditions may be responsible. The turtle's illness will generally manifest itself in other recognizable ways.

BUYING TURTLES

The illnesses to which captive chelonians are susceptible may be traced mostly to the lack of proper care. Once a turtle is sick, a spontaneous recovery is very rare; definite measures must be taken to reverse the conditions which brought about the illness. Before taking up what we know about turtle ailments, let us discuss the methods whereby we may at least assure ourselves that the specimen we are about to acquire is in good condition to begin with. Sick turtles, or other herptiles, for that matter, are seldom found in the wild. Nature is no respecter of ill health or old age, and no creature survives long when it has become infirm. We may therefore assume that a turtle we have captured ourselves is in good condition. A turtle purchased from a dealer, on the other hand, may have been subjected to gross mistreatment from the time of its capture.

I would not buy a turtle that has been kept under filthy conditions, allowed to go without water over a long period, or that is in contact with other turtles that seem in bad condition. It is better to patronize those dealers who care enough about the welfare of their live wares to assure them conditions of reasonable comfort while awaiting a sale. Perhaps the first and easiest thing to assess, in the case of a juvenile chelonian, is the hardness of its shell. A few turtles and tortoises have a naturally soft shell. This is true of the pancake tortoises and the aptly named soft-shelled turtles. Other turtles should have a reasonably hard, firm shell. The eyes should be bright and alert, without a trace of film or exudate of any kind. The area about the nostrils should be free of any discharge. The shell should be without eroded or eaten-out spots. The weight should be good, and this can be readily determined by anyone who has had some little experience with turtles. Normally, a turtle or tortoise feels quite heavy for its bulk. The head, neck, and limbs should be checked for the presence of whitish spots that may indicate a fungus infection. It should be without lumps or sores. Finally, it should be placed in several inches of water, if an aquatic or semi-aquatic

Chuckwalla, *Sauromalus obesus.* Photo by J. K. Langhammer.

Earless lizard, *Holbookia maculata.* Photo by F. J. Dodd, Jr.

Collared lizard, *Crotaphytus collaris.*

Zebra-tailed lizard, *Callisaurus draconoides.* Photo by F. J. Dodd, Jr.

species, and its actions carefully noted. With due time allowed for a hydrostatic adjustment, a turtle should be able to dive and swim well under water. A specimen that floats on the surface and seems to make an effort to go under but cannot do so is in bad shape indeed. This last test is not applicable to tortoises or to those emydid turtles, such as the box, whose normal existence is on land. These days keepers of turtles are able and willing to pay high prices for desired specimens, so the insistence on a thorough examination before purchase does not seem unreasonable.

The mail order business in turtles and other herptiles has become an important part of the animal trade. In building up a collection, it may seem desirable to acquire specimens from a dealer or trader some distance away. Like other businesses, the selling of animals is competitive and is likely to become even more so in the future. Most dealers rely heavily on repeat orders and do not consider it profitable, over the long run, to ship unhealthy animals. Besides, most dealers are basically honest. Terms are clearly spelled out on their price lists, and nearly all dealers guarantee live delivery of the animals they ship. When one wishes to obtain only chelonians that are in the very best of shape, however, a brief telephone call to the seller can tell the prospective purchaser much more than a price list description. The importation of turtles from other countries falls into another category entirely. It seems that luck plays an important part in the successful consummation of every importation from abroad.

With proper care, a turtle or tortoise may live many years in confinement. Our knowledge of these fascinating relics of past ages is increasing, and much can be learned from observations of captive animals. Serological and other studies in the laboratory are helping to clarify the relationships between turtles, and I think it is safe to say that these herptiles will be the first about which we will have a reasonably complete knowledge.

III

Alligators, Caimans, and Crocodiles

CROCODILIANS IN GENERAL

Alligators, crocodiles, caimans, and gavials combine to make up a reptile order of their own, the order Crocodylia, generally divided into three families: the Gavialidae, the Alligatoridae, and the Crocodylidae. There are some two dozen species recognized. All crocodilians are much alike in form and habits, but they differ greatly in the extent of growth they achieve. It may come as a surprise to some to learn that one species, at least, grows to only four feet, while several others seem not to exceed six feet. Each tropical and subtropical portion of the globe has one or more kinds of crocodilians. All live in the immediate proximity of water, but none is able to live entirely in water and none is able to survive long without water. Thus we have a group of truly amphibious animals that are indigenous to warm climates. If we keep these facts in mind we are more likely to have good results in keeping them in captivity.

The identification of the various crocodilians which come on the animal market is not an easy task for the novice, since the characters which differentiate the species are very technical ones, based on the position and relationship of the bony shields of the back and the number and position of teeth. Persons seeking rarities in reptiles will browse the establishments of animal dealers. If a cage or aquarium contains a large number of individuals, often one or two will stand out as being "different," though not in any easily definable way. Such a specimen may well be of one of the rarer types. Baby crocodilians

Green anole, *Anolis carolinensis.* Photo by G. Marcuse.

Leopard lizard, *Crotaphytus wislizenii.* Photo by J. K. Langhammer.

Clark's spiny lizard, *Sceloporus clarki.* Photo by F. J. Dodd, Jr.

Spiny lizard, *Sceloporus nelsoni,* Mexico. Photo by F. J. Dodd, Jr.

can range in price from a couple of dollars to well over a hundred dollars, and herptile hobbyists do not differ from others in continually seeking bargains. Take the "odd" one home and have fun identifying it in your leisure time.

All crocodilians lay eggs; the eggs are laid on land, in a situation which will provide the necessary heat and moisture for their development. Some species remain near their nests to protect the eggs from the predations of creatures which consider them a delicacy. Would-be hunters of crocodilian nests had best keep this in mind. Nests may be elaborate or simple, depending on the species. A baby crocodilian is among the most engaging of baby reptiles and from the very first will display all the characteristics of adult members of its kind. If treated properly, however, it will soon grow to a size that is not easily accommodated in the average private collection. A curious thing that I have not seen mentioned elsewhere is that under certain circumstances a baby crocodilian that is kept warm and fed well, but kept in a small cage, will have its growth limited by the area of its surroundings. I have seen this happen in the case of an American alligator which occupied for over ten years a cage about the size of a twenty-gallon aquarium. It was about a foot long when obtained and took perhaps two years to reach a length of two feet. Beyond this point, it did not grow but remained vigorous and in apparently the best of health. It was kept at a constant temperature of eighty degrees and fed exclusively on goldfish and other aquatic animals. It became very tame—a veritable pet—and assumed the heavy body build of an adult, but remained adjusted in size to the aquarium it occupied. It had a bathing pool sunk in a floor of gravel, but entered it only at feeding times. It received sunlight only in the filtered form, through two thicknesses of glass. Whether such dwarfing of a specimen is always possible—or desirable—I do not know, but mention it only as an aside to the usual experience of having a young croc outgrow one cage after another. It would seem that spaciousness of surroundings, in addition to all the other factors of caring for a young crocodilian, plays an important part in the growth process.

Crocodilians of all sizes are well-equipped for defense, and even very small ones are best held just behind the head to prevent scratches from their sharp teeth and strong jaws. Specimens of three feet are best handled with thick leather gloves. Some crocodilians have an unvarying aggressiveness and remain vicious even after a long period of confinement. In the wild state a crocodilian will overpower and eat animals of large size. The man-eating propensities of a few kinds are well authenticated. Food may be seized on the land or in the water, but is always devoured in the latter element. Here the croc is perfectly at home, and I do not think many creatures have lived to tell the tale of an engagement with a large crocodilian. Crocodilians' jaws are very powerful in regard to biting pressure, but this power, strangely, cannot be exerted to open the mouth. It is possible for the average person to hold the mouth of a large crocodilian shut with only his hands. This may be witnessed in the alligator-wrestling shows.

Crocodilians display great agility—in and out of water. An effective means of defense and offense is provided by their powerful tails. This is swung with great swiftness and can easily topple a man if the blow comes from a large specimen. With its muscular tail the crocodilian swims gracefully and well. Some species enter the ocean and swim far from shore. Crocodilians run well out of the water and do so with the body well raised from the ground. They seem incapable of sustaining this means of locomotion over a long period, however. Some of the larger types are genuinely dangerous animals and will kill and eat a man as they would any other mammal of similar size. Even such good-dispositioned species as our American alligator will sometimes display suspicious activity in this respect, especially in those places where it is under legal protection and has come to the state of contempt bred by familiarity and non-molestation.

All crocodilians are completely carnivorous. To sustain good health, they must receive an adequate intake of vitamins and minerals. I consider small fishes, fed whole or chopped, the best food for juveniles. Larger specimens may be fed mice and rats, as well as other vertebrate animals. Their calcium requirements are high and adequate portions must be provided if normal health and growth are to be ensured. Sunlight is a great asset if judiciously provided and the animals are not allowed to become overheated. All species do best in a temperature of 80 to 85 degrees. Whether kept in a large aquarium or other type of cage, they must be provided with water in which they can completely submerge, but must also be provided with a land area for completely drying out, as they would on the banks of their native rivers. They seem to be subject to fewer diseases than lizards, turtles, or snakes. Rickets will develop in malnourished captives; with the

Tree lizard, *Urosaurus ornatus,* southwestern U.S. Photo by F. J. Dodd, Jr.

Brown-shouldered lizard, *Uta stansburiana,* southwestern U.S. Photo by F. J. Dodd, Jr.

Texas horned lizard, *Phrynosoma cornutum.* Photo by J. K. Langhammer.

Short-horned lizard, *Phrynosoma douglassi*, western U.S. Photo by J. K. Langhammer.

long, slender-snouted crocs, rickets can result in gross deformity. Crocodilians live to a great age—possibly approaching that of some turtles. They grow rapidly and are likely to add a foot or more to their length each year under especially favorable conditions.

Crocodiles and alligators should not be mixed with other reptiles or amphibians, nor should they be mixed in sizes among themselves. Cuts and bruises are frequent from fights and these can be swabbed with iodine and will usually heal without complications. Baby crocodiles should have their mouths examined periodically. Their teeth should be clean and if encrusted, as seldom happens, can be brushed with very soft bristles. This will seldom be found necessary if the animals are housed in clean and well-kept cages and liberally supplied with the right foods. Such an examination of the teeth and mouth can be made while the reptile is basking with its mouth open. In their first months of captivity, crocodilians sometimes void large numbers of intestinal worms. These become fewer in number as time goes on and often disappear entirely. They appear to be of little consequence to their hosts.

Young crocodilians are often considered to be delicate, but they will do well if fed often on the right foods and given enough heat. Photo by M. F. Roberts.

Crocodilians from temperate regions hibernate in the natural state during the cooler months, while those of some tropical areas may estivate. Either of these inclinations may be carried over into captivity and cause an apparently quite healthy reptile to go off feed for a period of time. In anticipation of such a fast, the keeper of crocodilians should make every attempt to keep his specimens well nourished. They will thus have the weight to carry them through several weeks or even months of abstention from food. I would recommend that a baby crocodilian be fed not less often than every other day. This will mean a considerable amount of cleaning, as it is essential that a young crocodilian's water be kept free from pollution. Generally, it will not be practicable to remove a croc from its permanent home for feeding—a system often used with turtles. Many baby crocodilians will not feed in unfamiliar surroundings.

Crocodiles and alligators are subject to fewer disease conditions than other reptiles. Sometimes, however, there appears a cracking and sloughing of the outer epidermis, a condition which is probably related to excessive dryness. It can be alleviated by massaging with pure petroleum jelly. Crocodiles and alligators continually lose and replace teeth in the wild, but in captivity they may lose this capacity because of poor feeding habits. Once again, it is essential to provide the baby crocodilian with its natural food supplemented with small amounts of vitamins and minerals.

I do not think that any private collector has anything like a complete collection of the crocodilians of the world; the rarity of many species and the rapid growth of the animals themselves form an effective barrier to the formation of such a collection without unlimited financial resources. Since they are so alike in habits and general appearance, a young specimen or two will well represent this entire order of living fossils.

GAVIAL

The most curious of the living crocodilians is the gavial, *Gavialis gangeticus*, the single member of its family, Gavialidae. Though growing to a huge size, more than twenty feet, it is not considered a dangerous species in its native haunts—the great river systems of India. It has greatly attenuated jaws that are studded with a massive array of closely interlocking teeth. Despite the great bulk of a fully grown specimen, its diet consists entirely of fishes, and its slender

Regal horned lizard, *Phrynosoma solare*. Photo by J. K. Langhammer.

Yucca night lizard, *Xantusia vigilis*. Photo by F. J. Dodd, Jr.

Broad-headed skink, *Eumeces laticeps.* Photo by F. J. Dodd, Jr.

Arizona alligator lizard, *Gerrhonotus kingi.* Photo by F. J. Dodd, Jr.

Indian gavial, *Gavialis gangeticus.* Photo by G. Marcuse.

snout seems an adaptation to this diet. The gavial is one crocodilian which must be handled with the best of care in captivity. Special attention should be given its diet, which should consist entirely of fish. These may be fortified with additional calcium and vitamins before they are tendered the animal. Though formidably arrayed with teeth, the jaws of a gavial look, and are, very fragile and easily broken. More than one gavial is today surviving in a zoo minus a portion of its snout—the result of a quarrel over food with a species of more robustness. Common in India, gavials are rarely imported and are among the most expensive crocodilians.

AMERICAN ALLIGATORS

The American alligator, *Alligator mississipiensis*, was once the most readily procurable crocodilian, but it is now rigidly protected throughout the southern United States. Dealers are no longer allowed to handle this animal.

If the mass commercial traffic in alligator skins and baby specimens for souvenirs had not been halted, this creature might today be on the list of those close to extinction. When any animal is threatened with extermination, generally the larger individuals disappear first. It is said that American alligators once abounded as twenty-foot monsters, but now any individual over twelve feet must be considered very large. Baby alligators are among the more handsome members of the crocodilian tribe, being jet black in ground color and crossbanded the length of the back and tail with bright yellow. They are somewhat hardier than many exotic crocodilians and can withstand lower temperatures, but this is not said with the intention of easing caution in the matter of providing a warm environment. Alligators hibernate in the winter but in captivity should be kept constantly in an environmental heat of 75 to 90 degrees, and this applies to air as well as water. Bits of lean raw beef and liver will be greedily devoured but do not constitute a complete diet; insects, earthworms, and fishes and other small vertebrates are needed. Easily-tamed, the alligator can often be handled easily even when fully grown—this in distinct contrast to many of the foreign crocodilians.

Adult alligators have dens to which they regularly retire. These dens are holes in river banks, and it is in them that the cooler months are weathered. Males grow larger than females and, except at breeding time, are likely to lead a solitary existence, driving off smaller reptiles and even devouring their own young when they are encountered. Courtship and mating take place in the water, and the

American alligator, *Alligator mississipiensis.* Photo by Wathen.

Gila monster, *Heloderma suspectum*. Photo by H. Hansen, Aquarium Berlin.

Island glass lizard, *Ophisaurus compressus.* Photo by F. J. Dodd, Jr.

Gecko, *Peropus mutilatus.* Photo by F. J. Dodd, Jr.

female constructs a rather elaborate nest for eggs. The nest consists of a mound of debris several feet in width and height. The eggs, numbering up to almost 75, are deposited in a central hollow which is then smoothed over. Two to three months are required for incubation; during this time the female remains close by. When the babies are ready to emerge she assists them by opening the nest with her jaws—the same manner in which she constructed it. Baby alligators have many enemies besides man, so probably only a few reach maturity. The cottonmouth moccasin may play an important part in keeping a population balance.

Baby alligators give voice to grunts in recognition of their keepers as providers of food. These noises become deeper as the young reptiles mature; in adult males, the grunts assume the proportions of a resounding roar which can be heard for great distances in the stillness of a bayou night. Baby alligators get accustomed to handling. In common with some other reptiles and amphibians, notably certain lizards and toads, they can be pacified by being laid on their backs and gently massaged on the stomach area.

CHINESE ALLIGATOR

The Chinese alligator, *Alligator sinensis*, is a close relative of the American alligator but is very much separated geographically, being found in eastern China. It is a small species, seldom growing to more than six feet. It is considered a rare animal and is seldom offered for sale by dealers. Together with the American alligator and the South American caimans it makes up the family Alligatoridae.

CAIMANS

The caimans are the crocodilians most commonly sold by pet dealers these days. They are imported from South America in immense numbers and have all but taken over the unenviable position once held by the American alligator in the pet trade. The little creatures most commonly seen are varieties of the widely-distributed spectacled caiman, *Caiman crocodilus*. Bony ridges in front of and around the eyes are responsible for the common name of these reptiles. All of the caimans are tropical reptiles, and this above all else should be kept in mind when one purchases a baby. They have a maximum length of about eight feet and show rapid growth under good conditions. Like other crocodilians, they are

The crocodiles (family Crocodylidae) differ visibly from the alligators and caimans (family Alligatoridae) by having the fourth tooth in the lower jaw visible when the mouth is closed; it is hidden in a pocket in the upper jaw in alligators. Photo by G. Marcuse of a young alligator.

entirely carnivorous and can be fed snails, earthworms, minnows, frogs, and other small animals. Their usual diet, unfortunately, is a much less nourishing one, consisting for the most part of scraps of raw beef and liver. Caimans generally will not take any spiced or cured meat or salted fish. If fed on bits of lean beef, this should be sprinkled with bone meal and a vitamin compound. Hamburger is not a good food, because it falls apart easily, and much of it is left to foul the water of the reptile's cage. Hatchlings of eight to ten inches can readily swallow whole pieces of meat the size of an almond nut. As with all of the crocodilians, some sunlight is a very great aid in promoting the health of captive caimans, especially during their first year. The aquarium or cage for caimans should be about equally divided between land and water, the latter being of about four inches in depth. In selecting a caiman from the aquarium of a dealer, pick the liveliest of the group—one that is ready to bite when picked up.

Tokay gecko, *Gekko gecko.* Photos by H. Hansen, Aquarium Berlin.

Madagascar day gecko, *Phelsuma madagascariensis.* Photo by H.
Hansen, Aquarium Berlin.

Many of the specimens we find have been poorly conditioned and are quite thin. Apathetic toward their surroundings, they lie limply about, awaiting an early end. Freshly-caught specimens are vigorous little animals, bright and strong, and will remain so if handled correctly. They tame after a while, but remain voracious and will leap from the water to grasp a piece of food offered to them. Caimans are today the least expensive of the crocodilians. It remains to be seen how long their tropical jungle homes will be able to supply the large numbers being sold as pets, not to mention the demands of the leather trade for the hides of grown specimens.

The largest member of the caiman and alligator family is the black caiman, *Melanosuchus niger*, of the Amazon Basin and Guianas. Its maximum length may be about fifteen feet, but few specimens of this size are captured alive. Babies of this species resemble small American alligators very much. Like other caimans, they do well if kept warm and provided with a nourishing diet.

I recommend a constant temperature range of 78 to 85 degrees for all crocodilians. They succumb almost at once to a really bad chilling. The critical low for the various crocodilians has not been established, but I would suspect that it might be surprisingly high. Undoubtedly, the most tolerant of the crocodilians in regard to temperature drops is the American alligator, but even this species must be kept very warm. Other kinds of caimans which are imported from time to time are the dwarf caiman, *Paleosuchus palpebrosus*, and the smooth-fronted caiman, *Paleosuchus trigonatus*, of the Amazon Basin. These are really small crocodilians, averaging around four feet.

CROCODILES

The family Crocodylidae contains the true stars of the world of crocodilians. Ranging in size from four-foot dwarfs to twenty-five-foot giants, the members of this family flourish throughout the New and Old World tropics. Zoo curators and keepers have long been aware of the differences in temperament among the various species of crocodilians. Among the present group we find some truly dangerous animals—feared in their native haunts and best handled with extreme caution in captivity. In comparison with alligators and caimans, the true crocodiles appear formidable, and their looks are hardly belied by their dispositions. The true crocodiles provide the only authenticated instances of habitual reptilian predation upon human beings. Few private collectors will have the inclination or means of keeping adult crocodiles in captivity, and even very few zoos are equipped to handle really large specimens. Babies are often offered for sale and, during their first two or three years, make interesting occupants of a collection. A fully-grown crocodile of one of the larger kinds may exceed a ton in weight. By comparison, a giant python may weigh in the neighborhood of 250 pounds.

The American crocodile, *Crocodylus acutus,* is the only one of its family which is found in the United States. In extreme southern Florida it frequents brackish coastal waters in small numbers. In Central America, Mexico, the West Indies, and South America it is an abundant reptile. Young specimens are olive-tan, with dark cross-striping along the back and tail; as the animal grows these markings become obscure and finally are lost entirely, leaving a plain dark brown or black animal. I had owned many alligators before I acquired my first crocodile, and it presented an interesting contrast in behavior to the former. It would bask in the sun for hours at a

American crocodile, *Crocodylus acutus.* Photo by G. Marcuse.

Day gecko, *Phelsuma* sp. Photo by H. Hansen, Aquarium Berlin.

Leopard gecko, *Eublepharis macularius.* Photo by H. Hansen, Aquarium Berlin.

Tree lizard, *Calotes calotes*. Photo by H. Hansen, Aquarium Berlin.

time with its jaws agape—a habit I have not observed among alligators. It would occasionally utter a long, drawn-out grunt—this with open mouth—which was very different from the noises made by the baby alligators. It was an agile creature, and though slender in comparison with alligators of the same length, it seemed more powerfully muscled. It became very tame, but its strenuous twisting made it always a difficult animal to pick up and hold for long. In connection with the handling of crocodilians it should be advised that they never be picked up or allowed to hang by the tail. The proper grasp is a firm one just behind the head, the other hand supporting and restraining the rear portions of the reptile. Freshly-caught crocodiles may have leeches attached to them, mostly about their legs. These are easily removed with forceps.

Nile crocodile, *Crocodylus niloticus.* Photo by L. E. Perkins.

Slender-snouted crocodile, *Crocodylus cataphractus*, Africa. Photo by G. Marcuse.

The Nile crocodile, *Crocodylus niloticus*, is a species which is greatly feared by the natives of African villages. A sixteen-foot example can easily kill a man. In the taking of any prey species, the crocodile's mode is to seize the victim and bring it to deep water, where it can be held until it drowns. Unable to swallow massive objects, the crocodile reduces its victims to manageable pieces by twisting and tearing the bodies in its powerful jaws, which are equipped with long, sharp teeth. If two crocodiles seize the same animal, they will fold their limbs and twirl about in opposite directions, tearing their victim apart. Crocodiles fight among themselves, especially when hungry, and serious injury or death may be the result of such quarrels. Alligators and caimans cannot match the dental equipment of the true crocodiles and are likely to come out the worse in any dispute with their vicious relatives. The situation was once reversed at Ross Allen's Reptile Institute in Florida, when a huge crocodile somehow managed to thrust its head into a pen containing a large alligator. The latter seized the crocodile's head and went into the characteristic rolling. The injuries inflicted proved fatal.

Another of the man-eaters is the salt-water crocodile, *Crocodylus porosus*, of Asia and Australia, which may reach twenty feet in length. Even as babies these reptiles show a great exhibition of temper and for a while some may not feed in captivity. It frequents estuaries

Tree lizard, *Calotes versicolor,* Afganistan to southern China. Photo by H. Hansen, Aquarium Berlin.

Frilled lizard, *Chlamydosaurus kingi.* Photo by G. Marcuse.

Household agama, *Agama agama,* Africa. Photo by Dr. Otto Klee.

mostly but has been seen far offshore in salt water. Crocodiles of this and other kinds may be successfully force-fed, but force-feeding should be resorted to only when the animal has fasted for some time and there seems little likelihood of its taming sufficiently to partake voluntarily of food. Fresh whole fish are best used for force-feeding; the fish should be inserted head-first into the reptile's throat and placed as far back as possible. Wooden blunt-tipped forceps may be used to minimize damage to the angry reptile's teeth and mouth when it clamps shut. Most crocodiles will eat after they have been in captivity for a short time, and it is not desirable to maintain a specimen of any herptile which does not feed voluntarily.

Muggers are Asiatic crocodiles known scientifically as *Crocodylus palustris*. Widespread and very abundant, they are timid animals and somewhat alligator-like in disposition. Like alligators, they have broad and massive heads. Occasional examples have become predaceous upon humans, but with this species the rule is here excepted. In India, muggers are often corraled in a semi-domesticated state; they are said to breed well under such conditions. Muggers have an average length of about twelve feet. An example of this size would require about twelve pounds of meat a week to keep it in good condition.

Two species of dwarf crocodiles are recognized. One, the Congo dwarf crocodile, *Osteolaemus osborni*, is considered the smallest living crocodilian, with an adult length of about four feet. The other, the West African dwarf crocodile, *Osteolaemus tetraspis*, is but slightly larger. Little is known of the habits of either of these rare reptiles.

The false gavial, *Tomistoma schlegeli*, stands in a genus of its own. It is the most slender-snouted of the true crocodiles and superficially resembles the true Indian gavial. False gavials are found on the Malay Peninsula, Sumatra, and Borneo. Like all other crocodilian species with excessively slender snouts, false gavials can be quickly and permanently deformed if fed on the wrong kinds of foods during their early years. Fish constitute the main fare of these animals in the wild state and must be provided in captivity. If a young false gavial is fed on meat, the snout will not lengthen in natural conformity with the growth of the infant, but instead will hook upward, with the teeth growing in every which way. If natural sunlight or the substitute of a sun lamp is not available, it is especially important to

False gavial, *Tomistoma schlegeli,* in top and side views. Photos by
G. Marcuse.

Water lizard, *Physignathus cocincinus,* southern Asia. Photo by H. Hansen, Aquarium Berlin.

Water lizard, *Physignathus lesueuri*, Photo by H. Hansen, Aquarium Berlin.

to make sure that all baby crocodilians receive vitamin and mineral supplements to their regular diets.

Frequently the reptile man is asked to explain the difference between an alligator and a crocodile. The question is asked, generally, by someone who thinks that the names denote quite different animals. This is not so. The alligators, caimans, crocodiles, and gavial are very closely related, more so than the members of other orders of herptiles. It is true that the animals we know as crocodiles are usually more vicious and harder to tame, but even in this matter of temperament there are exceptions. Muggers, which are true crocodiles, tame readily in captivity, whereas caimans of some kinds are often hard to handle and resemble the worst of the crocodiles in this respect. A simple answer to the question of the difference between an alligator and a crocodile must revert to details of dentition. Simply put, with the crocodiles the fourth tooth of the lower jaw remains visible when the mouth of the reptile is closed. With the alligators and caimans, this tooth fits into a socket in the upper jaw and is thus not to be seen when the mouth is closed. Some of the caimans are very like crocodiles in appearance, and this matter of tooth difference can serve to enable anyone to determine whether a questionable specimen is a caiman or a crocodile.

Crocodiles in general, no matter how abundant they may be in their Old World jungle homes, will command a better price than the more common caimans. Persons engaged in the selling of reptiles are almost always aware of the identity and true value of their wares. The American crocodile is usually the only true crocodile which can be purchased for a moderate sum.

IV

Native American Lizards

The lizards of the United States are a fascinatingly varied group of reptiles that will well repay the effort expended on their behalf in providing suitable conditions for them in captivity. None grows to a really large size, and most are readily procurable.

Unlike the snakes and other reptiles which often make a quick and good adjustment to cage life, lizards are a bit more demanding in their requirements. Also, they usually don't live as long as other captive reptiles. This may be due to the fact that many of the smaller kinds are naturally short-lived, as many of the smaller snakes are believed to be. This may not be the whole story, however, for in exceptional cases even the smallest lizards have lived for very long periods. It is a very rewarding accomplishment to maintain a varied group of lizards in good health.

Lizards belong to the suborder Sauria and are often referred to, collectively, as saurians. They are quite closely related to snakes; the latter have, in fact, been derived from them. The smaller lizards, especially the secretive kinds, are often mistakenly identified as salamanders—even by herpetologists in the field, where a snap judgment of a scurrying creature has to be made! All lizards differ from salamanders in having a scaly, usually dry skin; salamanders have a moist, scaleless skin which feels clammy and often sticky to the touch. Some lizards have no legs; the legless lizards are few in number in the United States, and where they are found they are commonly regarded by local residents as snakes. Like most other lizards, they have eyelids and external ear openings that immediately separate them from the snakes, which have neither. The Southwest

Sail-tailed water lizard, *Hydrosaurus amboinensis.* Photo by H. Hansen, Aquarium Berlin.

Knight anole, *Anolis equestris.* Photo by G. Marcuse.

Spiny iguana, *Ctenosaura hemilopha*, Mexico. Photo by F. J. Dodd, Jr.

is the stronghold of the lizards in the United States, followed by the Southeast. As one proceeds toward the North, the numbers and kinds of these sprightly forms diminish, because lizards are warmth-loving animals; most of the 3000 lizard species live in the tropics. In New England, for instance, any lizard is an exceptionally rare find.

Lizards live in trees, on the ground, and in subterranean tunnels. Matters of habitat and moisture requirements must be taken into account if they are to be kept in health. Most lizards in this country are diurnal, but there are a few kinds which are active by night. Lizards are among the cleanest of animals in captivity and, once set up in an appropriate cage, require but little attention. Like snakes and turtles, they are quiet animals and not likely to disturb their neighbors, in this respect, at least. Many species have a fragile tail, and no lizard should ever be handled by its caudal appendage. In most species, the tail is likely to break under the slightest stress, while those species that have a more durable tail can suffer a vertebral injury if allowed to twist about or hang by this member. With the single exception of the Gila monster, the lizards of the United States are harmless to man; most can inflict no more than an inconsequential nip. Many of the more active types become very tame, readily accepting food from the hand. If several lizards are kept in a cage, there is likely to be a great deal of activity, especially if conditions are to their liking. Some will breed and produce fertile eggs. Others produce living young. Some lizards of the United States rival the most beautiful exotic forms in their coloration and markings. There are few handsomer saurians than the male collared lizard in his breeding adornment.

AMERICAN GECKOS

The family Gekkonidae has only a few representatives in this country, of which the most familiar and best adaptable to vivarium life is the banded gecko, *Coleonyx variegatus*. This delicate little three-inch lizard of the southwestern deserts is yellowish with a series of dark bands across its back. Like most geckos, it is nocturnal and issues from rock crevices at dusk to prowl and search for food in the form of small insects. Its wanderings during the night may take it a considerable distance from its home, and it may be encountered on highways after dark. When caught it will attempt to bite and may emit a squeal. During the spring the species deposits two eggs. Banded geckos are accomplished climbers, the adhesive qualities of their toes enabling them to scale the smoothest surfaces and even walk across ceilings. In captivity, banded geckos should be provided with pieces of bark or rocky caverns in which to pass the daylight hours.

Similar in size to the banded gecko is the Mediterranean gecko, *Hemidactylus turcicus*, an Old World gecko that has become well established at various places in the southern United States. Geckos in general seem little afraid of humans, and *H. turcicus* is among those which readily take up an abode in or near houses. Insects are attracted to light, and where geckos are common a good place to look for them at night is on the window screens of dwellings.

DESERT IGUANA

Few lizards have been as widely kept as pets as the members of the family Iguanidae. Typically Western Hemisphere inhabitants, the members of this family are known collectively as iguanids. A rather large denizen of our southwestern deserts is the desert iguana, *Dipsosaurus dorsalis*. Growing to a foot or more in total length, this lizard inhabits some of the hottest and dryest country and can be found actively foraging during daylight hours when the temperature may be well over 100 degrees. Like that of many desert reptiles, the

Banded gecko, *Coleonyx variegatus*. Photo courtesy American Museum of Natural History.

Common iguana, *Iguana iguana*. Photo by H. Hansen, Aquarium Berlin.

Rhinoceros iguana, *Cyclura cornuta.* Photo by H. Hansen, Aquarium Berlin.

true beauty of this lizard can be appreciated only at close range. In a vivarium, under good lighting, its delicate shadings of gray and brown, reticulated with lines and striations, produce a uniquely handsome animal. The species is an active one and will readily part with its tail. Eggs may number from two to eight and are deposited in the summer, the babies emerging late in that season or in the early fall. Young and adults feed on insects and tender foliage, usually the buds and blossoms of desert plants. Clover blossoms are relished by captives. I would consider a temperature of 95 degrees to be ideal for this species in captivity.

CHUCKWALLA

If the sunshine and constant dry heat they require can be provided, certain desert lizards make very attractive additions to a collection. One of these is the chuckwalla, *Sauromalus obesus*. Dull brown, olive, or even black, the mature chuckwalla is a heavy-bodied lizard but one which can sprint away at great speed when it feels itself in danger. Its habit is to dash into a rock crevice and then inflate its body if attempts at removal are made. The skin is rough and granular, making it almost impossible to extract the lizard without injury when it is pressed tightly against the walls of a crevice. Chuckwallas

Chuckwalla, *Sauromalus obesus*. Photo by L. van der Meid.

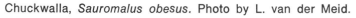

Earless lizard, *Holbrookia maculata*. From Van Denburgh.

are very tame in captivity and will feed on succulent greens. A wide variety of fruits, flowers, and leaves should be offered. These may be difficult to provide, especially during the cooler months, and this is just one of the difficulties of keeping these fine lizards alive over a long period. Another is their constant demand for heat and sunshine. Perhaps *Sauromalus* is one of those few reptiles which will do best only in their native regions. The species lays eggs, and the young present a rather startling contrast in color to their parents, being mottled and crossbanded.

EARLESS LIZARDS, ZEBRA-TAILED LIZARD, FRINGE-TOED LIZARD

Several rather nondescript little lizards inhabit the desert wastes of our southwestern states. Two of these, *Holbrookia maculata* and *Holbrookia texana*, called earless lizards, are readily identified by the absence of an external ear opening. Small and fast, they are active during the day and are insectivorous. When running they curl their tails upward, presenting the vividly-barred undersurface.

A similar species is the zebra-tailed lizard, *Callisaurus draconoides*, notable for the fact that it is one of our fastest lizards, having been clocked at 18 miles per hour. At top speed it will rear upon its hind legs and progress in this fashion, a habit common to certain other lizards. Its food requirements are blossoms, tender leaves, and insects.

Island iguana, *Cyclura baelopha*, West Indies. Photo by H. Hansen, Aquarium Berlin.

Basilisk, *Basiliscus basiliscus*. Photo by H. Hansen, Aquarium Berlin.

Curly-tailed lizard, *Leiocephalus carinatus*, West Indies. Photo by H. Hansen, Aquarium Berlin.

Zebra-tailed lizard, *Callisaurus draconoides.* From Van Denburgh.

Fringe-toed lizard, *Uma notata.* From Van Denburgh.

The fringe-toed lizards of the genus *Uma* form another group of desert species noted for their alacrity when pursued over desert dunes and their habit of disappearing suddenly into the fine sand. In captivity these lizards will devour insects and also smaller lizards— a fact to be kept in mind. All require a great deal of heat and sunshine, but they also require shady places to which they may retire. Perhaps most reptile collectors will tend to regard these small desert lizards chiefly from the standpoint of food for certain desert snakes. For this purpose they can, if necessary, be killed and kept frozen until needed. Each, however, has a life history of its own, and with the majority this has been little studied. Observation in captivity under favorable conditions could provide us with much information about these smaller desert lizards.

COLLARED LIZARD

The collared lizard, *Crotaphytus collaris*, is an outstanding species among our native lizards. A foot long and of robust build, it is an abundant inhabitant of rocky desert terrain. The color patterns of the male and the female are quite different, but both have the characteristic and vivid double black collar. Females are generally fawn colored or gray, taking on a speckling of red during the breeding season. The males are truly handsome animals, especially in some of their racial variants. Bright green is the predominant color, but over-laying this is a profuse spotting of white, yellow, or red. The throat is washed with a deep orange. For a desert lizard, the present species may be considered fairly hardy in captivity. A dry, warm cage is essential; either natural sunlight or a substitute must be provided or these bright and energetic little animals soon fall into a state of indifference, ceasing to feed and soon succumbing, one by one. The collared lizard furnishes us with an example of the many beautiful reptiles that have requirements that cannot easily be met, particularly in northern latitudes. Because of their beauty and interesting habits, lizards of this kind are much in demand, but unless careful thought is given to their needs, few will survive for any length of time in captivity. Vitamin and mineral compounds intended for human consumption flood the market these days. Mixed with such food as these desert species normally eat, they can be of assistance in maintaining difficult species. Collared lizards are largely carnivorous, but most individuals will take lettuce leaves and other plant material as

Keel-tailed lizard, *Tropidurus torquatus,* South America. Photo by G. Marcuse.

Helmeted iguana, *Corythophanes cristatus*, Central America. Photo by H. Hansen, Aquarium Berlin.

Collared lizard, *Crotaphytus collaris*. From Van Denburgh.

well. Anyone who has caged these aggressive lizards with smaller animals has probably had the sad experience of learning, first-hand, how pugnacious they are. They will unhesitatingly devour any such small vertebrates that they can overcome, including other lizards and snakes. The collared lizard is an oviparous species and deposits up to a dozen eggs in early summer. The eggs hatch about ten weeks later, producing charming little editions of the adults.

LEOPARD LIZARD

The leopard lizard, *Crotaphytus wislizenii*, is a close ally of the collared lizard and, like it, a ferocious predator. Reddish-brown in general color, with numerous spots covering the body and legs, it does not have the huge head of the latter, but it seems not in the least handicapped by this deficiency, for it, too, feeds upon almost any other reptile that can be swallowed and even some that can't. More than one leopard lizard has been found choked to death by the size of the prey it had attempted to swallow. It is a fast-running, diurnal lizard which, because of its extreme wariness, is not easily noosed.

ANOLE

The green anole or American "chameleon," *Anolis carolinensis*, has probably found its way into more homes in this country than any other lizard. It is a member of a genus of over 300 species and

Leopard lizard, *Crotaphytus wislizenii*. From Van Denburgh.

Green anole, *Anolis carolinensis*. Photo by M. F. Roberts.

Common chameleon, *Chamaeleo chamaeleon*. Photo by H. Hansen, Aquarium Berlin.

Crested chameleon, *Chamaeleo cristatus*. Photo by Dr. Otto Klee.

Jackson's chameleon, *Chamaeleo jacksoni*. Photo by K. Alexander.

subspecies, all very much alike in body configuration and habits, common throughout the tropical and subtropical portions of the Americas. The species under consideration is the only true native of the United States, but several other species have been introduced and apparently are successfully colonizing. Though not closely related to the geckos, anoles have a toe development which enables them to climb smooth surfaces with much the same facility of the latter. The true chameleons are Old World reptiles and have little in common with our anoles except the ability to change color. In our green anole, the change from brown to green is caused by alteration of the pigment cells of the skin and may be the response to various stimuli such as temperature, light, and emotion. A resting anole is usually brown during the day, turning green at night, but fright and other stimuli will cause it to turn green at any time.

Another curious feature of the anole is the possession of a throat fan which can be distended at will. Anoles are lizards with territorial convictions, which can be readily observed in a cage containing a number of specimens. Males will distend the pink throat fan and bob the head to warn off other males from their territory. A six-inch anole is fully grown and makes a hardy and vivacious inmate of a collection of reptiles. It should be provided with a fairly humid cage; the foliage should be sprinkled from time to time, because it is from hanging drops of water that the lizards will obtain their liquid nourishment. Captives can be maintained over long periods on a diet of mealworms, but a varied diet of flies and other insects is to be preferred. Anoles' tails are very fragile and readily lost. If the break is incomplete, with part of the original tail left in place, a new tail may form beside the old one, causing the lizard to have two tails. A specimen with this deformity came into my possession recently, and it seemed in no way handicapped by the extra tail. This habit of parting with the tail is common to many families of lizards. The new tail will seldom resemble the original one and it is possible to tell at a glance whether a lizard has its original tail or a regenerated one, since the latter is usually shorter and of different scalation from the original. Under conditions of repeated partial breaking, it is possible to produce lizards with three or more tails. These freaks are curious to the layman but of little interest to the herpetologist. Among the reptiles, only the lizards—and not all of them—are able to regenerate lost tails.

It is interesting to establish a colony of, say, a dozen anoles in a large aquarium or other cage. Abundant foliage should be supplied, and the cage should be well lighted. If possible, it should be provided with some sunlight for at least part of each day. Under such conditions, these vivacious little lizards will follow much the same activity as they would in their natural haunts. Territories will be established, and breeding may take place, the tiny eggs being deposited at intervals under bark or rocks in a moist situation. Anole babies, like most other infant reptiles, receive no parental care and are soon stalking their own food supplies in the form of small insects. Growth is quite rapid, and the species may equal or exceed what would probably be its natural life span in captivity.

Despite the large number sold as pets, the anole is still a very familiar reptile throughout the South, where it frequents trees, shrubs, vines, and the environs of old houses. Large numbers may be caught at night with the aid of a flashlight. It is far too abundant in its native haunts to warrant any "farming" by the wholesale suppliers of this little lizard. It is about the least expensive lizard that may be bought by the private collector.

SPINY LIZARDS

The spiny lizards, often called "swifts," form another group of very common lizards which are admirably suited to life in a vivarium. Mostly creatures of dry regions, they abound in some places but are difficult to catch because of their speed and cunning maneuvers when being pursued. Like squirrels, they attempt to keep rocks or tree trunks between themselves and their would-be captors. Two persons working together from opposite sides of a fallen tree or boulder will have better luck than one. Like many other lizards, spiny lizards will quickly part with their tails. None grows to a very large size—even the biggest western species attain a total length of about a foot. It is useless to provide any of the spiny lizards with a container of drinking water. Their habit is to lap drops of water from foliage or rocks. They are active by day and retire to favorite hiding places at dusk.

The eastern fence lizard, *Sceloporus undulatus*, is fairly typical of its genus, bristling, as it does, with coarse, sharply-tipped scales. Males may be easily distinguished from females by the bright bluish-green blotches on their stomachs and throats. This species deposits eggs, but some others produce living young. A very dry cage, liber-

Girdle-tailed lizard, *Cordylus warreni,* southern Africa. Photo by H. Hansen, Aquarium Berlin.

Parson's chameleon, *Chamaeleo parsonii,* Africa. Photo by Dr. Otto Klee.

Girdle-tailed lizard, *Cordylus cordylus,* southern Africa. Photo by G. Marcuse.

Western fence lizard, *Sceloporus occidentalis*, west of Rocky Mountains. Photo by Muller-Schmida.

ally furnished with pieces of bark and a few stones, forms an ideal home for several lizards. They become quite tame and will readily accept mealworms and other insects from one's fingers, with a studied care not to bite the hand that is feeding them. Their sharp claws enable these agile lizards to run rapidly over any surface which is rough in the slightest degree. Unlike geckos, they cannot walk up the straight sides of an aquarium; they are, however, fair jumpers and their cages are best kept covered. Sunlight or a substitute is a requisite for the successful keeping of spiny lizards. They show little of their normal vivacity in a dark cage. Eastern fence lizards have several subspecies which extend the range from the South well into the West. In the east, the New Jersey pine barrens are the northernmost limit of the species.

Some of the western spiny lizards are especially attractive. One of these is the rock crevice spiny lizard, *Sceloporus poinsetti*, of New Mexico and Texas. With its jet-black collar and vividly banded tail, one of these lizards can be seen at a distance. But one seen is by no means one caught, for these beautiful lizards move quickly among the rocks and boulders of their habitat and will usually succeed in eluding any would-be captor. Insects make up the bulk of the diet of the rock crevice spiny lizard, but buds and leaves are occasionally eaten. Several live young are born in the spring and are miniatures of their parents, although they have a more distinct pattern of banding on their bodies. A temperature of 80 to 85 degrees is recommended for this species.

Clark's spiny lizard, *Sceloporus clarki*, is another fine species and one of the largest found in the United States. In general, the larger spiny lizards are hardier in captivity than their smaller cousins. These lizards reach the height of their colors and activity when the sun is high; on cloudy days they may remain concealed and will seldom show any interest in food at such times. I suppose that everyone who has kept lizards has his favorite kinds; of our native lizards I would consider the spiny lizards among the best for pets or exhibition purposes.

The spiny lizards have a number of small relatives which have been placed in the genera *Uta*, *Urosaurus*, and *Streptosaurus*. They are mostly tree- and rock-dwelling lizards of arid and semi-arid regions. They are easy to care for but perhaps not as captivating as their larger relatives.

HORNED LIZARDS

Probably there are not many people who do not have at least a passing acquaintance with the horned lizards. Formerly called "horned toads," these lizards are among the herptiles frequently

Rock lizard, *Streptosaurus mearnsi.* From Van Denburgh.

Red tegu, *Tupinambis rufescens.* Photo by H. Hansen, Aquarium Berlin.

Caiman lizard, *Dracaena guianensis*. Photo by H. Hansen, Aquarium Berlin.

brought home as souvenirs from the West. Placed in unnatural surroundings with insufficient heat, they rarely live as long as six months in the average household. Even under really good conditions, with an adequate supply of unfiltered sunshine and a cage temperature of around 85 degrees, few horned lizards live more than a year or two. Wild horned lizards are believed to feed chiefly upon ants, and a diet of this sort cannot be readily provided in captivity. In the absence of their natural food, various other kinds of insects may be given. Mealworms will be taken but do not constitute a proper diet.

The Texas horned lizard, *Phrynosoma cornutum*, abounds in some areas and is the species very often brought home by travelers. Like most other horned lizards, the present species is adorned with a crown of prominent spines on its head. It has a squat body, short legs and tail, and obviously is not built for a great deal of running. Horned lizards are active during the hottest part of the day and at night bury themselves in sand. The last item is a very important one to consider in providing a home for these quaint little lizards. A four-inch bed of very fine, dry sand should cover the bottom of their cage. Horned lizards do not normally nose about seeking escape, thus scraping and bruising their snouts. Therefore, a cage of all-screen construction is suitable and will provide the dryness and ventilation they require.

Coast horned lizard, *Phrynosoma coronatum.* From Van Denburgh.

Regal horned lizard, *Phrynosoma solare.* From Van Denburgh.

An interesting feat performed by some individuals is the squirting of streams of blood from the corners of their eyes. This usually occurs only when the reptile is roughly handled or badly frightened. We do not know for sure whether the horned lizard does this voluntarily or not. Some specimens feign death when first captured.

A species of our westernmost coastal region is the coast horned lizard, *Phrynosoma coronatum.* Somewhat more elongated of body than the preceding species, this one presents an even more bristling appearance. It does quite well in captivity if kept dry and very warm. Drinking water for this and other horned lizards can be presented once in a while on a lettuce or cabbage leaf. A fine, mistlike spray of water from an atomizer can be squirted occasionally on the lizards themselves, but this should be done only when the sand of their cage is sure to dry out quickly. No horned lizard is able to tolerate prolonged dampness. An adult may measure in excess of six inches from snout to tail tip. The short tail of this species and others of the genus does not break and regenerate like that of many other lizards. One would think that the horny armament of these creatures would deter any creature from attempting to make a meal of them. Such is not the case, for certain desert snakes eat them quite regularly.

The beautiful regal horned lizard, *Phrynosoma solare,* is one of the largest and finest species. In the United States it is confined to Arizona and is protected by the laws of that state, so is not often to be

Ameiva, *Ameiva ameiva*. Photo by Dr. Herbert R. Axelrod.

Sand lizard, *Psammodromus algirus,* northern Africa. Photo by H. Hansen, Aquarium Berlin.

Wall lizard, *Lacerta muralis*. Photo by H. Hansen, Aquarium Berlin.

had from dealers. The head spines reach a magnificent development in this species, forming a circlet about the head. These may be employed defensively by the twisting and turning of a newly-captured specimen but, for the most part, this and the other horned lizards are among the most inoffensive of reptiles and are a charming part of our desert wildernesses.

NIGHT LIZARDS

The night lizards of the family Xantusidae are secretive and nocturnal animals which were once considered rare. Two genera and four species are found in the Southwest and are among the commonest lizards. The yucca night lizard, *Xantusia vigilis*, fully-grown at four inches or less, resembles the snakes in lacking functional

Granite night lizard, *Xantusia henshawi*. From Van Denburgh.

eyelids. The vertical pupil of its eye is clearly an adaptation to night-prowling habits, though an occasional individual may be found abroad in hours of daylight. The usual hiding places are crevices among rocks and among the leaves of plants. Species of the United States bring forth their young alive—usually in the number of one to three. Night lizards feed upon insects and other arthropods. One kind, the island night lizard, *Klauberina riversiana*, grows to the tremendous size—for a night lizard—of eight inches and is confined to the islands off the coast of southern California. It is frequently seen during the day and is said to include in its diet the leaves, blossoms, and seeds of plants. In captivity all night lizards should be given ample hiding places in a dry cage.

Island night lizard, *Klauberina riversiana.* From Van Denburgh.

SKINKS

Cosmopolitan in distribution and well represented in the United States are members of the family Scincidae, commonly known as skinks. Skinks of this country are smooth, shiny lizards of secretive habits. Herptile hunters make it a point to overturn rocks and strip the bark from fallen trees along their routes of travel. If skinks are at all common, a number of them will certainly be uncovered in this way. The slippery surface of a skink's skin makes it difficult to hold, and skinks have a way of nosing themselves out of one's grasp. Their tails are fragile and easily broken. Although short-limbed, skinks can make good progress over favorable terrain, so collecting them in numbers is no easy task. Because they are generally found in damp areas, their cages should have both moisture and dryness in equal proportions. Skinks will sometimes mate in captivity under very favorable conditions and produce fertile eggs which are sometimes guarded by the female. Some natural sunlight is undoubtedly beneficial, but skinks can apparently do without it if other conditions are right. Most species will find and drink from a small water dish. Insects and other invertebrates are eaten, and the larger species will not hesitate to devour baby mice.

Brueggemann's wall lizard, *Lacerta muralis brueggemanni*. Photo by H. Hansen, Aquarium Berlin.

Sand lizard, *Lacerta agilis*. Photo by H. Hansen, Aquarium Berlin.

The small ground skink, *Lygosoma laterale,* abounds in some areas of the Southeast. Brown above and light below, this lizard may be considered fully grown when only four inches long. It is quite salamander-like in configuration and frequents damp places that are the favorite haunts of insects and other small invertebrates upon which it feeds. Eggs numbering one to five are deposited in such situations and require about two months to hatch. The ground skink is one of the many herptiles of whose life history we know little.

An attractive addition to any collection of herptiles is the five-lined skink, *Eumeces fasciatus,* of the south-eastern states. In the past there has been much confusion in the naming of skinks, and with the present species the young are so much different from the adults that they were long considered a distinct species! When it breaks free of the egg the tiny five-lined skink is a vividly marked animal. The ground color is black and the stripes which run the length of the back are yellow or white. The tail is blue. As the reptile grows toward its adult length of nearly eight inches, the colors become more and more obscure, leaving a plain brown lizard. The adult female retains faint stripes and does not grow as large as the male, which loses all trace of stripes and develops a widely-swollen reddish head. In the rural South these large, vicious-looking males are called "scorpions."

Efforts to collect this and other skinks with a noose are usually fruitless. They do not permit close approach and even if the collector succeeds in getting the noose over the lizard's head the smooth, shiny creature will, likely as not, manage to slip out of it and scurry off to cover. Possibly the best method of capturing these skinks and other diurnal lizards is by stripping the bark from fallen and decaying trees in the early spring and at night. During such collecting ventures it should be carried in mind that one is likely to encounter other and somewhat less pleasant creatures in company with the lizards. Many skinks will try to bite when first captured, and the larger specimens, especially the heavy-jowled males, can inflict a painful squeeze and tend to hang on. Their highly-polished bodies make them rather difficult to hold, and the tail will break readily. Five-lined skinks like a moist environment but also like to sun in a dry place, so any cage for them should provide both damp and dry places, as well as hiding places such as slabs of bark or small houses. Insects and spiders are eaten, but some skinks will accept a beaten egg and shredded raw beef mixture that is placed in a shallow dish. This greatly simplifies

Southeastern five-lined skink, *Eumeces inexpectatus*. Photo by F. J. Dodd, Jr.

feeding them when insects are not abundant. If necessary, vitamin drops may be added to this diet. Skinks may not look like good climbers, but they are, and in some portions of their range they are to be found well up in trees. Mating takes place in the spring when the lizards have emerged from their winter quarters and the eggs are deposited in wood pulp in mid-summer. Skinks are among the few reptiles which exhibit any parental solicitude toward the developing babies. A female will remain coiled about her eggs during the incubation period of about six weeks, but she shows no interest in the babies after they have emerged from their shells. A temperature range of 78 to 85 degrees is ideal for any of our North American skinks.

Likely to be confused with the five-lined skink because of their similar coloring and habits are the broad-headed skink, *Eumeces laticeps*, and the southeastern five-lined skink, *Eumeces inexpectatus*. Differences in scalation cause the demarcation of the three forms. The broad-headed skink reaches the impressive length of over twelve inches. All three species are found in the same broad geographical range.

Green lacerta, *Lacerta viridis.* Photo by H. Hansen, Aquarium Berlin.

Eyed lizard, *Lacerta lepida.* Photo by H. Hansen, Aquarium Berlin.

Sand skink, *Neoseps reynoldsi.* Photo by F. J. Dodd, Jr.

Glass lizard, *Ophisaurus ventralis.* Photo courtesy American Museum of Natural History.

The Great Plains skink, *Eumeces obsoletus*, is another large species. Like the previously-mentioned skinks, this species undergoes a color transition from the young to the adult stage. Tan or light grey, the mature animal is rather attractive. This species, like many other North American skinks, would make an ideal lizard for study if it were not for its secretive habits. Deprived of hiding places, these lizards do not thrive.

Many other kinds of skinks are found throughout the United States. One of these is the small sand skink, *Neoseps reynoldsi*, of Florida, a species which is believed to be in the evolutionary process of losing its limbs. These are of little use to the reptile in its subterranean abode. Whether this is truly a rare lizard, or simply one which is not seen often, is not known. Very little is available concerning the sand skink's life history. Most specimens are taken in relatively dry situations.

WHIPTAILS AND RACERUNNERS

Lizards of the family Teiidae are commonly called whiptails and racerunners. Long-tailed and fast runners, either of these names well describes *Cnemidophorus*, the genus to which all the teiids of the United States belong. The six-lined racerunner, *Cnemidophorus sexlineatus*, bears a superficial resemblance to the striped skinks but has a proportionately much longer tail and is never shiny. Racerunners live in dry, rather open areas and are strictly diurnal. They

Racerunner, *Cnemidophorus gularis*. From Van Denburgh.

Striped lizard, *Lacerta trilineata,* Balkans to Asia. Photo by H. Hansen, Aquarium Berlin.

Yellow-throated plated lizard, *Gerrhosaurus flavigularis*. Photo by G. Marcuse.

Red ground skink, *Lygosoma fernandi,* Africa. Photo by J. K. Langhammer.

live entirely on the ground, actively hunting insects, and taking quick flight if approached closely. The western whiptail, *Cnemidophorus tigris*, is found in one or another of its varieties over much of the Southwest. It is like the racerunner in size and habits, flicking its tongue out and in as it progresses over the ground in search of food. Although some of these lizards reach a fair size—over twelve inches— none of the kinds found in this country is able to bite with any effectiveness. Their skin has a dry, soft texture; this makes the lizards easy to hold, once they have been caught—a feat requiring no mean ability on the part of the captor. These lizards will do well only if kept very dry and warm. Mealworms and other insects will be eaten and some individuals will partake of a meat and egg mixture. Handling one of these slender and fragile-looking lizards, it is hard to imagine that it is a close relative of the strong and robust tegus of South America.

ALLIGATOR AND GLASS LIZARDS

Lizards, as a group, are harder to keep alive over long periods than most members of the other major reptile groups. One family, however, produces species which make a quick and satisfactory adjustment to captive conditions. This is the family Anguidae, represented in this country by the alligator lizards and the glass lizards. The southern alligator lizard, *Gerrhonotus multicarinatus*, sometimes called the plated lizard, will live for years in a dry cage that has a sand base and contains rocks and pieces of bark for hiding. Curiously enough for a terrestrial lizard, it seems unwilling, at times, to drink from a low water container and must be provided with sprinkled leaves. Serpentine of body, with rather short legs and a very long tail, its actions when moving along in search of food remind one of a snake. The impression is enhanced by the continual flicking of the lizard's tongue as it explores holes and crevices. *G. multicarinatus* and the other alligator lizards have strongly keeled scales along the back, and each flank has a fold of skin running from the ear to the tail, giving them an emaciated appearance. Alligator lizards differ from species to species in their breeding habits, some laying eggs while others produce living young. The present species deposits up to twenty eggs during June, July, or August. Hatching takes place nearly two months later, and the babies shift for themselves as soon as they are free of the eggs. They measure three to four inches in

Southern alligator lizard, *Gerrhonotus multicarinatus.* From Van Denburgh.

over-all length at time of hatching and can reach an adult length of twenty inches. An example this long is so slender, however, that it could hardly be regarded as a large lizard. Many lizards will part with their tails if handled or grasped by that appendage; the present lizard goes a step further, having the ability to voluntarily throw off the tail and leave it writhing violently to decoy its pursuer.

The northern alligator lizard, *Gerrhonotus coeruleus,* is a smaller species than the preceding and differs from it in having its babies born alive in late summer. A brood will often consist of six or seven baby lizards. None of the alligator lizards could be called really beautiful, but those from Arizona, *Gerrhonotus kingi,* have a more boldly defined pattern of crossbands than the others of this country and their upper jaws are adorned with black and white spots. Alligator lizards can and will devour nearly any small living creature, including spiders and scorpions, that they can swallow. They should not be mixed with other lizards in a cage because of this propensity. Western lizards all, the members of this genus can be found in many habitats, but perhaps the best place to look for them is along the course of streams or in other places where there is some moisture.

Blue-tongued skink, *Tiliqua nigrolutea.* Photo by H. Hansen, Aquarium Berlin.

Striped mabuya, *Mabuya striata*, southern Africa. Photo by H. Hansen, Aquarium Berlin.

Northern alligator lizard, *Gerrhonotus coeruleus*. From Van Denburgh.

In the East the family of anguids is represented by the glass lizard, *Ophisaurus ventralis*, and its allies. Because of the absence of legs, these lizards are often mistaken for snakes. Eyelids and external ear openings are features which will readily separate these or other legless lizards from the snakes. Usually some shade of black, olive, or brown, glass lizards are not colorful, but their adaptability to cage life more than makes up for this. Glass lizards have smooth and shiny scales which permit them to make good progress when underground, where they seem to spend much of their time. They are entirely carnivorous and in addition to the insects they encounter they readily consume birds' eggs, other lizards, small snakes, and earthworms. In captivity they will take an egg and chopped raw beef mixture. It is not essential to provide them with soil in which to burrow—a piece of bark or small house will meet the requirement of a place to retire. Our native glass lizards attain a length in excess of three feet and in a lizard of this size the tail will account for more than two feet! Despite their streamlined build, the glass snakes project a clumsy image when they attempt to slither away. They lack the graceful motions of a typical serpent and, in fact, even feel quite different when handled. Most will attempt to bite when first caught, but as a rule they tame readily and are soon feeding from their keeper's fingers. The island glass lizard, *Ophisaurus compressus*, and the slender glass lizard, *Ophisaurus attenuatus*, are the two other species found in the United States. All three differ little in habits.

190

BURROWING LIZARDS

Like the snakes, the lizards have many species which spend virtually all of their time underground. One of these is the worm lizard, *Rhineura floridana*, of the family Amphisbaenidae. Confined to Florida, this lizard has no eyes and no external ear openings. When grown it may measure a foot in length and greatly resembles a large earthworm. It frequents areas of well-drained soil and feeds upon insect larvae and earthworms. Specimens may be found by raking through leaf-mold; after a heavy rain they may be found on the surface. Coloration is usually a delicate shade of pink or lavender. The young are hatched and are surprisingly large—about four inches. An aquarium makes a good home for worm lizards if the bottom is covered with several inches of sandy soil, topped with an inch-deep layer of leaf mold. A moderate humidity may be obtained and sustained by periodic spraying. Burrowing lizards of this family require no sunlight.

Another of our burrowing lizards is the California legless lizard, *Anniella pulchra*, the sole native member of the family Anniellidae. The present lizard is a silvery gray in color and reaches a length of nine inches. In general structure the species is similar to the worm lizard, but it has tiny eyes with functional eyelids. Babies numbering

California legless lizard, *Anniella pulchra*. From Van Denburgh.

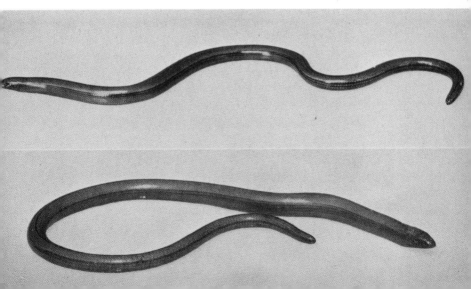

Gidgee skink, *Egernia stokesii,* Australia. Photo by H. Hansen, Aquarium Berlin.

Cunningham's skink, *Egernia cunninghami.* Photo by Dr. Otto Klee.

Sand skink, *Eumeces schneideri*, western Asia to northern Africa. Photo by H. Hansen, Aquarium Berlin.

European glass "snake", *Ophisaurus apodus*. Photo by J. K. Langhammer.

two to four, usually, though rarely a single baby, are born alive in the fall. This lizard requires an aquarium set-up similar to that described for the worm lizard. Excessive dampness is harmful and hardly less so is complete dryness. A happy medium must be reached and therein lies the key to the successful keeping of these secretive lizards. Temperature should be maintained at about eighty degrees. Burrowing lizards of this and the preceding family are rarely to be seen in any cage which provides the correct conditions for then. Keeping them in captivity is a little like keeping a cage full of invisible lizards.

POISONOUS LIZARDS

The family Helodermatidae contains one genus and two species of poisonous lizards. Our native species is the famous Gila monster, *Heloderma suspectum.* Large in size, bizarre in coloration, and grotesque of form, in many ways this lizard is the most interesting one we have. The scales of the Gila monster are very beadlike in character on the back, sides, head, and tail. Each one is rounded and set in relief—the total effect produced is like that of a piece of Indian beadwork. Black and pink prevail as the colors, and no two of these lizards are exactly alike. The head is blunt and swollen and so is the tail, which becomes very heavy in a well-fed lizard but diminishes markedly in size during times when its owner is not eating regularly.

Captive Gila monsters will live for years on a diet of beaten eggs and raw meat. In the wild state, small mammals as well as bird and reptile eggs are eaten. Captives generally show little interest in any other reptiles which may be caged with them. Several specimens may be fed in a low dish containing the semi-liquid mixture of eggs and meat. It is interesting to watch them slowly lap up the contents, periodically raising their heads to allow it to flow down their throats. One egg and a teaspoonful of minced raw beef each week will keep an adult in fine condition.

Gila monsters escape the worst of the desert heat by remaining in burrows during the day. At dusk and during part of the night they may be met prowling in brushy country or even crossing highways. As the reptiles slowly crawl about, they constantly flick out their forked tongues, in this manner picking up scents which are conveyed to paired orifices in the roof of the mouth. These tell the animal what is edible and what is not. Provided with sharply clawed and strong feet, the Gila is well equipped to unearth the eggs of tortoises, lizards, and snakes. If interfered with, a wild Gila monster can move with surprising alacrity and is quite ready to defend itself. Its jaws are large and powerful; once they have fastened on something, it is most difficult to break the hold. Grooved teeth channel the lizard's venom into the bitten object. Some human fatalities from the bite of *Heloderma* are on record. Even without the presence of venom the jaws would be capable of inflicting a most painful injury. There is no specific serum for the treatment of a Gila monster bite.

Captive Gila monsters that are kept indoors soon abandon all inclinations to defend themselves by biting and settle down to a phlegmatic existence, showing no nervous reactions toward humans. They do best in a plain cage which can be easily cleaned. Though true desert reptiles, captives will enter a low dish of water and soak for long periods. Unlike other desert lizards, they do not require sunlight for their well-being. A large Gila may measure two feet in length and makes a spectacular exhibit, but should never be handled carelessly, despite its apparent docility. Females deposit their large

Gila monster, *Heloderma suspectum*. Photo by G. Marcuse.

Papuan monitor, *Varanus salvadorii,* Papua New Guinea. Photo by Dr. Otto Klee.

Sand monitor, *Varanus gouldii*. Photo by Dr. Otto Klee.

Head of a Gila monster, showing poison gland on lower jaw. From Van Denburgh.

eggs, numbering usually five or six, in mid-summer. The four-inch-long babies hatch about a month later.

In this country, Arizona is the stronghold of the Gila monster, and for over fifteen years it has been protected by the laws of that state. It is our only poisonous reptile that enjoys such protection and this was brought about in consideration of the diminishing numbers of the animals in their natural haunts. The species ranges into northern Mexico. Fine specimens could once be purchased for as little as five dollars; now one can expect to pay ten times this amount for one of the few specimens which come on the animal market. The Mexican beaded lizard, *Heloderma horridum*, is the only close relative of the Gila monster and, like it, is poisonous. Its care in captivity is basically the same as that recommended for the Gila, but since it is a larger reptile it requires more commodious quarters. A temperature range of 75 to 80 degrees is ideal for both members of the genus.

V

Exotic Lizards and the Tuatara

FAMILY GEKKONIDAE

In tropical and semi-tropical regions the variety of lizards increases greatly. Lizards, in one form or another, seem to be everywhere—by day and by night. The small lizards of the family Gekkonidae, the geckos, are mostly nocturnal creatures. When the multitude of sun-worshipping lizards have retired for the day, an army of geckos emerges to enliven the night. It is not alone in their night-time activities that these lizards stand apart from most others; they are different in other ways, too. Most geckos' eyes lack movable lids and have the unblinking stare of snakes; their toes are equipped with clinging pads which enable their owners to run quietly over walls and even ceilings; some have a loud call which is used frequently. There are many genera and species of geckos, all of them interesting, and most are adaptable to life in a vivarium.

TOKAY GECKO

The tokay gecko, *Gekko gecko*, is one of the largest species and is imported more frequently and in greater numbers than the others. Fully grown at twelve to fourteen inches, the tokay is usually gray, liberally sprinkled with red dots. As with other geckos, the colors may darken or lighten from time to time. The massive head of this lizard is equipped with a cavernous mouth. A large specimen in my collection would readily devour any smaller lizard, as well as small mice and all kinds of insects. Tokays have good appetites and probably thrive best on small daily feedings. Imported specimens

Yellow monitor, *Varanus flavescens.* Photo by H. Hansen, Aquarium
Berlin.

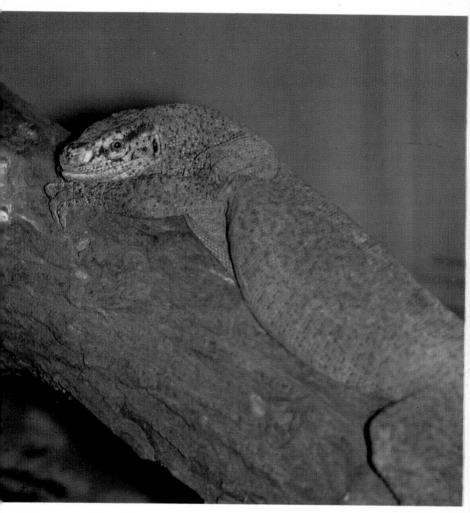

Steppes monitor, *Varanus exanthematicus,* southern Africa. Photo by H. Hansen, Aquarium Berlin.

have frequently been without food or water for some time and are quite emaciated when they reach the cages of retailers, but a tokay in good health has a well-rounded appearance. Many geckos voluntarily

Wall gecko, *Tarentola mauritanica*, Mediterranean area. Photo by G. Marcuse.

take up their abode in human dwellings—the tokay is one of these and so should not feel too much out of place in an apartment!

The tokay gecko's voice is quite loud, and the sound is the one from which the animal gets its common name: "to-kay." It is not a harsh or altogether unpleasant sound, though I imagine that a number of specimens could create quite a din. Mine would usually start calling at 3 o'clock in the morning and stop at 4:30—a rather early alarm clock!

Geckos like the present species should be kept in glass-fronted wooden cages of the type used for the larger snakes. They remain lethargic and inactive during the daylight hours, clinging to the top and sides. At dusk they awaken and spend most of the evening hours scampering about in search of food. No smaller animal of any kind should ever be housed with geckos. The temperature range should be 70 to 85 degrees. Water should be provided by the liberal sprinkling of a piece of bark or some very sturdy foliage plant; this should be done each evening. All geckos can bite and many are quite ready to. They should be lightly but firmly grasped just behind the head when it is necessary to handle them. Like other lizards, and reptiles in general, they do best with a minimum of handling. They may be allowed the run of a reptile room, providing no small animals in uncovered cages are exposed to their predations.

MADAGASCAR DAY GECKO

Tastes differ, and perhaps no two herpetologists would agree in their choices of the world's most beautiful lizard. My own vote would be for the Madagascar day gecko, *Phelsuma madagascariensis*. There are many green lizards in the world, some with subtle shadings and others with handsome patterns, but the day geckos stand alone in the intensity of their color. Scattered over the green body color are streaks and spots of scarlet. There is nothing garish about the creature, yet the simple colors combine to produce an effect which looks positively artificial, especially when the lizards are housed under good lighting. They are not very sociable animals, and if several are kept together in a large cage they usually remain well separated.

Madagascar day gecko, *Phelsuma madagascariensis*. Photo by G. Marcuse.

Girdle-lizard, *Platysaurus* sp., family Cordylidae. Photo by H. Hansen, Aquarium Berlin.

Dull monitor, *Varanus* sp. , northern Africa to southwestern Asia. Photo by G. Marcuse.

An unidentified *Platysaurus*. Photo by H. Hansen, Aquarium Berlin.

These and the other day geckos are, as their name implies, diurnal creatures which enjoy sunlight in moderate amounts and a cage that provides some humidity. A small limb with branches attached will help to make these tree-dwellers feel at home. Unlike the majority of geckos, the *Phelsuma* species have round pupils, and this imparts a benevolent expression quite unlike that of their slit-eyed nocturnal relatives. None of the day geckos grows to a large size, seven inches being about average for an adult *P. madagascariensis*.

The geckos are commonly thought of as climbing forest lizards, but some live in areas of great drought and could properly be called desert lizards. Oddly, the body forms of the many species are similar; it is in the tails and feet that differences show up. Nearly all geckos reproduce by means of eggs, though a few live-bearing forms are known from New Zealand. Two, but sometimes only one, eggs constitute the mode for the family. So close has the association of some species with humans become that the eggs are often deposited behind the shutters of houses. More usual places are under stones and beneath the rotten bark of fallen trees.

Leopard gecko, *Eublepharis macularius*. Photo by G. Marcuse.

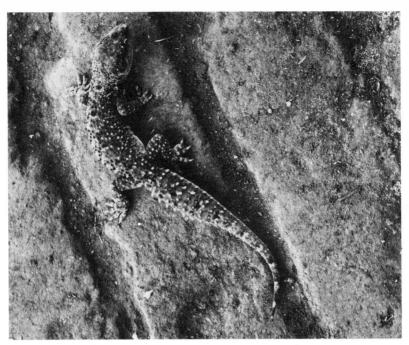

Brook's gecko, *Hemidactylus brooki*, Africa. Photo courtesy American Museum of Natural History.

Saddle-backed gecko, *Hemidactylus triedus*. Photo by R. Pawley.

Eastern garter snake, *Thamnophis sirtalis sirtalis.* Photo by J. K. Langhammer.

Rosy boa, *Lichanura trivirgata.* Photo by F. J. Dodd, Jr.

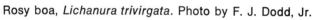

Washington garter snake, *Thamnophis sirtalis pickeringii.* Photo by J. K. Langhammer.

Eastern ribbon snake, *Thamnophis sauritus.* Photo by J. K. Langhammer.

Turkish gecko, *Hemidactylus turcicus*. Photo by F. J. Dodd, Jr.

Sand gecko, *Teratoscincus scincus*. Photo by G. Marcuse.

An unusual variant of the leopard gecko, *Eublepharis macularius.* Photo by R. Pawley.

LEOPARD GECKO

The attractive leopard gecko, *Eublepharis macularius,* reaches the fair size of about eight inches and is one of the fat-tailed species, living on the ground among rocks and doing well in a semi-desert type of vivarium. This species, unlike the great majority of geckos, has movable eyelids. Another desert form is the sand gecko, *Teratoscincus scincus,* an animal whose skin has smooth scales, quite unlike the wart-like scalation of most geckos. The saddle-backed blotched gecko, *Hemidactylus triedus,* is a member of a genus that is world-wide in its distribution. Many of its forms are very tiny creatures which require sympathetic care on the part of their keeper, particularly in regard to feeding. Others, like the robust Turkish gecko, *Hemidactylus turcicus,* and the house gecko, *Hemidactylus frenatus,* are larger and easier to care for.

Northern water snake, *Natrix sipedon sipedon.* Photo by F. J. Dodd, Jr.

Northern brown snake, *Storeria dekayi.* Photo by J. K. Langhammer.

Flat-tailed water snake, *Natrix sipedon compressicauda,* two color phases, Florida. Photos by F. J. Dodd, Jr.

FAMILY PYGOPODIDAE
SNAKE LIZARDS

The Pygopodidae, a family of limbless lizards confined mostly to Australia, is a group about which little has been learned. Like many Australian reptiles, they come on the animal market very rarely, and most zoos do not have them. Lacking limbs in most of their species, they glide about like snakes and like snakes have lidless eyes which they clean by means of their tongues. Some give voice to various sounds, like the geckos, to which these strange creatures seem most closely related. The species about which we know a little deposit eggs and are carnivorous: lizards and grubs have been taken by captives. There are some twenty species, a few of which are distinctly burrowing animals. Collectively they are known as snake lizards. One of the better known of them is the attractive Burton's snake lizard, *Lialis burtonii*, of Australia and New Guinea.

FAMILY AGAMIDAE

Some of the most attractive vivarium animals are supplied by the lizards of the family Agamidae. These lizards which make up this family are the Old World counterparts of the more familiar iguanid lizards of the New World. Like the latter, they are strong and active animals which forage by day. In captivity, few will do well unless given sunlight in which to bask. No agamid grows to a really large size, but some are thickset and, though only three feet in length, require large cages if their normal activity is to be seen. Some show rather elaborate courtship displays, and nearly all reproduce by means of eggs.

FLYING LIZARDS

Southeastern Asia and the East Indies are the native lands of the numerous small saurians which have long been called "flying" lizards—something of a misnomer, for the fragile little creatures never actually fly but are able to make extended glides from tree to tree by means of folds of skin which can be distended to support the light body. The "wings" are supported by elongated ribs, much like an umbrella, and the lizard is able to land gracefully quite some distance from its take-off point. In some species, the wings are brilliantly colored. *Draco* is the name of the genus of flying lizards; many species are recognized. They are tree lizards and few ever descend to the ground except to deposit their eggs, which may number from three to five or more. Average length for the various members of the group is ten to eighteen inches. A well-heated cage provided with many branches and twigs can be used to keep captives, but they are delicate lizards, none having lived very long in captivity. Lizards that feed largely upon ants, as the flying lizards do, are very difficult to keep over long periods. Other types of insects do not seem to form a satisfactory substitute. What little we know about the flying lizards indicates that the animals feed largely upon ants in the wild state.

TREE LIZARDS (CALOTES)

One of the difficulties we encounter in writing a non-technical account of the smaller tropical lizards is in the matter of names. In many, the scientific name seems absurd when translated, and often the species do not have native names, or, when they do, the names

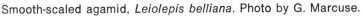

Smooth-scaled agamid, *Leiolepis belliana*. Photo by G. Marcuse.

Kirtland's water snake, *Clonophis kirtlandi* (sometimes placed in the genus *Natrix*), north-central U.S. Photo by J. K. Langhammer.

Juvenile racer, *Coluber constrictor*. Photo by J. K. Langhammer.

Blue racer, *Coluber constrictor,* color pattern found in central U.S. Photo by J. K. Langhammer.

Striped whipsnake, *Masticophis lateralis.* Photo by F. J. Dodd, Jr.

relate to some imagined characteristic that the species in question do not really possess. *Calotes* is a widespread and abundant genus of lizards which lack a good common name. Let us call them variable tree lizards, for such they truly are or, perhaps more simply, calotes. They are Asiatic in origin and may number in excess of twenty distinct species, most of which are small, slender tree-dwelling forms that are noted for their rapid changes of color, particularly about the head. *Calotes calotes* is a slender and active tree lizard that can be kept alive in captivity over long periods under the best of conditions in regard to sunlight, heat, and abundant insect food. The species has a beautifully colored head of orange, red, yellow, and green—these colors suffusing into a bright red when the lizard is excited. The body is green and the tail is long and whiplike. Their pretty colors show off best in a warm cage, 75 to 80 degrees, that permits the normal running and jumping that these creatures enjoy.

SMOOTH-SCALED AGAMID

The smooth-scaled agamid, *Leiolepis belliana*, is one of the ground-dwelling members of its family, living in burrows and including vegetation in its diet. It grows to about eighteen inches. Its back is olive or brown with a speckling of yellow; this coloration gives way on the flanks to vivid bars of black and orange, while the belly is orange or red. Captives are not secretive, and the males do much harmless fighting among themselves. They should be kept warm and dry, their cage-floor covered with fine sand or dry soil.

TOAD-HEADED AGAMIDS

The toad-headed agamids (*Phrynocephalus neydensis* and related species) are hot country animals which will not tolerate any degree of dampness in their cages. Some possess the ability to threaten enemies by opening the mouth and expanding flaps of skin on either side of the head. These threats may be backed with a sharp bite. Insects are their principal food and, like other strong-jawed agamids, they can easily crush the hardest beetles. Water should be given to them only in the form of drops on a leaf. These small lizards can jump well and often bury themselves in the sand.

Toad-headed agamid, *Phrynocephalus neydensis*. Photo by G. Marcuse.

WATER LIZARD

Many of the agamid lizards run to a certain monotony in form and habits, much the same as our iguanid lizards of southwestern United States. As among the latter group, however, certain forms stand out because of size, appearance, or unusual habits. Among the agamids, one of these is the water lizard, *Physignathus lesueri*, of Australia and New Guinea. This handsome lizard is one of the finest to be seen in captivity. It grows to a length of over three feet, much of this taken

Corn snake, *Elaphe guttata*. Photo by Dr. K. Knaack.

Western patch-nosed snake, *Salvadora hexalepis.* Photo by F. J. Dodd, Jr.

Glossy snake, *Arizona elegans,* western United States. Photo by J. K. Langhammer.

Rat snake, *Elaphe obsoleta.* Photo by F. J. Dodd, Jr.

up by the long, flattened tail. Olives and browns predominate as the colors on the back, but stripes and bands stand out in contrast. The neck is crested with spines and a wide, dark band extends from the eye backward. The belly is red. I think that one of the handsomest exhibits of reptiles I have seen featured examples of these large, semi-aquatic reptiles. The cage, really a huge aquarium, was about ten feet in length and had a water depth of eighteen inches. Running the length of the rear wall was a land area of sand, rocks, and stones which dropped abruptly at the water's edge. A background resembling a jungle river bank added a feature which would transpose the onlooker from an artificially heated reptile house of a modern zoo to the sluggish water's edge of a New Guinea river. Protruding from the water and overhanging its shore was part of a large tree, and reclining on this were several of the most beautiful lizards I had ever seen. This was my first acquaintance with the water lizards, which have remained my favorites among the agamids.

Water lizards will not do well in a small vivarium—they need space, lots of it. They are powerful runners on land, often using a bipedal locomotion, and equally at home in the water. A temperature of 80 degrees is suitable. In general, water lizards can be expected to accept as food any small invertebrates or vertebrates that are placed in their cage. Mice and birds are eaten readily. The species deposits its eggs in tunnels close to water.

FRILLED LIZARD

Sometimes imported from Australia and New Guinea is the frilled lizard, *Chlamydosaurus kingi*, a small species that would tend to pass unnoticed if it were not for its habit of expanding a wide frill about the head when the creature is alarmed. Small and slender, the present animal is likely to startle one who is unfamiliar with its ways. Normally, as when at rest, the reptile's wide collar lies folded inconspicuously against its sides, but a sudden fright throws the frilled lizard on the defensive. The mouth is opened and simultaneously the wide, nearly circular expanse of skin is erected, forming a collar which may be ten inches in diameter and having the flashing brilliance of coloring often seen in really dangerous animals. Captives become tame and spend most of their time on trees and branches, feeding readily on insects and small vertebrates; they soon lose all inclination to expand the frill.

Frilled lizard, *Chlamydosaurus kingi*. Photo by G. Marcuse.

Bullsnake, *Pituophis melanoleucus sayi*. Photo by H. Hansen, Aquarium Berlin.

Florida kingsnake, *Lampropeltis getulus floridana.* Photo by G. Marcuse.

California kingsnake, *Lampropeltis getulus californiae.* Photo by F. J. Dodd, Jr.

Bearded lizard,
Amphibolurus barbatus.
Photo by Muller-Schmida.

Water lizard, *Physignathus lesueuri.* Photo by H. Hansen, Aquarium
Berlin.

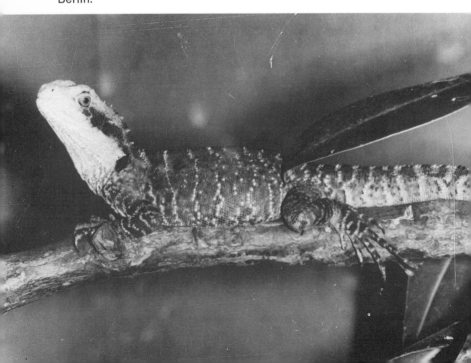

BEARDED LIZARD

Rather similar to the frilled lizard in the method of its bluff is the bearded lizard, *Amphibolurus barbatus*, also from Australia and New Guinea. Desert-inhabiting reptiles, bearded lizards should be kept warm and dry. Insects and occasional vegetable matter are eaten. This spiny 18-inch lizard lives well if properly cared for.

SAIL-TAILED WATER LIZARD

The sail-tailed water lizard is a very large agamid. Known to science as *Hydrosaurus amboinensis*, it attains a length in excess of three feet. The males have a large and showy tail crest. Though strongly built and quite ferocious looking, these semi-aquatic lizards feed to some extent, at least, on the tender leaves of waterside plants. They take to the water when alarmed and are strong swimmers. Only a very large enclosure is suitable for water lizards of this kind.

SPINY-TAILED AGAMAS

The spiny-tailed agamas (genus *Uromastix*) are often imported but seldom do well unless their requirements for heat and a dry atmosphere are provided. The black spiny-tail, *Uromastix acanthinurus*, is representative of the group and, like the others, is a desert dweller which subsists mostly on plant life and is much given to burrowing in the wild state. Young specimens will sometimes take insects. None of the spiny-tailed agamas is brightly colored...the principal adornment of these blunt-snouted desert-dwellers is their large, heavily armored tail, which can be used quite effectively for defensive purposes. Desert lizards of many kinds can do without drinking water if they are sprayed occasionally. They seem able to absorb liquid nourishment through the skin. Their cages must be kept very dry, however. A high temperature range is required and good ventilation is a necessity in maintaining these lizards. They show normal vivacity at 85 to 90 degrees.

THORNY LIZARD (MOLOCH)

Without doubt, one of the strangest-looking lizards in the world is the thorny lizard, *Moloch horridus*, of Australia. Most of us have seen horned lizards of the southwestern United States—some kinds are quite bristly and nearly all have prominent spines, especially around the head. The moloch appears as a gross exaggeration of a

Longnosed snake, *Rhinocheilus lecontei*, western United States. Photo by J. K. Langhammer.

Milk snake, *Lampropeltis triangulum*. Photo by F. J. Dodd, Jr.

Great Plains ringneck snake, *Diadophis punctatus edwardsi.* Photo by J. K. Langhammer.

Eastern hognose snake, *Heterodon platyrhinos.* Photo by J. K. Langhammer.

Hardwick's spiny-tail, *Uromastix hardwicki*. Photo by G. Marcuse.

horned lizard. Like the latter, it lives in dry, sandy places and seems to subsist mainly on ants and termites. For this reason, they are impossible to keep in an average collection for any length of time, since 1,000 or more ants may be eaten at a single meal. Moloch lizards deposit their eggs in January; the eggs hatch in February or March, the six to eight young being spiniferous replicas of their parents.

FAMILY IGUANIDAE

The family Iguanidae, like the family Agamidae, is a huge one, having some 700 species which are confined mostly to the New World. Among the many forms one finds a multitude of species which seem to have counterparts among the agamids. Parallelism of development, this is sometimes called. Indeed, the two families have been separated mainly on the basis of dental structure, and without reference to such detail most herpetologists would be hard put to distinguish the less-well-known iguanids from the agamids.

KNIGHT ANOLE

When we think of anoles usually it is in terms of the charming little lizards so well represented by our native species, but there are over 150 other species of anoles found throughout the warmer portions of Central and South America. Most, like *A. carolinensis*, are small lizards not exceeding six or eight inches in length, although certain very large species inhabit the islands of the West Indies. One of these is the knight anole, *Anolis equestris*, of Cuba, a species which commonly measures eighteen inches. Knight anoles are handsome reptiles, mostly green with a network of white markings. Their eyes are circled with blue and the distensible throat fan of the males is pale pink. Like their smaller relatives, they do well in a cage that is supplied with branches, where the anoles will spend much of their time. A damp cage is not suitable, nor is one which is completely dry. Anoles of all kinds must have careful attention paid to their moisture requirements. They require water, which must be provided in the form of drops hanging from foliage. They will not make use of a drinking dish. In the past, the larger species particularly have been considered delicate animals, but many will live a long time if kept warm, fed well on insects other than mealworms, and supplied liberally with water on leaves of plants. The knight anole is large enough to eat mice and small birds. Other giant anoles are found on Puerto Rico, Jamaica, and Hispaniola.

Knight   anole, *Anolis equestris*. Photo by G. Marcuse.

Western ringneck snake, *Diadophis punctatus regalis.* Photo by J. K. Langhammer.

Spotted night snake, *Hypsiglena torquata,* western United States and Mexico. Photo by J. K. Langhammer.

Reticulate python, *Python reticulatus*. Photo by H. Hansen, Aquarium Berlin.

Blood python, *Python curtus*. Photo by J. K. Langhammer.

IGUANAS

The common iguana, *Iguana iguana*, is a large arboreal lizard that is imported in great numbers for the pet trade. The pretty green babies one sees in such large numbers are often hatchlings that have been so weakened by lack of food during the most critical period of their lives that there is little hope of bringing them back to health. Iguanas in good condition are lively and vivacious lizards, most often a clear, bright green in color. Specimens that are mottled or that appear emaciated should be avoided. Perhaps it is best to buy a specimen that is out of the infant stage, say 15 to 18 inches long. These will cost a little more but are far more likely to do well in the home. The species grows to six feet and is eaten to some extent by the natives of the tropical areas where it occurs.

All iguanas should have roomy cages with plenty of stout branches for climbing and resting. They need abundant light, and some natural sunlight each day is very beneficial. The adults have the habit of resting on tree limbs overhanging water. When frightened they will drop off and swim away with great speed. Despite this, iguanas could not be described as aquatic lizards. I have never known any that would accept food in the water, and they seem content with just a small dish for drinking. The adults are chiefly vegetarian, but the young will accept animal matter as well as plants. Powdered calcium and a multi-vitamin should be mixed with the chopped fruits and vegetables that are offered. Bananas, pears, cabbage, clover leaves and blossoms, lettuce, and mealworms and other insects are among the many things appreciated by the growing iguana. Some specimens will become accustomed to feeding on the better kinds of canned dog food, which forms a readily procurable and nourishing diet, especially if vitamin drops and bone meal are added. Baby iguanas become very tame and show little of the nervousness exhibited by some lizards. Specimens that are kept alone seem to adjust more quickly than those kept in groups. This is true of nearly all herptiles, with the possible exception of certain turtles. One should never forget that iguanas are tropical lizards that require a great deal of heat—a temperature of 80 degrees suits them fine; their cage should be well ventilated. Artificial lighting is better than none and a bulb may be left burning overhead continuously during the day when an abundant supply of natural light is not available.

Other iguanas become commercially available from time to time. One of the rarest of these imports is the Fiji Island iguana, *Brachylophus fasciatus*, a handsome animal about three feet long which lives entirely on vegetation. The rhinoceros iguana, *Cyclura cornuta*, is a heavy-bodied, dull-colored member of the family. A fully grown male rhinoceros iguana is an impressive animal. The snout is provided with three horns and the stout body is crested with a row of spines. The legs are robust and the habit of the reptile is to walk about with its body well elevated from the ground. One must have a very large cage or outdoor enclosure to properly care for these huge ground lizards. They feed on vegetable and animal matter and become very tame in captivity, though fierce when first caught. A high temperature, at least 80 degrees, is required for them.

Cayman Islands rhinoceros iguana, *Cyclura caymanensis*. Photo by Muller-Schmida.

Rock python, *Python sebae.* Photo by J. K. Langhammer.

Boa constrictor, *Boa constrictor.* Photo by J. K. Langhammer.

Rainbow boa, *Epicrates cenchris.* Photo by G. Marcuse.

Brown sand boa, *Eryx johni.* Photo by G. Marcuse.

237

The South American iguanids of the genus *Polychrus* are interesting little arboreal lizards that are quite like chameleons in a few respects. Their bodies are highly arched and flattened from side to side, as in most tree lizards, while the toes of their feet are opposable to allow a firm grasp on the branch of a tree. The eyes are rather bulbous and the tail partly prehensile; in addition, the lizards are able to change color to a considerable degree. They feed chiefly on insects. *Polychrus acutirostris* and *Polychrus marmoratus* are the species most frequently imported.

BASILISKS

The basilisks (genus *Basiliscus*) form a small group of tropical American iguanids that have long been favorites in reptile collections. The males are adorned with crests along their backs and tails, while

Basilisk, *Basiliscus basiliscus*. Photo by G. Marcuse.

the females lack these and are more ordinary-looking. Large specimens may reach the length of three feet, of which much is taken up by the long tail. Basilisks live near water and are noted for their ability to run for short distances across the surface of water. Primarily lizards of the trees, they do well in the type of cage recommended for anoles. Some will eat pieces of soft fruit, but in general the several species are carnivorous and in addition to insects will take small mammals and birds. Because of their bizarre adornment, males cost more than females. If possible, the basilisks' cage should have a sizeable container of water. A temperature of 75 to 82 degrees is recommended.

Spiny-tail iguana, *Ctenosaura acanthura*, Central America. Photo by G. Marcuse.

Curly-tailed lizard, *Leiocephalus carinatus*, West Indies. Photo by G. Marcuse.

Green tree boa, *Corallus canina,* orange young. Photo by J. K. Langhammer.

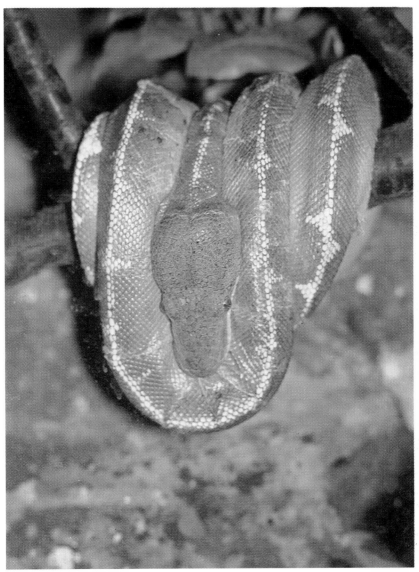

Green tree boa, *Corallus canina,* adult. Photo by H. Hansen, Aquarium Berlin.

Keel-tailed lizard, *Tropidurus semitaeniatus*, South America. Photo by G. Marcuse.

Marine iguana, *Amblyrhynchus cristatus*, Galapagos Islands. Photo by G. Marcuse.

MISCELLANEOUS IGUANIDS

Tropical America has dozens of genera of small iguanid lizards that can be kept over long periods in captivity. Specimens of the genera *Corythophanes*, *Leiocephalus*, and *Tropidurus* are a few of the kinds imported. Many do not have common English names. The appearance of a lizard can often provide clues to its habits. Species with flattened bodies are generally ground dwellers, while those in which the body is compressed from side to side generally live in trees or bushes. Prehensile tails indicate arboreal habitats, while a flattened tail may indicate that its bearer is at least semi-aquatic.

Mountain chameleon, *Chamaeleo montium*, Cameroons. Photo by Dr. Otto Klee.

FAMILY CHAMAELEONIDAE

True chameleons of the family Chamaeleonidae are found only in the Old World.

Africa and Madagascar are the homes of these lizards, only a few of the eighty or more species entering Europe and Asia. Chameleons are among the most highly specialized groups of reptiles, and numbered among them are some whose grotesqueness defies adequate verbal description. In size they range from pygmy species of two inches to giants of two feet or more. As a group they are admirably adapted to the life they lead. Slow-moving and flat-bodied, they

243

Diced water snake, *Natrix tessellata.* Photo by H. Hansen, Aquarium Berlin.

Checkered water snake, *Natrix piscator*. Photo by H. Hansen, Aquarium Berlin.

blend beautifully with the foliage of the trees and bushes that they seldom leave. Their feet have opposable toes which afford a sure grip on the branch of a tree. The tail is prehensile and is used effectively to anchor the lizard to its perch. From the blunt head project bulging eyes which are moved independently of each other, enabling their owner to concentrate on two or more widely separated objects. The tongue is extremely long and thickened at its terminal portion, like a club. When an insect or other small creature arouses a hungry chameleon's attention, the tongue is shot out in a motion too quick for the eye to follow. The sticky tip nearly always finds its mark and returns the hapless victim to the lizard's mouth. Chameleons are capable of rapid and drastic changes of color, and these can be brought about by any of a large number of factors—psychological and physical.

Chameleons have never had the reputation of being hardy or long-lived in captivity. Six months was once considered a good record of longevity. With the advancing of our knowledge concerning reptiles in general, however, the care we are able to provide has become more sophisticated. Lives of captives can now be measured in years rather

Flap-necked chameleon, *Chamaeleo dilepis*. Photo by G. Marcuse.

Meller's chameleon, *Chamaeleo melleri*. Photo by G. Marcuse.

than months, though they must still be considered among the more delicate of lizards. Possibly, as a group, the chameleons are naturally short-lived.

The common chameleon, *Chamaeleo chamaeleon*, is found from Palestine eastward along coastal North Africa to southern Europe. It measures about ten inches in length and is at home among thick branches in a good-sized aquarium or other cage. Chameleons are not sociable and a single one does quite well if a temperature of 75 degrees is maintained for it. Like other lizards, it will benefit from brief exposures to natural sunlight. Water must be provided by spraying the foliage of the lizard's cage, but this should be done lightly and in one section only, so that a situation of continual dampness does not obtain. Mealworms, flies, and spiders will be accepted; a daily feeding is recommended. The common chameleon, like most of its clan, deposits eggs.

Meller's chameleon, *Chamaeleo melleri*, is one of the largest members of the family. Fully grown individuals will eat small birds and mice and require a great amount of food to keep them in health. Jackson's chameleon, *Chamaeleo jacksoni*, is adorned with long projections resembling horns, as are several other species. The

Oriental rat snake, *Ptyas mucosus*. Photo by H. Hansen, Aquarium Berlin.

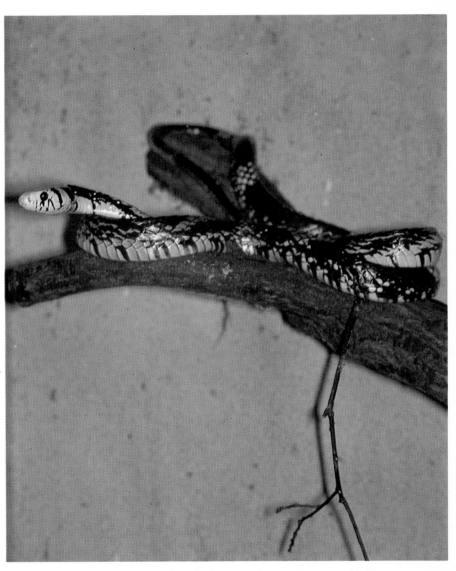

Black and yellow rat snake, *Spilotes pullatus*. Photo by H. Hansen, Aquarium Berlin.

African flap-necked chameleon, *Chamaeleo dilepis*, is commonly imported and lives fairly well, as do some of the dwarf chameleons. Some chameleons, especially among the smaller species and those from mountainous regions, give birth to living young.

FAMILY CORDYLIDAE

Some of the lizards of the family Cordylidae are known as sun-gazers or girdle-tails. The first name comes from their habit of squatting in a frog-like position with the forepart of their bodies raised; the other name comes from their sharply pointed scales, which reach the height of their prominence on the tail. These lizards are among the most heavily armored of reptiles; despite their small size—most are only twelve to fifteen inches in length—they are able to deal telling blows with their tails. They inhabit desert areas where there are outcroppings of rocks. Here they find a haven when danger threatens, their spiny bodies pressed closely to the sides of the recesses among the rocks. For desert lizards, the cordylids are particularly hardy in captivity, feeding well on arthropods and small

Giant girdle-tailed lizard, *Cordylus giganteus*. Photo by G. Marcuse.

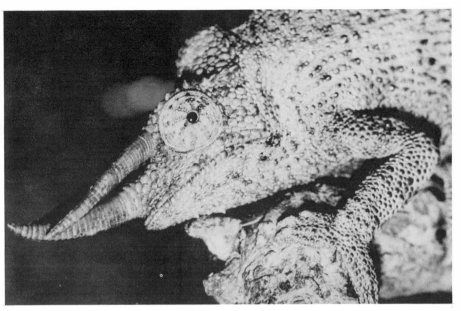

Jackson's chameleon, *Chamaeleo jacksoni*. Photo by Muller-Schmida.

Crested chameleon, *Chamaeleo cristatus*. Photo by Dr. Otto Klee.

Mussurana, *Clelia clelia.* Photo by G. Marcuse.

Coluber species. Photo by G. Marcuse.

Cuban racer, *Alsophis angulifer,* Cuba. Photo by H. Hansen, Aquarium Berlin.

Leopard snake, *Elaphe situla,* southern Europe and western Asia. Photo by Dr. K. Knaack.

Smooth girdle-tailed lizard, *Cordylus coeruleopuretatus*, southern Africa. Photo by G. Marcuse.

vertebrate animals. They should be kept at a temperature of 80 degrees. They are not brightly colored lizards, being mostly brownish or yellowish. The giant girdle-tailed lizard, *Cordylus giganteus*, is the largest of the more familiar members of the family, reaching a length of eighteen inches in exceptional cases. All cordylids produce their babies alive.

FAMILY TEIIDAE

The tropical lizards known variously as tegus, caiman lizards, and rainbow lizards are members of the family Teiidae. There are a great number of species in this family, but only a few are really well known. The common tegu, *Tupinambis teguixin*, is a large species and is attractively marked with white on a shiny black dorsal surface. The species may reach a length of four feet; old males tend to develop enormous heads and powerful jaws. The similar golden tegu, *Tupinambis nigropunctatus*, is also a very large species. Its appearance is quite shiny, the yellow markings standing out in contrast to the black body. The red tegu, *Tupinambis rufescens*, is an attractive animal that is not as readily available as the other two. The tegus are tropical American lizards and should be kept at a temperature of 80 to 85 degrees. They are ferocious creatures when first caught and can inflict considerable damage with their strong jaws. They tame readily, however, and may then be handled without show of bad temper. As is the case with many tropical reptiles, a single chill can kill a tegu without its showing any signs of ill health beforehand. Reptiles of temperate climates tend to develop symptoms of respiratory malfunction when they have been chilled. With tegus and other tropical forms death may ensue before there are any observable symptoms of bad health. In captivity tegus can be maintained indefinitely on a diet of raw meat and eggs. Mice, other reptiles, and small birds will provide some variety in their diet. Normally they are active lizards, but tame captives tend to move about little and rapidly gain weight under favorable circumstances.

The caiman lizard, *Dracaena guianensis*, is a teiid which looks much like its namesake. It frequents marshes and feeds mostly on molluscs. Nearly four feet when fully grown, it should have a large cage with a capacious container of water. The smaller teiids are often called rainbow lizards on the price lists of dealers in tropical reptiles. Mostly, they belong to the genus *Ameiva* and are closely related to our own racerunners, but more beautifully colored. All are carnivorous and reach an average size considerably inferior to that of the tegus.

Common tegu, *Tupinambis teguixin*. Photo by H. Schultz.

Green tree snake, *Leptophis ahaetulla*. Photo by G. Marcuse.

Green vine snake, *Oxybelis fulgidus* (top) and brown vine snake, *Oxybelis aeneus* (bottom). Photo by G. Marcuse.

Long-nosed tree snake, *Dryophis* sp. Photo by G. Marcuse.

Golden tree snake, *Chrysopelia ornata.* Photo by G. Marcuse.

Caiman lizard, *Dracaena guianensis*. Photo by G. Marcuse.

FAMILY LACERTIDAE

In Europe any mention of lizards is likely to bring to mind those kinds belonging to the family Lacertidae. These are the typical lizards of the Old World; the family is made up of a number of genera, *Lacerta* being the largest. Members of the family are found in Europe, Asia, and Africa and are among the commonest reptiles of these continents. Such familiar forms as the wall lizard, *Lacerta muralis*, the sand lizard, *Lacerta agilis*, and the viviparous lizard, *Lacerta vivipara*, adapt quite well to confinement in a suitable terrarium. The various species may be mixed providing there is no great disparity in size among them. The green lacerta, *Lacerta viridis*, is an attractive species, as is the eyed lizard, *Lacerta lepida*. Both of these will depart from the usual insect diet of the smaller lacertas and take a meat and raw egg mixture from a dish. Larger specimens will even devour mice and other small vertebrate animals. Occasionally lacertids will mate and produce fertile eggs in captivity. They should have a sandy cage that is provided with rocks and a spacious water dish. In a well-lighted cage there are few vivarium animals more attractive than an adult male eyed lizard. Lizards of the genus *Psammodromus* are closely related to those of the genus *Lacerta* but should have drier surroundings.

258

FAMILY GERRHOSAURIDAE

The family Gerrhosauridae is a small group of about two dozen species that are found mainly in South Africa and Madagascar. One of the more familiar species is the yellow-throated plated lizard, *Gerrhosaurus flavigularis*. Like many other members of its family, this species does well in a dry terrarium with rocky hiding places and a fairly high temperature. Some of the gerrhosaurids reach a length of two feet and all are oviparous.

FAMILY SCINCIDAE

Some of the most desirable and long-lived of the lizards belong to the family Scincidae. The life histories of only a few of the family's more than 600 species have been worked out in any detail. Known as skinks, they are mostly secretive reptiles that elude observation in the field. Larger members of the family reach two feet, but most skinks are tiny lizards of a few inches. Every continent has its skinks, but it is Australia that produces some of the most desirable types for captivity. The blue-tongued skinks (*Tiliqua scincoides*, *Tiliqua occipitalis*, *Tiliqua nigrolutea*) are large Australian lizards that are very similar in general appearance and habits. They live entirely on

Plated lizard, *Gerrhosaurus* sp. Photo by G. Marcuse.

False hognose snake, *Lioheterodon modestus,* Madagascar. Photo by H. Hansen, Aquarium Berlin.

Banded krait, *Bungarus fasciatus.* Photo by G. Marcuse.

Tentacled snake, *Herpeton tentacularum.* Photo by J. K. Langhammer.

the ground, move slowly, have broad and flat bodies with attractive crossbands or blotches, and flat, blue tongues. Large blue-tongues may reach two feet, but the average is closer to fifteen inches. They become very tame in captivity and do well on chopped raw beef particles mixed with raw beaten eggs. This may be varied with occasional feedings of insects or even young mice and birds. Under favorable conditions mating sometimes occurs; the babies are born alive after undergoing a primitive placental development within the body of the mother. Most live-bearing lizards simply retain the eggs, allowing them to hatch internally rather than buried in the earth or under a stone. With the blue-tongues and certain other skinks, the babies are nourished by the body of the parent while developing.

The skinks of the genus *Egernia* are a varied group, consisting of smooth-scaled types that burrow, others that have taken to a life in trees, and still others that live in rocky areas and have a coarse

Shingleback skink, *Trachydosaurus rugosus*. Photo by J. Warham.

scalation. Of the latter, the short-tailed spiny skink, *Egernia depressa,* and Cunningham's skink, *Egernia cunninghami,* are well known in zoological collections, where they thrive for many years if kept dry and warm. The oddest-looking Australian skink is the stump-tail or shingleback, *Trachydosaurus rugosus.* This inhabitant of dry areas has protruding scales and a short, thick tail. Coloration is some shade of brown or grayish-black with lighter underparts. It is a large, thick-bodied lizard which may approach two feet in length in exceptional instances. Insects, snails, fruits, and flowers form the natural diet of Australian skinks, but all of these reptiles are re-

Red ground skink, *Lygosoma fernandi,* Africa. Photo by R.G. Sprackland, Jr.

markable in the ease with which they adjust to foods they never encounter in the wild state. Individuals have been kept for long periods on table scraps! The stump-tailed skink's babies are born alive and almost always number two. These are quite large and begin to forage for themselves at once.

FAMILY ANGUIDAE

It is interesting that two closely related members of the family Anguidae have established longevity records of a quarter of a century or more in captivity. One of these, the "slow-worm," is a diminutive reptile of about eighteen inches when fully grown. The other, the European glass snake, *Ophisaurus apodus,* is a robust lizard which may reach four feet. Both are limbless lizards, like many others of

Shield snake, *Aspidelaps scutatus*, South Africa. Photo by H. Hansen, Aquarium Berlin.

Egyptian cobra, *Naja hajae,* northern Africa. Photo by G. Marcuse.

Arizona coral snake, *Micruroides euryxanthus,* southwestern U.S. Photo by J. K. Langhammer.

their family. The slow-worm, *Anguis fragilis*, is probably the most satisfactory reptile one can keep in captivity where space is very limited. The species is serpentine of body and without limbs, progress being made in graceful undulations. The coloration of the slow-worm is subdued, yet quite attractive in its various shades of metallic brown. These small lizards become very tame, learning to recognize their keeper and feed readily from his fingers. They seem to display an intelligence that is out of keeping with their appearance. Breeding in captivity takes place frequently; the three-inch-long babies are born alive and raised easily on a diet of finely chopped beef and raw eggs, well-mixed and proffered in a shallow dish. Insects, earthworms, and slugs are taken with equal relish. A dish of water should be available always, and means of burrowing and hiding provided. A temperature range of 70 to 75 degrees is suitable.

The European glass snake is a large lizard and one which does exceedingly well in captivity. A simple cage with a layer of fine gravel and a good-sized container of water provides the essential requirements. Eggs and chopped beef—that standby of lizard keepers—is readily taken by captives, as well as a variety of arthropods and small vertebrate animals.

European glass snake, *Ophisaurus apodus*. Photo by G. Marcuse.

Spiny-tailed monitor, *Varanus acanthurus*, Australia. Photo by Muller-Schmida.

FAMILY VARANIDAE

Monitors (genus *Varanus*) belong to the family Varanidae. Some are small reptiles of less than a foot in total length, while others grow to a very large size. The Komodo dragon, *Varanus komodoensis*, may reach twelve feet and a weight of 300 pounds, making it the world's largest lizard. All of the monitors are tropical reptiles and should be kept at a temperature in the 80 to 90-degree range in captivity. They are active lizards, and freshly caught specimens can be expected to spend much of their time seeking a means of escape from their cage. Like snakes, they often rub their snouts sore in their probing of corners and attempts to push out screening or hardware cloth. Fortunately, most specimens will tame after a while. Some, though, remain hostile over long periods—lashing out with their tails upon the slightest provocation. Even a very small monitor can produce a stinging lash with its tail. If such a blow is inflicted on a hand, it will develop into a raised welt. The claws of monitors are long and very sharp and a carelessly handled wild monitor can do much damage with them as well as with its strong jaws. Monitors are amazingly strong animals, and it is quite difficult to hold one without being bitten. They do not readily relinquish a hold they have secured; any effort to pull a specimen away from a seized

Dark sea snake, *Astrotia stokesii,* Pacific Ocean. Photo by R. Steene.

Rhinoceros viper, *Bitis nasicornis*. Photo by J. K. Langhammer.

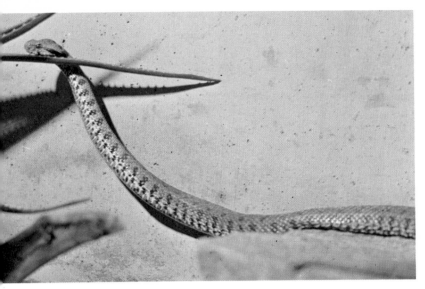

Radde's viper, *Vipera xanthina,* Armenia. Photo by Dr. Otto Klee.

Gaboon viper, *Bitis gabonica*. Photo by J. K. Langhammer.

Tree monitor, *Varanus prasinus*. Photo by G. Marcuse.

object will only result in a tightening of the hold. A young Nile monitor, *Varanus niloticus*, once seized hold of a forefinger while I was moving it during cage-cleaning. Though only two feet in length, it produced a laceration which served as a practical illustration of what a big specimen could do. It refused to let go until placed under water.

In my opinion, the monitors are among the most interesting of reptiles. Some are extraordinarily beautiful animals, especially when young. None seems to grow very rapidly, though detailed observations are lacking in the literature. A baby water monitor, *Varanus salvator*, in my collection grew from 13 inches to 19 inches in less than a year. It could be expected that its subsequent growth would be at a slower pace.

A few of the monitors which are commonly imported are the lace monitor, *Varanus varius*, the yellow monitor, *Varanus flavescens*, and the sand monitor, *Varanus gouldii*. The tree monitor, *Varanus prasinus*, is an arboreal animal that seldom reaches the United States.

Ocellated monitor, *Varanus timorensis*, Australia. Photo by Dr. Otto Klee.

Palm viper, *Bothrops lateralis,* South America. Photo by G. Marcuse.

Russell's viper, *Vipera russelli.* Photo by H. Hansen, Aquarium Berlin.

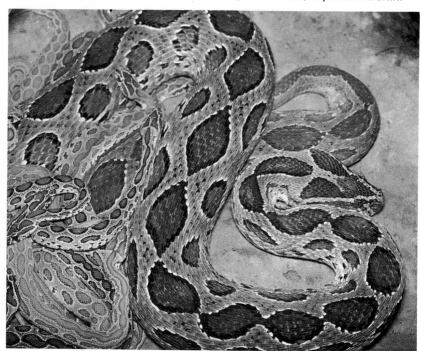

Bushmaster, *Lachesis muta*. Photo by H. Schultz.

Rough-neck monitor, *Varanus rudicollis*, Malaya to Borneo. Photo by Dr. Otto Klee.

Among the different species of monitors there is to be noted a difference in temperament similar to that found among the various species of crocodilians.

Monitors are carnivorous and will devour anything they are capable of dismembering and gulping down. The species which live in or near water will readily eat fish and some, like the water monitor, seem as well adapted to an aquatic existence as the crocodiles. Whole animals should be fed to monitors whenever this is possible, to provide the vitamins and minerals required to prevent the nutritional

Papuan monitor, *Varanus salvadorii,* Papua New Guinea. Photo by Dr. Otto Klee.

Copperhead, *Agkistrodon contortrix*, two subspecies. Photo by G. Marcuse.

Cantil, *Agkistrodon bilineatus*. Photo by J. K. Langhammer.

Eastern pigmy rattlesnake, *Sistrurus miliaris miliaris*. Photo by J. K. Langhammer.

deficiencies that develop among improperly cared-for monitors, especially the juveniles. If meat is fed, it should be fortified with bone meal and a multi-vitamin preparation. Rickets quickly manifests itself among young monitors that are not adequately nourished. A weakening of the rear limbs is the first symptom. Young monitors cannot be bought cheaply from retailers in the United States. Some kinds rarely come on the animal market at all.

Monitors do not require in their enclosures the imitative accessories of soil or rocks that are provided to other kinds of lizards. Ease of cage-cleaning should be the foremost consideration. Generally, this can be best accomplished with a plain floor covered with several thicknesses of paper. A large container of water should be available, and the aquatic species will spend much of their time submerged. It is a fascinating experience to raise a baby of one of the larger types. The Asiatic water monitor is a most attractive little creature during its early years and will quickly develop into a veritable pet. Monitors do not divest themselves of their tails, like some other lizards. Once lost, the tail of a monitor does not grow back. Small specimens should be handled like small crocodiles, a firm grasp being taken just back of the head while the other hand restrains the rear legs and supports that part of the reptile's body. With tame specimens, such precautions are unnecessary.

FAMILY AMPHISBAENIDAE

We will close our discussion of exotic lizards with a few remarks about the worm lizards of the family Amphisbaenidae. If it were not for the fact that they are sometimes offered for sale I would be inclined to bypass them in a general book on reptiles. Persistent burrowers, the worm lizards of the tropics are seldom seen above ground. Most burrowing reptiles do poorly in captivity unless provided with a means of tunneling through soil or sand. But the few accounts we have of the present strange creatures indicate that they will thrive in a container with only a thin layer of wood pulp which is kept moderately damp. The white-bellied worm lizard, *Amphisbaena alba*, is imported occasionally and is one of the larger species, measuring as much as two feet in length. It resembles a giant reddish earthworm. Worm lizards of this and other species may have little place in a small collection of reptiles, but any specimen would surely be a conversation piece among herptile enthusiasts!

Bornean earless monitor,
Lanthanotus borneensis
(above), Borneo. A very rare
family of one species, related to
the monitors. Photo by R. G.
Sprackland, Jr.

Flattened girdle-lizard,
Platysaurus torquatus (right),
southern Africa. The
Cordylidae is a rare family
with few species. Photo by
R. G. Sprackland, Jr.

Cape flattened girdle-lizard, *Platysaurus capensis*, southern Africa.
Photo by G. Marcuse.

Southern pigmy rattlesnake, *Sistrurus miliaris barbouri.* Photo by F. J. Dodd, Jr.

Western pigmy rattlesnake, *Sistrurus miliaris streckeri.* Photo by F. J. Dodd, Jr.

Massasauga, *Sistrurus catenatus.* Photo by J. K. Langhammer.

Eastern diamondback rattlesnake, *Crotalus adamanteus.* Photo by F. J. Dodd, Jr.

Tuatara, *Sphenodon punctatus*. Photo by Malcom Davis.

THE TUATARA

The tuataras of the order Rhynchocephalia, family Sphenodontidae, resemble somewhat the iguanids and the agamids. They are confined to the offshore islands of New Zealand, where they are under the strictest protection. Therefore, they are seldom seen in captivity.

In its habitat, the tuatara is mostly nocturnal, inhabiting during the daytime burrows dug by petrels, seagull-like birds. At night it emerges to feed upon such invertebrates as it may come across. Like many true lizards, it is able to regenerate a lost tail.

Tuataras do not reach sexual maturity until nearly twenty years of age, and the species may, indeed, be one of the longest-lived reptiles. The species—there is only one, *Sphenodon punctatus*—reaches an adult length of about twenty-two inches. Females are smaller and their eggs are deposited in holes. Clutches may number up to two dozen and require fifteen months to hatch.

There is little possibility that the average reader will ever come into contact with a living tuatara. Perhaps no other reptile can thrive in such a low temperature—the captive tuatara seems to thrive best with an ambient Fahrenheit temperature of approximately 55 degrees!

VI

Harmless North American Snakes

SNAKES IN GENERAL

With the opening of the present chapter I must make a confession: among the multitude of living creatures inhabiting this planet, the snakes have always been my favorites. People who have a frank and open liking for snakes have, in the past, been regarded as a bit peculiar. To some extent, this attitude still prevails. Among enlightened people, however, there is a slowly-growing awareness of the inter-relationship and oneness of all forms of life—nothing vanishes without leaving the whole poorer as a result. As a boy, I was frequently embarrassed when asked why I liked snakes. In the face of the widespread prejudice against them, it seemed, somehow, wrong to regard such creatures with friendly interest. The situation is gradually changing as more and more people are getting to know snakes as they really are. This trend will continue and in time an interest in reptiles generally, and snakes in particular, will be regarded as no more unusual or demanding of explanation than a special interest in birds, mammals, or any of the other fascinating forms of life about us.

Snakes are the easiest of backboned animals to keep alive and in good health in captivity. A clean, dry cage with a container for drinking water is all that many species require. Like other reptiles, snakes are cold-blooded, and their activities are circumscribed by the temperature of their surroundings. With those from temperate

Western diamondback rattlesnake, *Crotalus atrox*. Photo by F. J. Dodd, Jr.

Mojave rattlesnake, *Crotalus scutulatus*, southwestern U.S. Photo by F. J. Dodd, Jr.

Prairie rattlesnake, *Crotalus viridis viridis.* Photo by F. J. Dodd, Jr.

Prairie rattlesnake, *Crotalus viridis nuntius.* Photo by F. J. Dodd, Jr.

climates, the temperature range for normal activity may be quite broad and is not likely to present any difficulties to those who keep them in captivity. Species which normally hibernate in the wild state seem able, in captivity, to relinquish this period of winter rest without harmful results. Many snakes feed infrequently, especially when out of the juvenile stage, and this further lightens the burden on their keeper. In a cage snakes do not exercise much, and a liberal feeding once a week will keep most species in good health. If a snake begins to fatten noticeably, the feeding intervals can be stretched to ten days or even two weeks. Usually but one defecation will follow a meal, and this makes it very easy to keep a snake's cage clean.

Snakes live exclusively on animal matter—none is known to accept vegetable substances. It will be noted from reading the chapters on turtles, crocodilians, and lizards that many of the troubles plaguing these reptiles in captivity arise from the lack of an adequate diet. Since snakes will accept only their natural foods or a reasonable approximation of them, they almost never suffer from dietary deficiencies. They either eat what is good for them—or not at all; those in the latter category are individuals which cannot adjust and constitute a very small minority. Such individuals can be forcibly fed, but more will be said about this in a later chapter.

In North America we have a well-varied and very interesting serpent fauna, consisting of well over a hundred species.

BLIND SNAKES AND BOAS

The blind snakes (family Leptotyphlopidae) and the boas (family Boidae) are mostly tropical snakes, but both families have a few representatives in North America. The Texas blind snake, *Leptotyphlops dulcis*, and the western blind snake, *Leptotyphlops humilis*, are diminutive burrowing reptiles that are confined to the south-central and southwestern portions of the continent. They are commonly twelve to fifteen inches long, brownish or even pink in color, with degenerate eyes that have all but lost their function. Ants and their pupae, as well as termites, make up the bulk of the diet of these snakes. In captivity, an aquarium with several inches of loose soil makes the best home for them. Most of their time will be spent beneath the surface in tunnels, but they occasionally make an appearance at night. They reproduce from eggs; their wormlike babies measure around four inches when they hatch. Because of the difficulty of providing captives with their natural diet and the fact that only seldom will they emerge from their burrows, they are probably the least suitable of snakes to keep. None of them will live very long if deprived of a burrowing medium, which should be kept slightly moist. A temperature of 78 to 85 degrees seems to suit them quite well.

The boas of North America appear as pygmies when compared with the large forms of the tropics. Rubber boas, *Charina bottae,* are stout-bodied, blunt-tailed snakes which seldom exceed two feet in length. Though quite secretive, they can climb well and seem at home even in water. Most specimens are captured near streams, in relatively damp situations. Instead of defending themselves by biting, rubber boas are likely to contract their bodies into a ball when handled. They remain timid in captivity and spend most of their time hiding or burrowing. Many do not feed readily, but those which do prefer lizards, small mammals, and birds. Babies number around six, usually, and are produced alive.

Rubber boa, *Charina bottae.* Photo by F. J. Dodd, Jr.

Sidewinder, *Crotalus cerastes,* southwestern deserts. Photo by F. J. Dodd, Jr.

Rock rattlesnake, *Crotalus lepidus,* southwestern Texas to Arizona and Mexico. Photo by J. K. Langhammer.

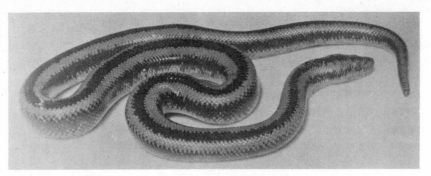

Rosy boa, *Lichanura trivirgata*. From Klauber.

The rosy boa, *Lichanura trivirgata*, is also a western snake and has habits similar to the preceding. It is a variable species in color—grayish, tan, or pinkish—with three fairly distinct dark bands running the length of the body. Like their larger relatives, the rosy and the rubber boas are constrictors, feeding mostly on warm-blooded prey. The males usually have tiny anal spurs.

All of the better-known non-poisonous snakes of North America belong to the family Colubridae. These are the typical snakes that are found nearly everywhere in any habitat that is capable of supporting reptile life. The colubrids vary much in size, form, and habits. It is much beyond the scope of this book to catalogue in detail structural differences among the species, range definitions, and subspecific variations. Rather, the aim is to present a broad picture of our serpent life, with special reference to the adaptability of the various species of snakes to life in captivity.

GARTER SNAKES

The garter snakes (genus *Thamnophis*) are perhaps the best-known snakes of this country. Most are characterized by the presence of stripes running the length of their bodies on a dark background. These stripes may be very vivid, somewhat obscure, or entirely absent, depending on the species, subspecies, or mutation in hand. A single population of the eastern garter snake, *Thamnophis s. sirtalis*, may have striped individuals, others in which the stripes are obscure or replaced by a checkerboard pattern, and others which are coal-black and lack all trace of pattern. Some of the western species, like

Checkered garter snake, *Thamnophis marcianus*. Photo by C. A. Hewitt.

the checkered garter snake, *Thamnophis marcianus*, and certain western varieties of *T. sirtalis*, are extremely pretty snakes.

Most garter snakes show their close affinity to the water snakes in frequenting areas that are plentifully supplied with ponds, streams, and other permanent water bodies. The types which are found in desert country follow the courses of streams and rivers. A few kinds are really aquatic, taking to the water when alarmed and swimming with the ease of the true water snakes. They depend on flight to escape enemies but when caught will put up a good show of defense, biting vigorously and often smearing their captor with a discharge from the anal glands. Captives tame quickly and permit themselves to be handled without the slightest intimation of hostility. A young friend of mine has a varied collection of reptiles and his special favorite is a black-necked garter snake, *Thamnophis cyrtopsis*, from Arizona. It is allowed the freedom of his dresser-top and has certain favorite resting places from which it never wanders far. The most extended foray of the handsome and trusting little reptile is to an adjoining desk, where it reposes beneath the keyboard of a portable typewriter. At first I was somewhat skeptical of an arrangement which allowed a small snake so much freedom, feeling that eventually it would wander away and become lost. But for months now it has been kept uncaged and serves as a practical illustration of the degree to which snakes can be tamed. Garter snakes average two to three feet in length. A few, like Butler's garter snake, *Thamnophis butleri*, may be fully grown when eighteen inches long; the giant garter snake, *Thamnophis couchi gigas*, on the other hand, grows to over four feet!

Garter snakes breed in the spring and the young are born alive in late summer, the broods occasionally numbering several dozens. Baby garter snakes can be reared without difficulty under the most ordinary of cage conditions. The eastern garter snakes feed largely upon earthworms and frogs; the western species and varieties tend to favor small fishes.

Black-necked garter snake, *Thamnophis cyrtopsis*. Photo by G. Marcuse.

Ribbon snake, *Thamnophis sauritus*. Photo courtesy American Museum of Natural History, from Pope's *Reptile World*.

RIBBON SNAKES

Ribbon snakes (*Thamnophis sauritus* and *Thamnophis proximus*) are slender, semi-aquatic members of the garter snake genus. They are frequently to be found basking on bushes which overhang a stream or pond. When alarmed they drop into the water, diving beneath the surface and hiding among aquatic plants. The eastern ribbon snake, *Thamnophis sauritus sauritus*, is a particularly attractive form, its bright yellow stripes standing out vividly on a black or dark brown body. Ribbon snakes are very active reptiles; captives usually remain alert and nervous for some time, though feeding readily enough on frogs, salamanders, and small fishes. Their babies are born alive and in smaller numbers than those of the typical garter snakes. The snakes of this group do not display the bewildering array of color variations seen among the garter snakes. Like the latter, they should be kept in dry cages with only a small container for drinking water.

BROWN SNAKES, RED-BELLIED SNAKES

The brown snakes (genus *Storeria*) are small reptiles, not often measuring more than a foot in length. The most familiar of the two species is the northern brown snake, *Storeria dekayi*, a secretive little

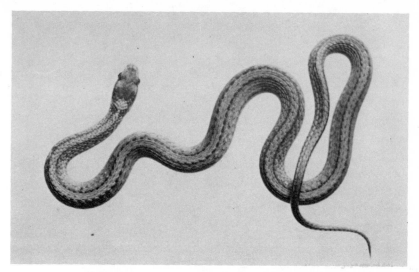

Red-bellied snake, *Storeria occipitomaculata.*

reptile which often lives in large numbers close to human habitations. In fact, in many years of collecting I have seldom found brown snakes in any wilderness area. However incongruous it may seem, any consideration of the habitat of the species immediately brings to mind city dumps and vacant lots. In such places they often abound, sometimes in company with the smooth green snake, *Opheodrys vernalis.* The really small kinds of snakes, like this species, seem much better able to tolerate moderately damp conditions in captivity than their larger relatives. Brown snakes can be successfully maintained under terrarium conditions, with a floor covering of earth and moss. They will also thrive in a plain wooden cage with bare floor, but means of hiding are a necessity for such a secretive reptile. Even when first caught the little brown snake will not bite. Its food consists largely of earthworms and slugs. The red-bellied snake, *Storeria occipitomaculata,* is closely related to the brown snake but differs in color, having a grayish or black dorsal surface and a bright red venter. Unlike the brown snake, the red-belly sticks to forest areas. Often many will be found around farm land that is skirted by areas of open woods. Their usual hiding places are under boards and flat rocks.

WATER SNAKES

Water snakes (genus *Natrix*) are common reptiles over much of the country. In the southeast they abound in numbers of species and in individuals. Most water snakes have brown, dark green, or black upper surfaces, more or less obscurely banded. They have keeled scales and stout bodies with conspicuously distinct heads. Frequenting the environs of water, they take to that element when alarmed and quickly dive out of sight. Aquatic animals of all kinds are eaten; most captives take readily to a diet of fresh fishes. In size, our water snakes range from small forms to species which exceed five feet in length. Large water snakes are formidable-looking and are often confused with the water moccasin, *Agkistrodon piscivorus*. The latter has a pit located between the eye and nostril, and this feature will immediately separate it from the harmless water snakes. Some water snakes fight viciously when cornered or noosed, and large specimens can produce lacerations which bleed freely but are not, of course, dangerous.

Green water snake, *Natrix cyclopion*, southern United States. Photo by F. J. Dodd, Jr.

The northern water snake, *Natrix sipedon sipedon*, lives well in captivity and becomes very tame, readily feeding from the hand. Perhaps no snake is more easily taken care of than a water snake. Their easily-procured diet of fresh or canned fish is at once an asset and a drawback—for fish tend to leave a lingering odor about the quarters of water snakes. This can be minimized by feeding the reptiles—at least the tamer ones—out of their cages. Correlated with their feeding habits is the production of watery feces which are odoriferous and often smeared over the cage bottom. These, then, are the drawbacks of keeping water snakes. A single water snake will require more attention to the cleanliness of its cage than six or more mouse-eating snakes of the same size.

The red-bellied water snake, *Natrix erythrogaster*, of our south-eastern waterways is a truly beautiful reptile in the contrast between its rich brown dorsum and bright red belly. It tames readily and makes a most attractive exhibit. The green water snake, *Natrix cyclopion*, and the brown water snake, *Natrix taxispilota*, grow to a huge size and are somewhat less adaptable to cage-life. Baby water snakes of all species are handsomely blotched little creatures, and most are easily raised.

Red-bellied water snake, *Natrix erythrogaster*. From Ditmars, *Reptiles of North America.*

Juvenile racer, *Coluber constrictor*. From Ditmars, *Reptiles of North America*.

RACERS AND WHIPSNAKES

The sleek, fast-moving racers, *Coluber constrictor*, are particularly interesting snakes. In one variety or another they are found from coast to coast. Those of the West are plain olive or brownish snakes with light bellies, while the eastern variety is a plain black snake with an area of white confined to the chin. The young, which are hatched from eggs, differ very much from the adults, being grayish or white with reddish-brown blotches. These begin to fade in the second summer and some racers only slightly over two feet in length have already turned completely black. As adults, the racers average between four and five feet. Among the many specimens I have caught, I have failed to find any that were a full six feet, though this measurement is often cited as the uppermost limit of their growth potential.

Racers are snakes with personality—one never knows what to expect from a specimen encountered in the field. Nearly all books on reptiles say that these snakes glide away like a streak when encountered. This may be true of racers that are met while prowling for food, but I have found that like many other snakes, racers often make no attempt to escape when discovered. This may be particularly true in the more remote areas where their contact with humans has been minimal. On a warm day only a few months ago, while hunting for rattlers, I came upon a cloister of four racers on a rocky hillside. They had recently emerged from their hibernating quarters and all about them were holes and crevices that would have provided a secure retreat. Each of the snakes was awake and alert and fully aware of the presence of my hunting companion and me, as evidenced by their head movements and the flicking of their tongues. Not one of these snakes made any attempt to escape until I had actually clamped my hands down over the mass of them. Two managed to squirm out of my grasp and two were made captive. On countless other occasions I have noted a tendency on the part of racers to scorn flight unless actually molested. I am speaking of racers in rather wild country, where they have been little persecuted. Possibly those which have had frequent contact with people have come to learn the advantage of the flight pattern.

Angry racers will fight viciously, but even the largest specimens can produce little more than superficial scratches with their teeth. Here again, we find racers that do not even attempt to bite when first caught. Many reptile hobbyists have given up on racers, considering them delicate and difficult to handle in captivity. Kept in a cage which has no hiding place and constantly harassed by a procession of people, the captive racer is likely to spend most of its time seeking escape or angrily striking at the objects of its annoyance. Such an animal rarely shows any interest in food, and is likely to damage its snout beyond repair. All racers dislike handling or restraint of any kind; this is true even of those which are well adjusted and have been in captivity and feeding well for many months. Sympathetically cared for, with allowance made for its flighty nature, a racer can become the favorite of a collection of snakes. My method of taming racers is the same I use with the other more nervous types of reptiles. First, I attempt to capture the reptile with as little shock to its nervous system as possible. This generally means seizing it by mid-body, then restraining the head while it is being put into a collecting bag. The snake is never allowed to dangle or attempt to shake loose from a neck-grasp. I never put more than one specimen in a collecting bag. This is securely tied and the snake remains in it for three or four days at least, the bag not being opened during this time. Awaiting the snake at the end of this quieting-down period is a clean and dry cage of moderate size—not more than two-thirds the length of the reptile. This has a glass front but the sides and top are of wooden construction. A small cardboard box with a two-inch hole cut in the side is held in place in one corner of the cage with a heavy rock. The bag is placed in the cage, after being untied, and the snake is allowed to make an acquaintance with its new home. After a couple of days the bag is removed and a container of water which cannot be tipped is furnished. By this time, the snake will have come to regard the cardboard box as a place of refuge and for a while will not venture from it very often. Food in the form of a dead mouse is now offered. If this is not eaten within a few daylight hours, it is removed and the snake is allowed a further few days to adjust before the feeding attempt is repeated. Live mice will serve only to further agitate an already nervous reptile, and in my opinion have little advantage over

Adult racer, *Coluber constrictor*, midwestern subspecies. From Ortenburger, courtesy University of Michigan Museum of Zoology.

dead ones in the feeding of snakes. It was once thought necessary to feed snakes live animals only, but experience has repeatedly demonstrated that any snake which will eat a live mouse will eat a dead one just as readily. The converse is not true, for many snakes which will readily eat dead mice show little interest in live ones.

Getting back to our racer—once it has accepted a mouse it is on its way toward becoming a contented and longlived captive. Eventually it will come to show a great deal of recognition toward its keeper and will even feed from the hand. Racers eat practically any small animal they can overcome and this includes smaller snakes of all kinds. Mice are the favorite food of captives. They are diurnal snakes and seldom move about much at night. Non-constrictors, they simply swallow their food alive in the wild state. The young are hatched from eggs and during the first year of their lives feed largely upon insects, small frogs and salamanders.

Whipsnakes (genus *Masticophis*) are closely related to the racers and have similar habits. Some, like the coachwhip, *Masticophis flagellum*, may attain the enormous length—for a snake of this country—of eight feet. The western forms, of which the striped whipsnake, *Masticophis lateralis*, is one, are often very pretty reptiles. None of the whipsnakes can tolerate even the slightest dampness, though they drink frequently and should be provided with a small dish of water that cannot be tipped. Active snakes all, they require proportionately more food than the slower-moving species.

PATCH-NOSED SNAKES

The patch-nosed snakes (genus *Salvadora*) are delicately formed desert reptiles that much resemble the whipsnakes in their habits. They have a broad dorsal stripe of yellow or tan, bordered by darker lines on the sides. The snout is much flattened and enlarged, im-

Coachwhip, *Masticophis flagellum*. Photo courtesy American Museum of Natural History, from Pope's *Reptile World*.

Western patch-nosed snake, *Salvadora hexalepis.* From Van Den-burgh.

parting a short-headed appearance. With their large eyes and quick, nervous movements, snakes of this genus are reminiscent of small birds. A western patch-nosed snake, *Salvadora hexalepis,* in my collection at the time of writing is very active by day but strangely, for a diurnal snake, will accept its weekly meal of a small dead mouse only at night! It does not attempt to bite when handled, but has the peculiar habit of suddenly throwing its body into a gyration about its own axis. This makes it a very difficult snake to hold when it has its mind set upon going elsewhere.

INDIGO SNAKE

Among the native snakes, an outstanding species is the indigo snake, *Drymarchon corais.* Commonly six feet or more in length, the highly-polished blue-black scales of this handsome reptile shine with an iridescence under good lighting. The variety found in the southeast is known as *D. c. couperi;* the Texas subspecies is *D. c. erebennus* and is not as attractive, having a brownish overcast to its color. Both varieties live very well in captivity, feeding upon small mammals, birds, reptiles, amphibians, and fishes. Some individuals can be conditioned to a diet of raw beef strips. Technically classified

Indigo snake, *Drymarchon corais*. Photo courtesy American Museum of Natural History.

as a near relative of the racers and whipsnakes, the indigo is, in its demeanor, an altogether different snake. It is nowhere very abundant, so the capture of an indigo is generally the highlight of a day's collecting. It is generally found in the more remote, sandy areas where tortoise burrows are numerous. Captives do well only if kept warm and dry; if these conditions are fulfilled they can be expected to outlive nearly all other kinds of snakes. Indigo snakes are the most expensive of our native serpents, and the supply seems never equal to the demand for them. Most private collectors do not own more than a single specimen, but those who have collected indigos in numbers tell us that they fight viciously among themselves when caged together. This is a rare trait among snakes of the same species that are of approximately the same size.

RAT SNAKES

Rat snakes (genus *Elaphe*) are common and familiar reptiles over much of the eastern half of the country. Generally of moderate to large size, some kinds are boldly patterned and among the most beautiful snakes in the world. All are constrictors, and their ceaseless search for mice and rats brings them into close proximity to human

Corn snake, *Elaphe guttata*. Photo courtesy Univ. Florida Press, from Carr and Goin's *Guide to Reptiles, Amphibians and Freshwater Fishes of Florida.*

Black rat snake, *Elaphe obsoleta obsoleta*. From Ditmars, *Reptiles of North America.*

dwellings, where such rodents often abound. They are not fast-moving snakes, and those encountered in the field will often stand their ground and vigorously defend themselves, contracting their forequarters and striking with a sharp hiss. Individuals may retain a readiness to bite even after months of captivity, but this is very unusual. The average rat snake makes a quick adjustment to cage life and shows little of the nervousness displayed by some other kinds of serpents.

The corn snake, *Elaphe guttata*, is a beautifully blotched species that feeds largely upon mice. Its gray or orange ground-color is overlaid with large red saddles that are bordered by black. The belly is handsomely checkered in black and white. Though the species may rarely reach six feet, such specimens are uncommon and any over four feet must be considered quite large. Like the other rat snakes, the present species climbs well but most often is found on the ground. It is both diurnal and nocturnal, depending in some measure on weather conditions. Few are found abroad on really hot days—but this is true of nearly all kinds of snakes.

The north-central states are the home of the fox snake, *Elaphe vulpina*, another of the blotched rat snakes with rather subdued tones of yellow and brown. The head has a metallic luster and the species is often confused with the copperhead, *Agkistrodon contortrix*. Fox snakes receive their common name from their habit of emitting an odor like that found around a fox den. They do this only when freshly caught; once placed in a cage they become the personification of good nature, feed readily on rodents and birds, and live a seemingly contented existence. The species does not often exceed four feet in length but has a stout build. It is a favorite of those who have kept it in captivity. Unfortunately, it is one of those snakes of rather limited distribution and is not often available from dealers.

The black rat snake, *Elaphe obsoleta obsoleta*, is the largest species of its genus in North America. Six-foot specimens are not rare, and occasional individuals grow much larger. Typically, it is a snake of wooded hillsides, often found in association with timber rattlesnakes, copperheads, and black racers. Superficially, it resembles the latter, but is a stouter snake, has a more angular and distinct head, is slower-moving, and its scales are keeled; those of the racer are smooth.

A conspicuous snake in the Carolinas, Georgia, and Florida is the yellow rat snake, *Elaphe obsoleta quadrivittata*. This brightly-hued

Yellow rat snake, *Elaphe obsoleta quadrivittata.* Photo courtesy University of Florida Press, from Carr and Goin.

Texas rat snake, *Elaphe obsoleta lindheimeri,* Texas and Louisiana. Photo courtesy American Museum of Natural History, from Pope's *Reptile World.*

snake, banded longitudinally with four blackish stripes, is often seen in trees. A more usual habitat is the environs of sheds and abandoned buildings which have become the congregating places of large numbers of rodents. Like other rat snakes, this species deposits about two dozen eggs in early summer. These hatch about eight weeks later, the babies measuring twelve to fourteen inches. In color and pattern they are very much different from the parent snakes. They are boldly blotched with brown on a gray ground color, this coloration fading as growth progresses until the plain yellow of the adult prevails when the young snake is about half-grown. A few adults retain traces of the juvenile pattern in obscure, barely-discernible blotches between their characteristic stripes. Baby rat snakes of this and the other species differ from the adults in the matter of food requirements. Adult rat snakes live exclusively upon warm-blooded prey and the eggs of birds. The juveniles will accept frogs, insects, and lizards.

An especially beautiful rat snake inhabits southern Florida, particularly the Everglades. The Everglades rat snake, *Elaphe obsoleta rossalleni*, as the subspecies is called, is a bright orange snake, growing to very large size, and often entirely lacking the striping of the more widely-distributed yellow rat snake. I would call this the handsomest of the larger North American snakes. Unfortunately, the species loses some of the intensity of its color when it has been in captivity for a long time. Whether this tendency could be overcome by the addition of vitamins to the diet of captives is not known, but it would be interesting to experiment along these lines.

PINE SNAKE, GOPHER SNAKE, BULLSNAKE

The pine, gopher, and bullsnakes were once divided into several species but all are now regarded simply as varieties of *Pituophis melanoleucus*. All are large and showy serpents with pointed heads and strong, constricting bodies. Economically they are among our most valuable reptiles, frequenting agricultural areas where they feed mostly on rodents that are injurious to crops. A small filament in the mouth permits them to hiss more loudly than any other snakes in this country; this, coupled with the vibration of their tails and lunging strikes at the object of their annoyance, causes wild specimens to appear quite formidable.

Pine snake, *Pituophis melanoleucus melanoleucus*. From Ditmars, *Reptiles of North America*.

The pine snake, *Pituophis melanoleucus melanoleucus*, is a large black and white snake which makes the pine barrens of New Jersey a favorite hunting ground of the reptile enthusiasts of nearby cities. Often five feet or more in length, the species is stoutly built and makes a good display animal. Many become very tame in captivity and will feed readily in or out of their cages; a few remain erratic in disposition and tend to bite if provoked. Mice are the favorite food of captives, and the species seems to have but a moderate requirement for water. This means that a permanent water container may be dispensed with and, instead, water offered at weekly intervals. This may assist in maintaining dry quarters for these snakes, for they can easily tip most dishes with the weight of their bodies.

A western relative of the pine snake is the bullsnake, *Pituophis melanoleucus sayi*, a yellow-brown reptile that is one of our largest snakes, with recorded lengths in excess of eight feet. Despite its large size and diurnal habits, this and the other members of the genus tend to spend much of their time hiding if a box or house is provided. Such means of concealment are in no way necessary for the successful maintenance of captives, for they calm down quickly in captivity and show little nervousness. Bullsnakes are large enough to be allowed to roam about a house occasionally, providing there is no means of exit. The various species of *Pituophis* are very responsive to any contact stimuli and seem most contented when confined alone. Recently I had occasion to cage together a large black racer and a bullsnake of similar size, but of greater body bulk. The racer was an active snake and its meanderings brought it into frequent body contact with the bullsnake. At each such contact, the bullsnake would vigorously arch its body, casting the racer away with some force. The racer would retaliate by frequently biting its cagemate. Both snakes fed readily before they were housed together. Occupying the same cage, each refused to eat and persisted in its fast until they were separated. A five-foot bullsnake requires a mouse each week to maintain a normal weight and state of health in captivity.

KINGSNAKES

The eastern kingsnake, *Lampropeltis getulus getulus*, and some of its relatives are famous for their habit of overcoming and devouring other kinds of snakes, even the poisonous species. The present species is lustrous black, banded over its entire length with regularly spaced markings of white or yellow. These fork and connect with each other along the sides, producing an effect like that of a chain. The average

Eastern kingsnake, *Lampropeltis getulus getulus.* From Ditmars, *Reptiles of North America.*

California kingsnake, *Lampropeltis getulus californiae,* two color varieties. From Van Denburgh.

kingsnake is about four feet long and quite thick-bodied and power-fully muscled. It is a constrictor, and captives will subsist indefinitely on a diet of small rodents. Several kingsnakes will get along very well together, but the introduction of an unrelated species will throw a cage of kingsnakes into a state of turmoil. The newcomer will be seized and quickly dispatched, and two kingsnakes are likely to start swallowing it from opposite ends. This can be catastrophic, for when their heads meet the larger specimen will often engulf the smaller one. For this reason, kingsnakes should be carefully watched while feeding. The bites of our native poisonous snakes seem to have little effect on kingsnakes, aside from the mechanical injuries which their needlelike fangs may produce. Rattlers in particular seem to recognize the kingsnake as an enemy and will hump their bodies in an endeavor to thwart the encircling attack of their adversary. They seem to realize that a stabbing strike, so effective against other animals, would be useless in dealing with a kingsnake. They employ their fangs only when actually seized.

Kingsnakes, in their many forms, are secretive reptiles and productive collecting entails the overturning of logs, stones, and pieces of trash. Often they are numerous in the vicinity of ponds and streams, seeming to prefer an environment that is at least moist. Some individuals will bite when first caught but nearly all quickly lose this trait and become the most docile of captives. The species deposits up to two dozen eggs which hatch in about six weeks. Baby kingsnakes of twelve to fourteen inches do not differ from the adults much in color. They feed mostly on newborn rodents, lizards, and smaller snakes.

MILK SNAKE

The eastern milk snake, *Lampropeltis triangulum*, is one of the kingsnake's smaller relatives. It is a slender gray reptile, saddled with closely set blotches of brown or red. The undersurface presents a checkerboard pattern. In snake-poor New England, this species is one of the more attractive, and is quite common in some areas. Usually it can be found basking only in the early spring. At other times it is a nocturnal reptile that spends its days in hiding. Although small in

Speckled kingsnake, *Lampropeltis getulus holbrooki*. Photo by J. G. Walls.

size—the average milk snake is about thirty inches long and has a body diameter of a half-inch, a milk snake can produce a more painful bite than many larger snakes. It has a habit of biting without warning, then chewing, once it has obtained a good hold. Milk snakes have the reputation of doing poorly in captivity. This may be true of most individuals, but occasionally a specimen will feed well and thrive for a number of years. I would regard it essential to provide a piece of bark or other hiding place for so secretive a reptile. Specimens kept in a bare cage tend to wander about hour after hour, seeking seclusion or a means of escape. Of one thing you can be sure—if there exists the smallest opening in a cage housing a milk snake, the reptile will be sure to find it and effect an escape. I once lost a milk snake in this way in an apartment. Curiously, it turned up one early morning many months later and appeared in better condition than when it escaped. What it ate, if it did, or where it obtained liquid nourishment, are puzzling questions.

Milk snake, *Lampropeltis triangulum*. Photo courtesy American Museum of Natural History, from Pope's *Reptile World*.

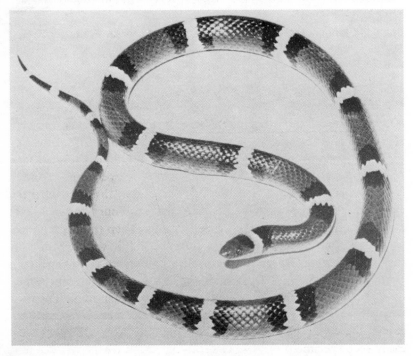

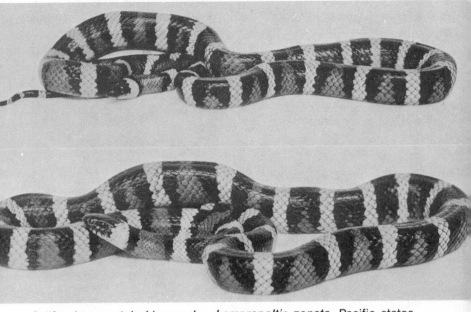

California mountain king snake, *Lampropeltis zonata,* Pacific states. From Van Denburgh.

RAINBOW SNAKE, MUD SNAKE

Although placed in different genera, the rainbow snake, *Abastor erythrogrammus,* and the mud snake, *Farancia abacura,* are closely allied and of similar habits. Both are large, very colorful burrowing species of swampy areas, confined to our southeastern states and the Mississippi valley. The rainbow is handsomely striped with red and black, while the mud is a shiny black species with pink blotches along its sides—extensions of the all-pink belly. Four feet would be an average length for either species. Efforts to keep these attractive snakes in captivity met with little success until it was determined that they fed mostly on the aquatic salamanders of the genera *Amphiuma* and *Siren.* This did not improve the situation much, for these salamanders can seldom be obtained in quantities. Then it was learned that these finicky eaters would accept nearly any aquatic animal that bore the scent of the salamanders. Now collectors can easily keep specimens of these colorful snakes if a frozen salamander

Rainbow snake, *Abastor erythrogrammus*. Photo by F. J. Dodd, Jr.

is rubbed against frogs or fishes before they are offered to the snakes. Either species will live indefinitely in an aquarium with several inches of water and no land area. In the South, newly-hatched babies can often be found crossing causeways in enormous numbers.

HOGNOSE SNAKE

The eastern hognose snake, *Heterodon platyrhinos*, is one of several kinds of curious serpents that are found mostly in dry, sandy areas. Though quite short, their very broad and heavy bodies give them a rather formidable appearance. This is backed by a show of bluff that has few peers among reptiles. The neck is broadly expanded while the diminutive reptile hisses loudly and strikes boldly at its tormentor. If these antics do not succeed in scaring the aggressor, the snake will turn over on its back and violently twist about, as though in agony, then finally lie still with mouth opened and tongue protruded. A specimen in this condition hangs limply if handled, but if placed in a crawling position will quickly flop over on its back and remain so until danger has passed. Tame specimens abandon this behavior and become very desirable inmates of a reptile collection. They will seldom take food other than frogs or toads, however, and this is considered by some a drawback. All-black hognose snakes are not

Eastern hognose snake, *Heterodon platyrhinos*. Photo courtesy Illinois Natural History Survey.

rare in elevated regions and, as with other snakes, occasional albinos are found. One such specimen was exhibited for at time at the Trailside Museum near Boston. It presented a beautiful study in pastels—the normally dark blotches faintly discernible in pink.

RINGNECK SNAKES

Ringneck snakes are seldom-seen denizens of our forested areas. Due to differences in size and color, they once were separated into a number of species. Now all are regarded as varieties of *Diadophis punctatus*. Eastern varieties generally do not exceed fifteen inches, while some western types reach a length of over two feet. Characteristic of the ringnecks is a black or slate-colored back and a red or orange stomach surface. The narrow ring just behind the head is a distinguishing feature. Ringnecks are able to tolerate some dampness in their cages and do well in planted terrariums if provided with a flat stone or section of bark for hiding. Earthworms and a variety of other animals are eaten, including snakes which are smaller than the ringnecks themselves.

GREEN SNAKES

The rough green snake, *Opheodrys aestivus*, and the smooth green snake, *Opheodrys vernalis*, are our only native bright green snakes, although this color is common in serpents of the tropics, especially those kinds which spend much of their lives in trees. Our green snakes are small and graceful reptiles; the smooth species has a

Ringneck snake, *Diadophis punctatus*. Photo courtesy American Museum of Natural History, from Pope's *Reptile World*.

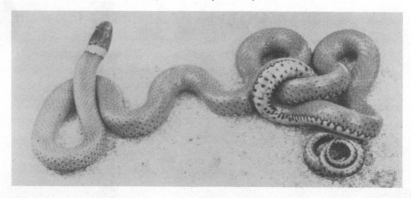

Smooth green snake, *Opheodrys vernalis*. From Ditmars, *Reptiles of North America.*

Rough green snake, *Opheodrys aestivus*. From Ditmars, *Reptiles of North America.*

maximum length of only about twenty inches, while the rough green may reach three feet or more. Either species may be kept in a terrarium, where they will feed on hairless caterpillars, crickets, grasshoppers, and spiders. The rough green snake climbs well and is usually found in bushes near water; the smooth green snake is more at home in damp meadows. The smooth green snake, particularly, tends to form colonies, outside of which specimens are seldom found. As a boy in Boston, I collected green snakes in the vacant lots which dotted the city. These places were nearly barren of vegetation and were, in fact, dumps. Among the rubble and pieces of trash, the beautiful little snakes seemed out of place. I did not realize it at the time, but I was never again to find smooth green snakes in such numbers.

In this chapter we have talked about representatives of our major groups of harmless native snakes. There are many species that are less familiar and about which we do not have much detailed information.

Glossy snake, *Arizona elegans,* western United States. From Klauber.

Longnosed snake, *Rhinocheilus lecontei,* western United States. From Van Denburgh.

Lined snake, *Tropidoclonium lineatum,* northern Mississippi R. valley west to Texas. From Ditmars, *Reptiles of North America.*

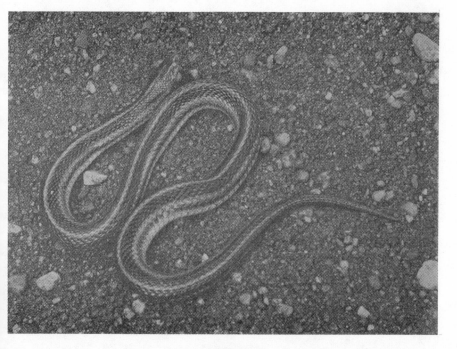

Shovelnosed snake, *Chionactis occipitalis,* southwestern United States. From Van Denburgh.

Most snake fanciers seem to have a preference for the larger species—these are more showy and, in general, easier to care for than the smaller kinds. Most of our larger snakes cannot stand dampness: they quickly develop fungoid conditions. Many of the smaller kinds, on the other hand, will thrive best in surroundings which imitate their natural habitats. It is possible for the herpetologist to elicit much new and interesting information regarding the smaller snakes under the semi-natural conditions of a terrarium.

VII

Non-poisonous Exotic Snakes

FAMILY BOIDAE

The family Boidae includes all of the really huge snakes of the world. Included in this family, however, are numerous smaller forms that have achieved little of the popularity of their larger relatives, but are, nevertheless, very interesting and often beautiful reptiles. Pythons and boas, as the members of this family are called, are very much like each other in many respects. Because of a fundamental difference in the structure of their skulls, they have often been separated and placed in subfamilies of their own. In their manner of reproducing, they differ in that the pythons deposit eggs while the boas give birth to live babies. In their many species and subspecies the Boidae are primitive snakes. Their ancient lineage is evidenced by such features as well-developed, paired lungs and, in most kinds, the trace of hind limbs. These are the "spurs" which may be seen at the base of the tail and are generally larger in a male than in the opposite sex. All pythons and boas kill their prey by constriction. Curiously, wild specimens will strike and hiss like other snakes, but never employ their powerful coils in defense until seized. Among the present snakes are some which tame readily, feed well, and live for a great many years in captivity; other kinds, however, are noted for their quick tempers and general intractability. A large boa or python is capable of producing severe lacerations with its long teeth and should, therefore, be handled with care unless known to be of good temperament. Some of the pythons and boas have exquisitely beautiful color patterns which, combined with large size and good disposition, make them deservedly the most popular of imported snakes. Some reptile hobbyists who once kept varied assortments of herptiles have come to confine their attention to the raising of giant snakes. Even a single specimen, well-cared-for, can provide a fascinating experience when raised from a baby of two feet or less to an adult weighing perhaps 200 pounds. Financially, baby pythons represent the soundest investment. The value of a growing youngster can easily increase tenfold during the first eight to ten years of its life. There is a ready market for large specimens, and those approaching record lengths may be negotiated for in terms of thousands of dollars. The large constrictors are notably inactive snakes and present few problems in the matter of housing. A very large specimen may be confined in a cage which would not do at all for one of the more active colubrids of moderate size. Boas and pythons have successfully been allowed the run of a house where no dogs, cats, or other small mammals are present. Caged, their general demeanor is to accept with indifference the limitation of movement caused by walls and glass. There is little of the probing for an escape route that is noticeable among some freshly caught snakes of other kinds. It may be that the mental processes of pythons and boas are not as highly evolved as those of other serpents, but if this is so we have no proof of it. I prefer to think of them as snakes which do not mind too much a close association with people!

The larger pythons and boas have a life expectancy of twenty to thirty years. This span is not in excess of that achieved by some captive colubrids and crotalids, snakes of only four to six feet in maximum length. This is a little surprising; among reptiles we can generally expect the largest forms to live the longest. Both pythons and boas produce at least one species which attains a length in excess of thirty feet.

RETICULATE PYTHON

Largest of the true pythons is the reticulate python, *Python reticulatus*, of southeastern Asia, the Philippines, and the East Indies. Among the most majestic of living snakes, the present beautiful reptile has a beautifully interwoven pattern of brown, gold, and black. The reddish eyes of an adult can be seen clearly. These, and the narrow line extending from the snout to the back of the head, are features which will distinguish this python from other Asiatic species. Baby pythons of this and other kinds usually feed quite readily and can be raised without difficulty. Larger specimens that have been taken from their native haunts are apt to be too reticent to eat for a long time after capture, so they are much less satisfactory than those which have been captive-reared. Like other large members of the genus *Python*, the reticulate deposits large eggs to the number of a hundred or more, occasionally, and these she broods by coiling about them until hatching time. Hatchlings may measure two feet in length and grow fairly rapidly under good conditions, for the first few years adding twenty inches or more to their length each annum. They prefer mice as food, while the adults can be maintained on a diet of chickens. Eighty degrees is a good cage temperature for pythons and boas of all kinds.

Reticulate python, *Python reticulatus.* Photo by G. Marcuse.

INDIAN PYTHON

The Indian python, *Python molurus*, is equally handsome, especially in its light phase, but is a somewhat smaller reptile than the preceding species. The two are sometimes confused by amateur herpetologists who are not critically familiar with the giant snakes. The colors are somewhat similar but in the present species the head marking has the appearance of an arrowhead, tapering to a point near the snout. It has long been recognized that the lighter variety of the Indian python tames more readily than the darker form and is, in general, a much prettier reptile. The situation is similar to that existing among the boa constrictors, *Boa constrictor*, in which the light phases are not only prettier but adapt much more easily to confinement than the darker forms. India, Ceylon, and the East Indies form the natural range of the Indian python. It spends much of its time in trees, and captives of all the larger pythons appreciate stout limbs in their cages. Like most other pythons, *P. molurus* lays eggs and coils about them during the incubation period. While brooding, the parent has an increase in body temperature.

Indian python, *Python molurus*. Photo by L. E. Perkins.

Indian python, *Python molurus.* Photo by G. Marcuse.

ROCK PYTHON

The central and southern portions of the African continent are the home of the rock python, *Python sebae,* another huge constricting snake which may grow to twenty feet or more. This, too, is a very beautiful snake which exhibits some variation in the intensity of its colors. Like the other large constrictors, captives will remain in a tank of water for long periods, especially before shedding or when digesting a meal. Zoos commonly provide these giant snakes with sizeable pools. Food requirements are small mammals in the case of babies; larger specimens take rabbits, chickens, and other warm-blooded prey. Feeding intervals can be spaced at ten days to two weeks with specimens that are well-grown. A twelve-foot python will keep well-nourished with a six-pound chicken every ten days. Larger amounts of food will be devoured if the opportunity presents itself but with snakes, as with humans, obesity shortens life. Overfed pythons may attain an enormous girth and a weight in excess of 250 pounds. Such specimens have difficulty moving about, seldom climb the trees in their cages, and often succumb to heart failure. I recently had the opportunity to examine a python weighing about 260 pounds though but slightly in excess of twenty feet in length. All pythons are relatively heavy-bodied snakes, but this particular example lacked the well-muscled sleekness of those which had a more normal weight and I believe it had been deliberately fattened to establish a weight record. Its demise shortly thereafter occasioned an autopsy which pointed to heart failure as the cause of death.

BLOOD PYTHON, BALL PYTHON

Among the smaller pythons frequently imported are the blood python, *Python curtus*, of Asia and the ball python, *Python regius*, of Africa. These are stout-bodied snakes that adapt quite well to captivity and seldom show any sign of bad temper. The former seems never to exceed ten feet in length, while the latter is fully grown at four or five. The blood python has an exceptionally beautiful coloration—some would call it the handsomest species of its genus. Ball pythons receive their common name from the tendency, noted among other constricting snakes as well, of coiling themselves into a ball when handled. The resultant mass of serpentine coils can be rolled about without relaxation on the part of the reptile.

OTHER PYTHONS

Australia and New Guinea and other Pacific islands have a number of fine pythons that are less frequently imported than the Asiatic and African forms. The carpet python, *Morelia spilotes variegata*, and the diamond python, *Morelia spilotes spilotes*, are, as their scientific names indicate, simply varieties of the same species. Both are handsomely patterned reptiles which average from six to ten feet in length. Unfortunately, captives usually live only a few years. The

Young carpet python, *Morelia spilotes variegata.* Photo by G. Marcuse.

amethystine python, *Liasis amethystinus*, is one of the world's longest snakes, occasionally reaching a length of 25 feet. It is a relatively slender snake with an attractive color pattern of brown and yellow. Particularly interesting is the black-headed python, *Aspidites melano-cephalus*, an eight-foot species that lives largely on the ground and has a black head and neck which contrast strangely with the banded pattern of the remainder of the snake. Pythons are not generally regarded as snake-eating serpents, but the present species is an exception: it attacks without hesitation even the deadliest of the Australian snakes. Its diet is not confined to other snakes, however. Captives become very tame and will eat nearly any warm-blooded creature that they are capable of swallowing. Due to the extreme elasticity of their jaws and skin, all of the pythons and boas are capable of swallowing animals much larger than their heads.

Black-headed python, *Aspidites melanocephalus*. Photo by Dr. Otto Klee.

BOAS

The most familiar of the giant constrictors are those known as boas, *Boa constrictor*. Natives of the tropical Americas, these snakes are a staple in the stocks of pet dealers. The species has a number of races which differ markedly in color and temperament. Those from Mexico and Central America are dark in color with rather obscure crossbars. The babies, with their huge heads, are rather sinister-looking little creatures. These northernmost forms of the boa constrictor are often hard to tame and resent all familiarity from human hands. The variety known as the red-tailed boa is a native of the Amazon jungles and is particularly beautiful—pale tan with ruddy crossbars that are widely separated and become red toward the tail. Boas of this variety make gentle and handsome members of any collection. Fully grown, at perhaps twelve feet, and in the prime of condition, they are among the most beautiful snakes. Babies of the boas are produced alive, generally in May, and a brood may consist of twenty or more infant snakes. These feed readily upon mice

Burrowing python, *Calabaria reinhardtii,* West Africa. Photo by Dr. Otto Klee.

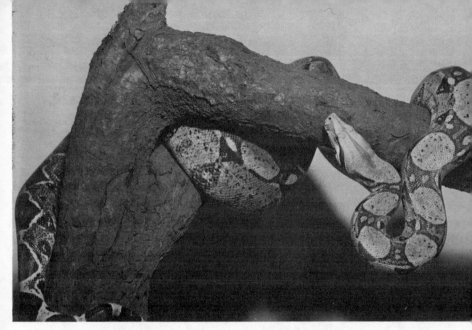

Boa constrictor, *Boa constrictor*. Photo by L. E. Perkins.

and grow rapidly. Like the pythons, the boas will enter a tank of water and soak for long periods. I do not consider it desirable to permit such baths to extend over a period of more than twenty-four hours, however.

Boa constrictor, showing variation in color pattern. Photos by C. A. Hewitt.

Though not especially adaptable to captivity, the anaconda, *Eunectes murinus*, of South America deserves special mention because it is the largest of New World snakes. A number of forms are recognized and all are very much alike in habits, frequenting jungle watercourses and feeding on mammals, birds, and reptiles. The yellow anaconda, *Eunectes notaeus*, grows to only about fifteen feet and is quite attractively marked as a baby, but these vivid yellow and black colors fade as they grow. The much-larger *E. murinus* is olive-brown with dark spots. Most anacondas tend to retain a morose disposition, in spite of which, however, individuals often live very many years when well cared for. One anaconda, at least, lived twenty-eight years in captivity.

Anaconda, *Eunectes murinus*.

Epicrates is another tropical American genus of boas which includes several well-known species. Because of its docile disposition and the beautiful iridescence of its scales, the rainbow boa, *Epicrates cenchris*, is a favorite in collections. The species ranges over a broad area of Central and South America. Examples from the northernmost portions of the range are brownish-gray and lack the spectacular beauty of those from Brazil, in which a reddish hue predominates. The Cuban boa, *Epicrates angulifer*, is one of the larger species, reaching a length of fourteen feet. It is not a colorful snake, being, for the most part, plain tan or brownish with a series of darker blotches running the length of the body. It is believed to feed mostly upon bats in the wild state; captives will accept other warm-blooded prey, but the species has such a persistently irascible disposition that many individuals cannot be persuaded to eat at all. Several smaller kinds of *Epicrates* occur in the West Indies. The Haitian boa, *Epicrates*

Rainbow boa, *Epicrates cenchris,* young. Photo by G. Marcuse.

angulifer striatus, averages about six feet in length and is rather slender of form. It lives well if kept at a temperature range of 78 to 85 degrees.

Tree boas form a small but interesting group of serpents that are admirably suited to an arboreal existence, having bodies which are much compressed from side to side and strongly prehensile tails. The green tree boa, *Corallus canina,* like its relatives, feeds mostly upon birds and is well able to capture such feathered prey with long and very sharp teeth. It is a beautiful reptile—emerald green above and yellow below, embellished along its back with narrow crossbands of white. As with the other boas, the babies are brought forth fully developed and differ from the adults in being of an orange color. None of the strictly arboreal boas reaches a large size; the present species runs four to six feet in length. It is essential that tree boas have their cage provided with a tree limb, where they will spend most of their time compactly coiled.

Rainbow boa, *Epicrates cenchris,* adult. Photo by G. Marcuse.

Green python, *Chondropython viridis*, New Guinea. Photo by G. Marcuse.

Green tree boa, *Corallus caninus.* Photo by G. Marcuse.

Rough-scaled sand boa, *Eryx conicus,* India. Photo by G. Marcuse

In striking contrast to the tree boas is a group known as sand boas (genus *Eryx*), which are short, stoutly formed snakes with bluntly tipped tails. They spend their lives entirely on the ground or burrowing beneath its surface; they inhabit dry areas of Asia, Europe, and Africa. One of the commonest species is the brown sand boa, *Eryx johni*, of India. Not exceeding a yard in length, this species and its relatives can be kept in a small cage with several inches of fine sand in which they will burrow. Small birds and mice are accepted readily and sand boas do well if kept dry and warm.

FAMILY COLUBRIDAE

The majority of the world's snakes belong to the family Colubridae. There is so much diversification of structure within this family that it has been divided into groups known as subfamilies. No herpetologist, in recent times, has been able to compile anything like a complete account of the snakes of this vast family. Such an endeavor could well occupy a lifetime of research. Changes of names among the many genera and species have been frequent and are still being made, as our studies give us a clearer picture of relation-

Hooded snake, *Xenedon merremi*, Brazil. Photo by H. Schultz.

ships within the groups. The synonymy presented in the literature is enough to discourage any but the most technical worker. Necessarily, therefore, we must glean our knowledge of the various species from fragmentary sources, including regional accounts and papers on individual genera and species. Most of the colubrids, as the snakes of this family are called, are the typical harmless snakes that predominate in every continent except Australia.

Many colubrids possess grooved fangs in the rear of their jaws. These fangs are used to inject venom into the natural prey of the snakes and can seldom be used effectively as a defense against humans. A few exceptions are notable, however, and I would regard it as judicious to handle rear-fanged snakes, especially the large ones, with caution. The boomslang, for instance, can cause the death of a human being.

The rear-fanged snakes' venomous properties have been little investigated. Many of them seldom bite when handled, and of those which do bite many cannot bring the tiny rear teeth into play unless a small, rounded surface is seized or a portion of loose flesh is grasped. The fingers, or the area of skin between two fingers, would be vulnerable. Among human subjects effects similar to those produced by the sting of a bee have been noted. Some of the tinier rear-fanged snakes are unable to break the flesh with their teeth. At our present stage of knowledge or, perhaps more correctly, lack of knowledge, common sense should be exercised in the handling of the rear-fanged serpents. In tropical regions, where the snakes of this type may be numerous, caution should be used in the handling of any snake which is not definitely known to be completely harmless. There is no sure way of identifying a rear-fanged snake in the field, unless one is critically familiar with the snake fauna of the area being collected. Some snakes of this type attain a good size, with a proportionately developed venom apparatus, but only two species, the twig snake and the boomslang, are known to be able to inflict serious bites upon humans. The former species has been recognized as dangerous only for the past decade. As a matter of course, I handle rear-fanged snakes, if they are of any size, with much the same precautions I use in the handling of vipers and others of the so-called deadly species. The characteristic of possessing enlarged and sometimes grooved teeth toward the rear of the mouth crosses several subfamilies of snakes and is found in arboreal, terrestrial, and aquatic forms. It is of little value in establishing relationships among the species. Any listing of all the known rear-fanged serpents would bring together a very artificial grouping of forms, many of whose closest relatives lack any trace of enlarged or grooved teeth.

Contrary to popular supposition, it is not necessary for these snakes to "chew" in order to inject venom. They are quite capable of delivering a serious wound by striking with open mouth, then immediately withdrawing. But in spite of the few known exceptions, we must regard nearly all of the rear-fanged snakes as harmless—at least as far as people are concerned.

WART SNAKE

Snakes show marvelous adaptations to their environments, and in this respect perhaps none exceeds the wart snake, *Acrochordus javanicus*, of Asia and northern Australia. Thoroughly aquatic, if removed from the water this strange snake flounders about and is unable to make much progress. Thick-bodied and blunt-headed, its skin hangs in loose folds and each scale is separated, not overlapping as in other snakes. The species lacks broad ventral plates which enable most snakes to move about on land. Instead, its belly is covered with a granular scalation. Wart snakes, the larger females of which may reach six feet, frequent streams, canals, and rivers and even enter the sea occasionally. They feed principally upon fishes, which they catch by quick snaps of their sharp-toothed jaws. The babies are born alive and may number twenty-five or more. This is one of the snakes which is annually caught by the thousands to supply the leather trade with fine and durable hides, which is perhaps one of the reasons why not many wart snakes are exported alive. They live fairly well under aquarium conditions if the water temperature is kept at a fairly high level...75 to 80 degrees. The valvular nostrils are placed at the tip of the reptile's snout, a peculiarity noted among many reptiles that spend most of their time in water. The species is able to remain submerged for long periods. Specimens are active mainly at night, reposing by day in the quieter shore waters of their native streams.

WATER SNAKES

The snakes of the genus *Natrix*, cosmopolitan in distribution and known commonly as water snakes, seem, in comparison to the highly

European water snake (also called grass snake), *Natrix natrix.* Photo by G. Marcuse.

specialized wart snake, to be but moderately suited for an aquatic existence. While they are excellent swimmers and divers, most spend much of their time on land, sunning near bodies of water into which they plunge and quickly disappear when frightened. Some species lay eggs while others produce their babies alive. While a few species of *Natrix* are prettily colored, most are clad in rather somber hues. The water snake *Natrix natrix* is a very çommon European species that does well in captivity. Adults are grayish with a yellowish-white collar. A fully grown snake of this species is about three feet long. A species of similar size, but rather more pretty, is the diced water snake, *Natrix tessellata,* of Europe and Asia. It resembles the preceding species in laying eggs, in contradistinction to the water snakes of North America, all of which produce their young alive. An Asiatic species of wide distribution is the checkered water snake, *Natrix piscator,* a reptile which shows much variation in color even among specimens from the same area. Usually a tan or brown snake with squarish black markings over much of the body, the checkered water snake occasionally may be enlivened with splashes of red or yellow. Although vicious when first caught, it soon calms down and makes an agreeable captive. The annulated water snake, *Natrix annularis*, is a pretty Asiatic species which differs from many of the Old World members of the genus in producing its young alive.

COMMON AFRICAN COLUBRIDS

The commoner terrestrial colubrids of Africa are frequently available from dealers in exotic reptiles. Particularly elegant, though not of large size or brilliant coloration, is the mole snake, *Pseudaspis cana*. This fine species is light brown; each scale of its moderately stout body is well defined, imparting a very neat appearance. The file snake, *Mehelya capensis*, has a light vertebral stripe running the length of its otherwise dark body, serving to accentuate the rather triangular body form. However well fed, file snakes have an emaciated appearance because of the prominence of the dorsal ridge. They are rough-scaled and strong constrictors, reaching a length of about five feet and feeding almost entirely upon other snakes. The beauty snake, *Psammophis sibilans*, is one of a group of several active and slender species that frequent relatively dry situations and are commonly known as sand snakes. They are rear-fanged and feed principally upon lizards. From their habit of prowling about human dwellings in search of rodents, snakes of the genus *Boaedon* are called house snakes. The brown house snake, *Boaedon fuliginosus*, is the species most commonly imported.

ORIENTAL RAT SNAKE (PTYAS)

Several very large, long-tailed serpents are prominent among the reptile fauna of Asia. One of these is the Oriental rat snake, *Ptyas mucosus*, an alert, very active snake which occasionally grows to ten feet. The color of this snake is brown or greenish-brown, obscurely crossbanded with rather dark markings. The scales about the mouth are lighter and edged with black; surmounting these are huge, ever-wary eyes. Rat snakes sell their liberty dearly and in captivity retain their wildness over a long period, but if carefully handled some individuals eventually tame down, feed well, and may live over long periods. In general, their actions are similar to those of the familiar coachwhips of the United States. Their diet includes such varied items as frogs, lizards, small mammals, and birds. In parts of their native land they are vigorously protected in recognition of their value as rodent destroyers. Wooded areas near water are favorite prowling grounds, and specimens encountered in the field will race away swiftly if escape is possible. Cornered, they flatten the neck vertically and with a short hiss strike at one's face. Because of this species' large size, a strike from an Oriental rat snake may be received in the would-be captor's face; the reptile's sharp teeth produce generous lacerations. The taming of a large rat snake is an achievement which will tax the patience of its keeper. It is best accomplished in the manner described in the last chapter, relating to the eastern racer of the United States. The cage used should, of course, be larger—in keeping with the much greater length of the present reptile. Oriental rat snakes deposit eggs which may be over two inches in length in the case of a large female.

LESSER INDIAN RAT SNAKE

A smaller species from Asia, sometimes called the lesser Indian rat snake, is known scientifically as *Ptyas korros*. Fully grown at five to six feet, it adapts more readily to captivity than the preceding species. Dark olive or brown is the predominating color, and each scale is margined with black. These Old World rat snakes, all of which are nonpoisonous, bear a resemblance to the cobras which inhabit the same areas. In connection with the use of their common name—rat snakes—it should be pointed out that these snakes are not be be confused with snakes of the genus *Elaphe*, which bear the same title. The latter are snakes of far different temperament.

BLACK AND YELLOW RAT SNAKE

Central and South America have large, partially arboreal snakes which, because of their feeding habits, likewise are called rat snakes. A really spectacular species is the black and yellow rat snake, *Spilotes pullatus*, possibly the largest member of the family, with a maximum length in excess of twelve feet. Like the Asiatic members of its genus, this snake is tamed only with much difficulty and patience. Captives will eat birds and their eggs, and mammals; they should be kept at a temperature no lower than 75 degrees, and care should be taken that freshly caught specimens do not injure themselves by striking against the glass fronts of their cages.

Mussurana, *Clelia clelia.* Photo by G. Marcuse.

MUSSURANA

Particularly handsome among the South American snakes is the species known as the mussurana, *Clelia clelia.* Feeding almost entirely upon other snakes, when fully grown at seven or eight feet the mussurana is able to overcome and devour most of the larger pit vipers that it may chance to encounter. The species is a powerful constrictor and is rear-fanged besides, though it has not been proven to have a bite which is dangerous to humans. The average mussurana is a very mild-tempered snake and will bite only under extreme provocation. It is an egg-laying species; the newly hatched young are very much different from the adults in coloration, having black heads and pinkish bodies with a light-colored band at the neck.

ROAD GUARDER

Another snake-eating snake is the tiny road guarder, *Conophis lineatus*, of tropical America. It, too, is one of the rear-fanged snakes and makes use of its venom-conducting teeth to subdue lizards and other smaller snakes.

ORIENTAL KING SNAKES, CHAIN SNAKES

Known variously as Oriental king snakes and chain snakes, the species of the genus *Dinodon* have the habit of rolling themselves into a ball when first captured. Snakes of this genus are confined to Asia, their banded color pattern causing them to be confused often with the dangerous krait of that continent. The head of the krait is but little larger than its neck, while the snakes under consideration have rather broad, flattened heads which are quite distinct. The red-banded chain snake, *Dinodon rufozonatum*, is a four-foot reddish-brown species with dark crossbands. As with the related species, it lays eggs and frequents the borders of streams or other marshy places

Black and yellow rat snake, *Spilotes pullatus*. Photo by Muller-Schmida.

where an abundance of frogs may be found. These, together with smaller snakes and lizards, make up its diet. *Dinodon* species have enlarged teeth, but these lack any trace of a groove. It is a night-roving animal and has eyes which are conspicuous in bulging slightly. The white-banded chain snake, *Dinodon septentrionale*, is a species of similar form and habits, but differs in its colors, having a grayish-brown ground color with more widely separated dark bands.

GOLDEN WATER COBRA

Snakes have picked up a variety of common names which more or less aptly describe their habits. Thus, in the golden water cobra, *Cyclagras gigas*, of South America we have a snake which displays habits like those of the true cobras, though it is not related to them. *C. gigas* has a yellowish belly; in the males this color extends to the back, where it is transversed by black or dark brown markings. The females are rather dull by comparison, being mostly brownish above. The species lays eggs and feeds on frogs and fishes. Imported specimens commonly measure four to five feet.

SPECKLED RACER

The speckled racer, *Drymobius margaritiferus*, is another pretty tropical American snake. It has a wide range in Central America and Mexico and has even been found in the extreme southern portion of Texas. About three feet when fully grown, this snake is black, with a yellowish spot on each scale. It frequents aquatic situations, though it is not a water snake in the sense of spending much of its time actually in that element. Frogs are eaten in captivity, and the snakes of this genus should be kept at a temperature of 75 to 85 degrees, in a dry cage, but with water available for drinking purposes at all times. The speckled racers are swift-moving species which commonly measure about three feet.

GENUS COLUBER

Related to the racers and whipsnakes of North America are a variety of Old World snakes of the genus *Coluber*. Though not constricting snakes, an occasional specimen, in overcoming its prey, will show a trace of what may be an evolutionary trend—toward or away from—the constricting method of overcoming prey. Coils may be used effectively, though loosely, to control and restrict the move-

The small scale wedged between the lower anterior edge of the eye and the upper labials is a hallmark of the genus *Coluber* throughout the world. Photo by L. E. Perkins.

ments of an animal that has been seized. The horse-shoe snake, *Coluber hippocrepis*, of southern Europe and northern Africa is a rather pretty species that is named for the marking on its head. Dark green snakes, *Coluber jugularis*, are part of the European fauna and are also found in Asia. The flowered snake, *Coluber florulentus*, and the Algerian snake, *Coluber algirus*, inhabit northern Africa. None of the snakes of this genus has a reputation for being very hardy in captivity. They range from about three to six feet in length and are very active in the wild state, actively foraging during daylight hours for small mammals, birds, and reptiles. In captivity they should be kept as free from annoyance as possible and, in general, require very

343

warm and dry cages. Though some frequent sandy areas, there is little point in providing sand as a floor covering for their cages, since they are not burrowing serpents. Sand will only make the task of cage-cleaning more difficult, and I consider it especially important to maintain the quarters of these snakes in the strictest state of cleanliness possible.

EUROPEAN CONSTRICTORS

The smooth snake, *Coronella austriaca*, is an inconspicuous reptile of Europe which in many respects resembles the milk snakes of the United States. It is a small snake, two feet in length, and spends much of its time hiding—both in the wild state and in captivity. Its color is brown, with a double row of dark spots along the back. The female produces from four to fifteen babies in the late summer; the babies arrive at sexual maturity in about four years. Captives, when they can be persuaded to eat, show a preference for lizards and baby mice. Other common and harmless constricting snakes of Europe are the leopard snake, *Elaphe situla*; the four-lined snake, *Elaphe quatuorlineata*; and the Aesculapean snake, *Elaphe longissima*. The first-named is a particularly beautiful snake, with black-edged red blotches on a ground color of yellow. Babies will eat lizards or very small mice; the adults feed largely upon grown mice and birds. It is a curious fact that some species of snakes which are considered delicate and short-lived in captivity occasionally produce an individual which thrives for many years. The leopard snake seldom lives a year, yet at least one individual lived in excess of twenty! We can find many parallels to this in the literature relating to the longevity of captive reptiles.

ASIATIC RAT SNAKES (ELAPHE)

Frequently imported from Asia are several species of large rat snakes (genus *Elaphe*) that are handsome in appearance, quiet in demeanor, and in general among the most satisfactory reptiles in captivity. The striped-tail rat snake, *Elaphe taeniurus*, is one of these kinds. Many snakes are striped, or banded, or blotched. In the present yellow, green, and black species we find a combination of all three patterns arranged in the most pleasing fashion. The head is pale, with a dark line extending backward from the eye to the angle of the jaw. The neck remains yellow for several inches, when a series of rather angular and broken dark splotches make their appearance and extend about half the length of the snake. These become smaller, finally disappearing toward the posterior portion of the body, where a broad yellow stripe takes their place, giving way along the sides to narrowly spaced spots. Looking at different sections of the snake's body, one might think that they belonged to at least three different snakes! This species reaches a large size, eight feet at least, and is a strong constrictor, feeding readily in captivity on rodents. Like the other rat snakes of its genus, *E. taeniurus* has a flattened abdomen which is sharply angular to its sides. This assists it greatly in climbing, and wild rat snakes of many species are frequently encountered in bushes and trees.

The keeled rat snake, *Elaphe carinata*, is also a very large species, but it has more sober colors than *E. taeniurus*, being mostly a plain brown reptile with indistinct darker markings on the forward portions of its body. The species is coarsely scaled and has a heavy body; it feeds upon rodents and, to some extent at least, other snakes.

TREE SNAKES

A veritable galaxy of tree snakes occurs throughout the warmer regions of the world. Some are so excessively slender and protectively colored as to be barely discernible when they repose among the vines and bushes which form their habitats. Others are not quite so attenuated in their proportions, and these types occasionally desert their arboreal sanctuaries to prowl on the ground. One of these is the handsome mangrove snake, *Boiga dendrophila*, of the Asiatic mainland and the offshore island groups. Mangrove snakes are commonly six to seven feet long and clad in lustrous black scalation over which are regularly-spaced narrow bands of vivid yellow. Few reptiles are more attractive as exhibits than the present snake as it coils compactly, as is its manner, on a bough in a well-lighted cage. The mangove is a rear-fanged snake and feeds on birds, mammals, reptiles, amphibians, and even fishes! Captives are best housed by themselves, for they will attack and devour other snakes nearly as large as themselves. Fully-grown examples seem to have a preference for birds. Reptile dealers generally offer this snake in four to six-foot-lengths. Juveniles and sub-adults rarely come on the market. Other species of the genus are often to be had, among them Blanding's tree snake, *Boiga blandingi*, and the dog-tooth cat snake, *Boiga cynodon*. Their habits are like those of the mangrove snake.

Mangrove snake, *Boiga dendrophila*. Photo by G. Marcuse.

Some of the most daintily-built and beautiful of the tree snakes belong to the genus *Leptophis* (called *Thalerophis* by some writers.) These are the green tree snakes and parrot snakes of the reptile trade. *Leptophis ahaetulla* frequently comes in with shipments from South America; *Leptophis diplotropis* comes from Mexico, as well as other species from other places. As I recall it, the first exotic snake I ever owned was a handsome three-foot *Leptophis*. Like its relatives, it fed readily on lizards. Supplying it with anoles taxed my boyhood financial resources during the months it was with me. This small snake introduced me to the prevalance of mites among tropical snakes. Soon after its arrival the minute red mites could be seen everywhere, in and out of the reptile's cage. Commercial preparations for the control of these pests were not available, so my "treatment" of the snake consisted of allowing it to crawl through a wet cloth which I held closely against its body. This particular tree snake was very adept at escaping from the smallest opening in its cage. I would always find it coiled up someplace nearby. It did not seem inclined to seek exit from the room by descending to the floor. One day, however, it disappeared, and I searched in vain for it for many days. With its escape the mite problem gradually resolved itself, though not to a complete extent for several weeks, at least!

VINE SNAKES

While the foregoing members of the genus *Leptophis* are very slender creatures, they appear robust when compared with the vine snakes (genus *Oxybelis*) of the tropical Americas. The green vine snake, *Oxybelis fulgidus*, reaches a length of five feet or more, while the brown vine snake, *Oxybelis aeneus*, is somewhat inferior in length. Vine snakes are incredibly slender reptiles and are next to impossible to see when coiled loosely in a bush. They feed chiefly upon lizards and possess rear fangs for subduing such quarry. It is absolutely essential to provide these and other true tree snakes with branches in their cages. A temperature of 75 degrees is satisfactory for them.

The long-nosed tree snakes of the genus *Dryophis* (*Ahaetulla*) appear to be closely related to the vine snakes, but are found in the tropics of the Old World. Some, like *Dryophis nasuta*, have a flexible

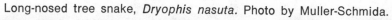

Long-nosed tree snake, *Dryophis nasuta.* Photo by Muller-Schmida.

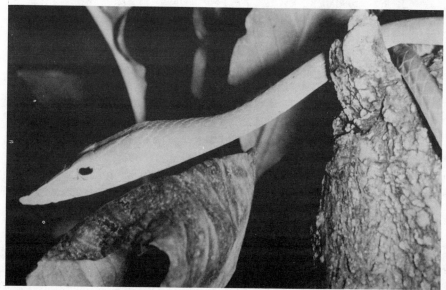

protuberance at the end of their long and slender heads, which feature adds to their grotesque appearance. *Dryophis* species bear living young, thus differing from those of the genera *Leptophis* and *Oxybelis*, both of which are oviparous. They will accept frogs, lizards, small mammals, and birds. Captives can be maintained indefinitely on a diet of American anoles. The bite of these snakes, when they can manage to imbed their tiny rear fangs, will produce, in humans, a swelling and pain like that caused by a wasp's sting. They seldom try to bite, however, depending mostly on bluff with open mouth to frighten enemies.

GOLDEN TREE SNAKE

Stories of flying snakes might be regarded as fanciful travelers' tales if it were not for the fact that the phenomenon has been sub-stantiated in part, at least, by the observations of scientific investi-gators. The snake figuring in these accounts is the golden tree snake, *Chrysopelia ornata,* and its close relatives. This small but very handsome reptile occurs in Asia and is not a rare snake. It is a tree snake but is somewhat stouter in build than many such serpents and is, perhaps, the prettiest of all in its coloration. There is considerable variation of pattern, but the golden tree snake is essentially a black species that is rather suffusely banded with lighter lines, between which occur delicate shades of red and yellow. The small head of this three-foot species is quite distinct from the neck; the eyes are large, with round pupils. While it cannot actually "fly" in the manner of birds and bats, without question this tree snake—and perhaps other kinds as well—is able to make long glides by compressing its lower surface into a concave form after it has launched itself into the air from a coiled position. Longer glides are in a downward direction but from the impetus of the take-off a position above that of the starting point can be attained if the distance is only a few feet. Motion pictures have recorded the simultaneous volplaning of a number of these snakes in their native jungle habitat. The effect produced is one that is not likely to be soon forgotten. Golden tree snakes make highly interesting and ornamental additions to a reptile collection, but unless confined in a really large cage they cannot be expected to show off their unusual abilities. Attempts to induce a flight artificially generally meet with failure, and I do not believe that the mechanism involved is one which relates particularly to

Golden tree snake, *Chrysopelia ornata*. Photo by Muller-Schmida.

escape from a threat. The species is rear-fanged, and golden tree snakes are quite ready to defend themselves by biting when freshly caught. No ill results from their bites have been recorded among humans, however. A wide variety of food is accepted in captivity, but the preference is for lizards. Captives do well if maintained at 75 to 80 degrees in a cage that has numerous branches for climbing.

BOOMSLANG

Throughout the present chapter there have been references to snakes possessing enlarged and sometimes-grooved rear fangs. None of the species considered so far has been proved capable of producing in a man anything but inconsequential symptoms following a bite, though once again I would urge caution in the handling of specimens, particularly of the larger species like the mangrove snake. Two species of rear-fanged snakes from Africa, however, both tree-dwelling and very slender of build, have caused fatalities among humans. One of these is the boomslang, *Dispholidus typus*, a four-foot snake that occurs over the greater portion of the African continent. It is a very common reptile in some portions of its extensive range, but bites do not occur often, because the boomslang takes rapid flight when disturbed. Fatalities have occurred most often among people who

Boomslang, *Dispholidus typus*. Photo by Muller-Schmida.

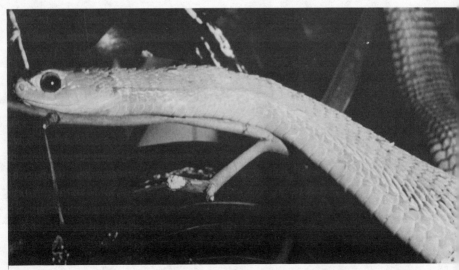

were attempting to capture a snake or were handling one after capture. The species inflates its throat vertically when annoyed; several tree snakes also do this. This is followed by an opened-mouth strike, followed often by a grasping and chewing action on the part of the snake. The boomslang is a plainly colored reptile and feeds mainly upon birds and their eggs, and lizards. This and the other rear-fanged species of snakes are nearly always these days designated as such on the price lists of reptile importers. They so closely resemble some of the harmless snakes, however, that there always exists the possibility of a misidentification. For a very great many years after its discovery the boomslang was not regarded as a dangerously poisonous serpent.

TWIG SNAKE

Another innocuous-appearing rear-fanged snake that is now regarded as dangerous to humans is the twig snake, *Thelotornis kirtlandi*, sometimes called the bird snake or the vine snake. Even more slender than the boomslang, this snake has similar habits, including the inflating of its throat when angry. Its range covers much of Africa, but the twig snake is, of course, missing from desert areas and is absent from the southern tip of the continent.

EGG-EATING SNAKES

A rather inconspicuous little snake of tropical and South Africa is famous for its capacity to swallow whole eggs that are enormous in proportion to the size of the reptile's head. This is the egg-eating snake, *Dasypeltis scaber*, a brown or tan reptile that has a spotted upper-surface and may grow to be a yard long. Egg-eaters are very common snakes and are quite often imported. Since there is a considerable demand for them, they are not among the least expensive snakes. Nearly all of our more familiar snakes have an astonishing ability to swallow large objects, and in the present species this ability has been even further modified to include eggs that appear huge in comparison with the small and slender snake that engulfs them. Egg-eating snakes possess a saw-like arrangement of bony projections in their esophagus. These cut into the shell of a bird's egg as it is being swallowed, and the pressure of the diminutive reptile's neck causes the shell to collapse. The shell fragments are later disgorged. A closely related species, the Indian egg-eating snake, *Elachistodon westermanni*, was once separated from *Dasypeltis* taxonomically because it has rear fangs, while the former does not. Both now occupy the same subfamily status.

SNAIL-EATING SNAKES

In contrast to the egg-eating snakes are the equally-peculiar snail-eating snakes (genera *Amblycephalus* and *Dipsas*), sometimes referred to as chunk-heads. Typically, these are slender tree snakes with string-like necks and tails. Their snouts are blunt and their lower jaws lack the median line which separates the scales of other snakes and makes possible much stretching of the skin when a large object is being swallowed. Snail-eating snakes extract their staple food from their shells with long, sharp teeth. The snail-eating snakes should be given branches among which to climb. They are not difficult to care for if a good supply of slugs or snails is readily obtainable.

Tentacled snake, *Herpeton tentaculatum*. Photo by G. Marcuse.

Cuban racer, *Alsophis angulifer,* Cuba. Photo by G. Marcuse.

OTHER COLUBRIDS

A group of thoroughly aquatic fresh- and brackish-water snakes occupy a section of their own within the broader scope of the family of colubrid serpents. They frequent waters of shallow depth, bring forth their young alive, and are rear-fanged. Some feed largely upon crabs, while others prefer frogs or fishes. The most unusual of the group is the tentacled snake, *Herpeton tentaculatum,* which has been reaching the reptile market in increasing numbers in recent years. These small and rather attractively marked snakes have two scaly appendages protruding from their snouts, the use of which is not known at present. In captivity tentacled snakes should be kept in an aquarium that has no landing place and is securely covered with screening or hardware cloth. A water-soaked branch should be held fixed in position at the bottom of about ten inches of water that is kept within a reasonable range of 78 degrees. The snakes will anchor themselves to the submerged branch with their tails. Small fishes are grasped as they swim near the snakes. Closely related to the tentacled snake, but lacking the nasal adornment of the latter, are the Asian snakes of the genus *Enhydris*. Like the *Herpeton* species they do well in a shoreless aquarium that has several inches of water. They progress in a rather awkward fashion when placed on land; many snap and bite viciously when removed from their element.

FAMILIES TYPHLOPIDAE, ANILIDAE

Distinct families of harmless snakes, members of which have not so far been discussed in this or the preceding chapter, are the Typhlopidae and the Anilidae. Members of the first family are wormlike reptiles ranging in size from a few inches to a couple of feet. Burrowing forms, they are rarely seen even in places where they are most common. Over 150 species are recognized, but they are almost never available commercially. They are related to the snakes of the family Leptotyphlopidae, which were taken up in the last chapter, and their care in captivity is the same. Representing the Anilidae, another family consisting of secretive and little-known snakes, is the beautiful false coral snake, *Anilius scytale*, a South American snake that reaches dealers in some numbers. Ringed brilliantly in scarlet and black, this snake bears some resemblance to the very venomous coral snakes, but is not related to them. It has vestiges of hind limbs, tiny eyes, and is of slender, cylindrical form. Imported specimens are generally around two feet in length and will eat small lizards and snakes. Like many other secretive reptiles, they will do well only if provided with means of burrowing or hiding.

VIII

Poisonous Snakes

Venomous snakes are the star attractions in any collection of reptiles, a fact which may be witnessed in any zoo that is fortunate enough to have a reptile house. Crowds may pass cage after cage, containing huge crocodilians, extremely rare turtles, lizards of bizarre forms and colors, and innocuous snakes, with little more than cursory inspection. But the cobras, mambas, vipers, and rattlesnakes stop such visitors in their tracks to observe with awesome awareness the often beautiful sinuous forms that have achieved notoriety because of their poisonous properties. In the better zoos, the poisonous snakes are treated with the degree of respect that is warranted by their awful capabilities. In the case of the more active and dangerous types, elaborate systems are employed with a view toward minimizing the possibility of bite casualties during such operations as feeding and cage-cleaning. Even so, accidents occur with rather disturbing frequency. Sera covering such medical contingencies are stocked by zoological parks for, in the cases of exotic poisonous snakes, they might otherwise not be available quickly when needed. The sera that are stocked by hospitals, when they have them at all, are usually of types that are antidotal only for the bites of local snakes.

If we were talking about reptiles solely from the standpoint of their suitability as pets, there would be little need to discuss the poisonous kinds. Poisonous snakes can, and often have been, tamed to the point where they permit handling. In this respect they do not differ much from their harmless relatives. Everyone who has kept many snakes knows, however, that even the most docile non-poisonous snake may have an "off-day" when it will bite if handled roughly or if it feels itself threatened. Poisonous snakes may, likewise, have such "moods," and this is one of the things which make them totally unsuitable as pets. One reads, not without a degree of amusement—tempered by concern—the letters which parents write asking herpetologists whether they think rattlers or cobras could be cared for safely by twelve- and fourteen-year-old sons and daughters! While maturity of judgment may be correlated only somewhat intimately with chronological age, I would strongly urge the teenager not to keep poisonous snakes—with or without parental permission. If an older person decides to keep one or more poisonous snakes in a private collection, it should be done with a thorough awareness of the dangers involved. In a few places there are municipal or state laws governing the keeping of poisonous snakes. This aspect should be given some attention before any are acquired. It is to be expected that the future will bring more such statutes, occasioned by the unhappy incidents of bites or escapes by captive specimens. I have been catching poisonous snakes in the field and keeping them under observation in cages for many years. I was bitten once—by a four-foot timber rattler—during an exceptional act of carelessness on my part while providing the creature with water. Severe envenomation accompanied the bite but, fortunately, recovery was uncomplicated, and there were no after-effects. Others have not been so lucky. Snakebite histories make gruesome reading. The subject will be discussed further when we talk about the methods of collecting reptiles in their natural haunts.

FAMILY ELAPIDAE

Some of the world's most infamous snakes belong to the family Elapidae—the group which includes cobras and mambas. Elapid snakes, as they are called, are found on all the continental land masses except Europe. In Australia, they predominate over other kinds, and that continent is the only one which has more venomous species than non-venomous species. Many of the Australian elapids are so small, however, that they are incapable of inflicting dangerous bites. Some are very secretive types which are seldom seen above ground. Australia has rigid codes protecting its fauna, and it is only occasionally that any poisonous Australian species is exported or available from dealers.

TIGER SNAKE

The tiger snake, *Notechis scutatus*, which receives its common name from the series of dark crossbands on a lighter ground color that run from the neck to the tail of the reptile, is a common but very dangerous reptile. This snake is usually three to four feet long, but in exceptional instances it may reach a length of five feet or more. Tiger snakes occur over much of Australia and are believed to be responsible for most of the serious bites in that country. Tested in the laboratory, the venom of this serpent has been found to be one of the most toxic known. The tiger snake produces large broods of living young, often to the number of thirty or more. This usually occurs in February or March, and the babies shift for themselves at once. Adult tiger snakes will eat small rodents and birds; it is likely that juveniles would include lizards in their diet. When angry, the tiger snake will spread its neck like a cobra and strike with great swiftness.

DEATH ADDER

Differing in form from most elapids, the death adder, *Acanthophis antarcticus*, is another Australian reptile that is quite common and widespread. Typically, elapine snakes are rather slender of build;

Tiger snake, *Notechis scutatus*. Photo by G. Marcuse.

some may be excessively so. Death adders, however, are thick and chunky, resembling the popular conception of a viper type. They may be gray or brown, with dark crossbands, and seldom exceed two feet in length. A broad, flat head and coarsely-keeled scales add to the picture of a snake which looks, and is, very dangerous. Death adders live fairly well in a dry and warm cage. Mice will be readily accepted by most captives, and a temperature of 75 to 80 degrees is recommended. Progeny are not numerous, a brood of babies numbering less than twelve on the average.

AUSTRALIAN BLACK SNAKE, MULGA SNAKE, SPOTTED BLACK SNAKE

The handsome red-bellied black snake of Australia, *Pseudechis porphyriacus*, is found mostly in swampy places and is an excellent swimmer. Like most other Australian snakes, it is not aggressive but will fight fiercely when cornered. Its venom is of lower toxicity than those of the tiger snake and the death adder. A large black snake may measure seven feet or more and is a very beautiful animal with a shiny black uppersurface and a belly which varies from pink to scarlet red. Angry specimens flatten the neck and strike readily enough, but do not rear from the ground as does a cobra. Babies are born alive. Of the Australian elapids, the black snake is one of the most satisfactory in captivity. It will devour small mammals and birds, as well as frogs and lizards. Closely related to the black snake are the mulga snake, *Pseudechis australis*, a brownish reptile with a pink undersurface, and the spotted black snake, *Pseudechis guttatus*, which differs from *P. porphyriacus* in having a grayish belly.

AUSTRALIAN COPPERHEAD, WESTERN BROWN SNAKE, TAIPAN

The Australian copperhead, *Denisonia superba*, is not related to its namesake of the United States. Southeastern Australia is the natural range of the copperhead; it frequents swampy areas and feeds largely upon frogs. A large example may be five feet long and is dark brown or black. Other Australian elapids which occasionally reach the cages of dealers are the western brown snake, *Demansia nuchalis*, and the taipan, *Oxyuranus scutellatus*, a dreaded reptile which may reach a length of ten feet and is considered the most aggressive and dangerous of that country's snakes.

AFRICAN GARTER SNAKES

A number of small snakes of the genus *Elapsoidea*, some of them prettily marked with bands of red and white, inhabit Africa. Often called garter snakes, they are in no way related to the American reptiles of the same name. Small and secretive, the African garter snakes seldom make any attempt to strike but will bite if much handled. Though only about two feet in length, the pretty members of this genus are true elapids and should be regarded with caution. In captivity, unless given adequate means of burrowing or at least remaining out of sight, they will seldom thrive.

KRAITS

The kraits (genus *Bungarus*) account for many deaths in Asia, where they are among the most common poisonous snakes. Sluggish by nature, they make little effort to get out of one's way and are frequently stepped on at night when they are prowling in search of the other snakes upon which they feed. Though largely terrestrial and secretive, some species ascend trees and have been found even on the roofs of houses. They seldom will make any attempt to bite unless touched, when they will swing their heads around quickly and grasp and chew on the offending object. Even this response cannot usually be elicited, especially during the daylight hours, when a freshly-captured specimen will often roll into a ball which conceals its head and remain in this position while being handled. In Oriental countries kraits are captured and sold as food; it is rather disconcerting to view the indifference with which they are handled in these places. Oriental vendors think nothing of grasping these large snakes with their bare hands, yet bites from them are few. Still, kraits are among the most dangerous of snakes, and one that is stepped on will certainly bite in retaliation. Kraits very often do not live well in captivity, which may be due in part to the fact that they are rarely provided with sufficient means of hiding. Cages for kraits should be quite large; at least a portion of it should be abundantly supplied with hollow logs and a profusion of bark slabs. The snakes can be expected to spend much of their time in seclusion but will issue forth at night in search of food. This is best provided in the form of smaller, harmless snakes, though in the absence of these other small reptiles, frogs, small mammals, and even fishes will be taken by some individuals. Characteristically, the kraits are banded snakes of three to four feet in length. Some of the more commonly imported species are the banded krait, *Bungarus fasciatus*, a quite handsome yellow and black species, and the Chinese krait, *Bungarus multicinctus*, a black and white form. The kraits are subject to much color variation; some may even lack bands, being of a single color over the entire body. As far as is known, all of the krait species lay eggs.

COBRAS

Cobras occupy a rather special niche in the serpents' hall of fame. Popularly, they are visualized as hooded serpents rearing from the basket of Hindu snake charmers and "dancing" to the accompaniment of the discordant tones produced by his fluted instrument. Cobras do not have a sense of hearing, as we understand it, and the specimens used in these performances sway from side to side in an effort to achieve an advantageous striking position at the body of the "charmer," which is also kept constantly in motion, to keep the reptiles off balance. In some cases, these snakes have had their fangs removed, but this is by no means always true. There is little question that the show is a dangerous one, and it is somewhat oversimplified by the foregoing comments. An intimate knowledge of the serpentine material used is a requisite, and this is not acquired without great risk. The spreading of a cobra's hood is accomplished by the serpent's elongated ribs and can be observed only in agitated snakes. Reports that cobras spread their hoods while sunning require confirmation. The development of the hood varies among the different species of cobras; some have little or no ability to expand the neck. Cobras which have become accustomed to cage life lie quietly about and resemble more ordinary types of snakes. Under ordinary conditions they do not make spectacular display animals. Many writers have said that cobras are the most intelligent of snakes. This may or may not be true, but certain it is that they are very alert, sometimes extremely aggressive, and at all times most dangerous reptiles to tamper with.

Several species of cobras have the ability to discharge venom from their fangs directly at the face of an antagonist. The ringhals, *Hemachatus haemachatus*, is especially notable for this, "spitting" accurately over a distance of six to eight feet in the case of an adult cobra which

Cape cobra, *Naja nivea,* southern Africa. Photo by G. Marcuse.

Egyptian cobra, *Naja hajae,* northern Africa. Photo by G. Marcuse.

measures about four feet in length. The ejection of venom is usually accomplished from a raised body stance, with the hood spread. In the case of a standing man, it would be directed upward toward his eyes. Temporary or possible permanent blindness can result if any of the spray enters the eyes, a more than likely occurrence. Immediate remedial measures consist of a thorough rinsing of the eyes and face with water, which should always be carried in spitting-cobra country. Captive ringhals are hardy and thrive over long periods of time if properly cared for. Frogs, rodents, and birds can be fed successfully. The ringhals produces its babies alive.

The typical cobras have an extensive range in Asia and Africa. There is a great deal of variation in colors and markings among the various species and subspecies of the genus *Naja*. The common cobra, *Naja naja*; the black-lipped cobra, *Naja melanoleuca*; and the black-necked cobra, *Naja nigricollis*, are a few of the kinds which are imported. The last-named is an accomplished "spitter"—quite as adept as the ringhals. Adult cobras of the commoner forms are usually five to six feet in length and have a moderately heavy body. All require a considerable amount of warmth and the species from arid situations, in particular, need a very dry atmosphere. They are active reptiles and should have large cages. To someone who has had experience in handling the snakes of the United States, including the poisonous ones, but has not tried to care for a cobra in captivity, I can suggest that a mental picture be drawn of a racer-like snake which has, in addition to its speed, a poisonous bite and the sometime-ability to accurately eject venom into one's eyes. This composite will give the reader some idea of the care which must be exercised in the handling of captive cobras. All retain a high-strung disposition in captivity and are easily provoked. Fights with each other are frequent. The *Naja* species reproduce by means of eggs, and a hatchling will rear its diminutive form, spread its hood, and strike the moment it is completely free of the egg.

A particularly dangerous snake is the king cobra, *Ophiophagus hannah*, of Asia, a species which has been known to reach a length of eighteen feet! An example of this size could rear itself to the height of an average man. Large specimens are often imported and are quite expensive, for the snake is not a really common one. Its color is usually an olive-brown, sometimes with pale bands. Babies are handsomely banded in black and white and may measure about

Spectacled cobra, *Naja naja kaouthia*. Photo by G. Marcuse.

twenty inches when hatched. The king cobra is one of the species of snakes which guard their eggs, which may number several dozens. Under favorable conditions king cobras have successfully bred and produced fertile eggs in captivity. Unlike the commoner cobras which will take a variety of warm-and-cold blooded animals, the present species prefers other snakes as food. Occasionally, a specimen may be trained to take other foods.

MAMBAS

Mambas (genus *Dendroaspis*) are confined to Africa, where they are justifiably feared by hunters and others who enter their haunts. All are long, very slender snakes; black, brown, or green may be the prevailing color. They look and act like tree snakes and can be confused with some of the innocuous forms of the latter. The black mamba, *Dendroaspis polylepis*, can grow to twelve feet; its relatives, like the green mamba, *Dendroaspis angusticeps*, are somewhat smaller. Mambas can be kept in a large cage which has branches for climbing. Food in the wild state consists of birds, mostly, but captives will take mice and often frogs and lizards. Being extremely active and prone to attack if interfered with, mambas should never be allowed the freedom of a room—as during cage-cleaning. Food and water should be introduced by means of long tongs, a careful watch being kept on the cage's inhabitants during this process. This rule should apply to the feeding and watering of all captive venomous snakes. Complete visibility of the occupant should be had during any work in a cage that does not have a dividing partition. In small cages, particularly, I never keep more than a single individual. Some snakes pay little attention to cage-cleaning, whereas others rush forward to investigate the cause of the disturbance. This may be particularly true of snakes which have been in captivity a long time and have lost their natural timidity. An animal which has lost its fear of humans is more dangerous than a freshly-caught individual, unless the loss of fear is accompanied by a corresponding loss of the inclination to bite when danger threatens. The more nervous types of dangerous snakes can rarely be brought to this degree of tameness, regardless of how kindly treated. Mambas are oviparous snakes and the eggs may

Green mamba, *Dendroaspis angusticeps.* Photo by G. Marcuse.

number about a dozen. Among the really deadly snakes of the world, the mambas must surely occupy a foremost position. I do not think there would be many recoveries from the fully-delivered bite of a large mamba unless the bite were treated rapidly and energetically.

CORAL SNAKES

North, Central, and South America are the homes of a number of small burrowing elapids that are called coral snakes (genus *Micrurus*). Brightly ringed with black, yellow, and red, the small members of this genus are very attractive reptiles and often have a close resemblance to certain harmless snakes which share their habitats. The eastern coral snake, *Micrurus fulvius*, is well known in the United States, where its bite has caused a number of deaths. In habits, the coral snakes are somewhat like the kraits: they remain hidden during the day and emerge at dusk to search for food in the form of other snakes and small lizards; they never bite except when handled or stepped on; they adapt rather poorly to average cage conditions and must be provided with a floor-covering of moss or wood pulp in which to burrow. A temperature range of 75 to 80 degrees is best for them. Most coral snakes do not grow larger than three feet—some are much smaller. The giant coral snake, *Micrurus spixi*, is an exception, attaining dimensions of four to five feet. Despite their gentle demeanor, coral snakes are very venomous reptiles, and no one should attempt to capture one without suitable tools.

FAMILY HYDROPHIIDAE

All of the strictly marine serpents have been placed in one family— the Hydrophiidae. Two sub-classifications have been made, depending on the degree of specialization shown by the various species for an aquatic existence. Most sea snakes give birth to living young in shallow shore waters, but there are several kinds which actually leave the sea and deposit their eggs on land. Marine snakes are widely-ranging and abundant in tropical waters of the Indian and Pacific Oceans. Great numbers of sea snakes are hauled in by commercial fishermen, who pick them up with bare hands and toss them back into the sea. Fatal bites sometimes occur from this carelessness, for all of the known sea snakes are poisonous and very dangerously so, though many species have a mild disposition. Size among the marine snakes runs from a couple of feet to over eight

Eastern coral snake, *Micrurus fulvius*. Photo by C. Hansen.

Banded sea snake, *Laticauda laticauda*. Photo by G. Budich.

feet. As a group, they show much variation in colors and pattern, and some are quite beautiful. All have flattened tails and seem as thoroughly at home in the water as the eels upon which they feed. Some species have been seen far out to sea in aggregations which numbered in the thousands, if not millions, of individuals. The reason for such concentrations is not known. Sea snakes are seldom available from dealers in reptiles, and we have learned little of their habits in either the wild state or in captivity. It is known that they can be maintained over indefinite periods in ordinary tap water and often accept food under these circumstances. One species, at least, has been cut off from the sea and now resides in fresh water.

Representative of the sea snakes which have not broken away completely from the land are such kinds as the banded sea snakes, *Laticauda laticaudata* and *Laticauda semifasciata*. These species have ventral scales which are broadened, like those of terrestrial serpents, and are able to make awkward progress on land. Some species of *Laticauda* are said to sun themselves on coral atolls; among these species we find the sea snakes that lay their eggs on land. The thoroughly aquatic species are represented by the yellow-bellied sea snake, *Pelamis platurus*, a dark brown or black reptile with a bright yellow belly and a vividly-banded tail. The belly scales of this snake are small and do not differ from the scales of the back. Such species rarely, if ever, voluntarily leave the water; they bear living young. I do not believe that any sea snake has been kept in captivity over a really long period of time, even in salt or brackish water. Most will live out of water for quite a while. The sea snakes are a fascinating group of reptiles and well worthy of the life study of a specialist.

FAMILY VIPERIDAE

Snakes of the family Viperidae, commonly called vipers, are found only in the eastern hemisphere and are absent from Australia. Typically, the snakes of this family are rather stout-bodied terrestrial reptiles, though some have taken to subterranean habits and others live in trees. With proper care, many do exceedingly well in captivity. Vipers and pit vipers do best with an absolute minimum of handling or other disturbances. The best captives are those which have been raised from infancy, and with many of the species this is not a difficult accomplishment if their feeding requirements can be satisfied. Adults which have been handled roughly at time of capture and hereafter often refuse to eat or will feed so sparingly that they starve to death. Force-feeding, a simple and safe operation in the case of a harmless snake, is a dangerous procedure with a poisonous one, and the trauma to the snake which accompanies such forcible handling is likely to outdo any good which may be accomplished. Likewise, the "milking" of a captive poisonous snake is a reprehensible practice and is justified only when there is a clear need for the venom, as in the production of snakebite sera or in experiments to determine the composition or toxicity of the product. In connection with the danger and difficulty of force-feeding venomous snakes, it might be well to bring out that in every aspect of their care in captivity the poisonous snakes present more problems than the harmless kinds. This is true in such everyday occurrences as feeding, cage-cleaning, assistance in the shedding of their skins, and giving treatment for parasites and minor illnesses. These are points to be considered when the time allotted to the care of a collection is limited. On the other hand, there is hardly a more attractive and interesting exhibit than a well-managed collection of poisonous snakes. The colors and patterns of some of the species are positively gorgeous. Most viperine snakes show little interest in escaping from their cages once they have quieted down and started feeding. In this they resemble the more phlegmatic of the boas and pythons.

BURROWING VIPER

The burrowing viper, *Atractaspis bibroni,* and its relatives form an interesting African group. Commonly less than two feet long, their slender and cylindrical forms are ideally suited to the underground life of the reptiles. A curious thing about them is the enormous development of the viper fang mechanism: the fangs are so long that they can be used with little effectiveness when the mouth is open. They often bite with the mouth closed, the viperine teeth exposed and projecting over the sides of the lower jaw. Unlike most other true vipers, the present species deposit eggs. They are nocturnal and feed upon small mammals, lizards, and other snakes. In captivity they should have a means of hiding. Possibly the best arrangement is one which provides a thin layer of soil and flat rocks or slabs of bark.

AFRICAN PUFF ADDER

Writers who attempt to evaluate the deadliness of the world's snakes with "the ten most" lists always include the forbidding-appearing African puff adder, *Bitis arietans*. There is little likelihood that anyone would mistake a puff adder for a harmless snake; everything about the reptile bespeaks sinister intent with capability to match. Five feet seems to be the greatest length attained by puff adders, and a specimen of this size is tremendously heavy-bodied. The yellowish-brown skin has interspersed over its surface a series of broad and much darker chevrons which are accentuated by light borders. There is some variation among specimens from different regions. Those from the drier areas tend to be lighter colored. Puff adders are difficult to see in their natural habitat and many accidents result from stepping on them. They are very common snakes and probably bite more people than any other African snake. In captivity puff adders do well, and large ones make sensational exhibits. Rodents, which often die within seconds after being bitten, are the preferred food. Young specimens are easily reared and are able to swallow small mice from the moment of birth, though some show a preference for tree frogs. Broods often number twelve or fewer babies. I mentioned earlier that I prefer to house only one poisonous snake in a cage, primarily for reasons of safety during cage-cleaning. Another reason is that if live mice or rats are fed to captive viperine snakes, the snakes may strike wildly and cause severe mechanical injuries to each other with their long fangs, though the various species are immune to the poison of their own kind. The fangs of a viper or large rattlesnake may be nearly an inch in length; with a few species this length is well exceeded. Any accidental penetration of the spinal area by one of these instruments, as has happened when two or more specimens were confined to the same cage, is certain to cause the death of the specimen so injured.

GABOON VIPER, RHINOCEROS VIPER

The Gaboon viper, *Bitis gabonica*, and the rhinoceros viper, *Bitis nasicornis*, are large and very beautiful relatives of the puff adder. The former may reach a length of six feet, while the latter is smaller. Rhinoceros vipers have horn-like appendages on their snouts and a beautifully-interwoven color pattern. Blue is not a common color among snakes, but it figures prominently on the head and back of

Gaboon viper, *Bitis gabonica*. Photo by G. Marcuse.

B. nasicornis, in combination with yellow, black, red, and brown. All of the African vipers of the genus *Bitis* require warm and dry quarters. A temperature of 78 to 85 degrees seems to suit them well. They are not active snakes but because of their huge bulk they should have a good sized cage. They seek to intimidate the observer by hissing loudly. Their strike is delivered with great swiftness, however, and is impossible to avoid if one is within range—a distance of perhaps a third the length of a coiled reptile.

HORNED ADDERS AND VIPERS

Bitis caudalis and *Bitis cornuta* are African desert species which possess enlarged and pointed scales over their eyes. These resemble horns and give these desert reptiles their popular name of horned adders. Their cage should have a sand covering on its floor, to the depth of several inches, and it is necessary to keep the temperature no lower than 78 degrees. The horned vipers, *Cerastes cerastes* and *Cerastes cornutus*, are also desert creatures, only about two feet when fully-grown. They spend much of their time buried in sand, with only their heads visible. None of these desert viperines has been kept over a very long period in captivity. The provision of natural sunlight or the substitute rays of an ultraviolet lamp is beneficial to them.

NIGHT ADDER

The night adder, *Causus rhombeatus*, of tropical and South Africa is a true viper but differs in many ways from most other African types. For one thing, it lays eggs, often in September, and its food consists mostly of frogs and toads—in contrast to the warm-blooded prey preferred by other vipers, especially forest species. Enormously developed venom glands are carried from the head well back into

Horned viper, *Cerastes cerastes*. Photo by G. Marcuse.

the body of these snakes; the purpose of this is not known. Night adders do not have the marked enlargement of head that is prevalent among viperine snakes and, adding to their innocuous appearance, are round pupils, though the reptiles are nocturnal to a large extent. Two to three feet is the average length of an adult, which is grayish-green and prettily blotched with dark rhombs along the back and stripes on the sides and head. An arrow-like design, its point toward the snout of the snake, is very prominent.

SAW-SCALED VIPER

Another curious little viper, *Echis carinatus*, has a wide range in Africa and Asia. Known as the saw-scaled viper, it is able to produce rather loud rasping noises by rubbing together loops of its body. Large examples are only two feet long and will eat insects in addition to the more usual viper fare of mice and small birds. Babies are easy to rear on a diet of small lizards. The species, like other African and Asian reptiles, requires a fairly high temperature, 78 to 85 degrees. Saw-scaled vipers are irascible in temperament and, as with all poisonous snakes, great care should be used in working with them.

COMMON ADDER

A common poisonous snake of Europe and the only one found in the British Isles is the common adder, *Vipera berus*. Curiously for a reptile from temperate regions, this species needs to be kept warm or it will not live in captivity. Even under the best of conditions, it is delicate and not easy to induce to feed. It is thus at variance with some of its very close relatives from warmer climates. These often thrive for years under careful management. Some writers have suggested that the common adder lives best if allowed to hibernate during the cold months. If this is true, it is not so of other snakes which normally hibernate but are not allowed to do so in captivity. Captive adders will sometimes accept mice, lizards, or fledgling birds; babies, which are born alive, show a preference for very small lizards.

EUROPEAN ASP, SAND ADDER

The European asp, *Vipera aspis*, is closely related to the common adder but can be distinguished from it by a slightly upturned snout. A further development of this feature is found in the sand adder,

Saw-scaled viper, *Echis carinatus*. Photos by G. Marcuse.

Sand adder, *Vipera ammodytes.*

Common adder, *Vipera berus.* Photo by H. Hansen, Aquarium Berlin.

Vipera ammodytes, a species that grows to the moderate length of about three feet and has the zigzag line down its back—a feature common to many of the European vipers. In captivity the present species flourishes indefinitely, but only if kept both warm and dry. In their manner of caring for reptiles, European herpetologists tend to favor semi-natural settings in their cages. These are very necessary in the cases of types which spend much of their lives underground, or those which live in trees. Most terrestrial snakes, however, will do better in cages which can be easily cleaned and do not hold dampness.

KUFI

Vipera lebetina is one of the largest species of the genus and is found in portions of three continents. Adults reach a length of five feet and are able to consume rats as well as smaller rodents. Its large size and the proportionate quantity of venom it is able to inject make the kufi, as this snake is sometimes called, a very dangerous one. Mem-

Kufi, *Vipera lebetina.* Photo by G. Marcuse.

bers of the genus *Vipera* are characteristically snakes which produce small to very large broods of living babies. The present species follows this mode of reproduction in some portions of its range, while in others it deposits eggs. An inconsistency of this type has been noted with some other serpents, though it is not a common phenomenon.

RUSSELL'S VIPER

The most formidable of its group is the large and handsome Russell's viper, *Vipera russelli*, of Asia. Its color pattern is quite distinctive, consisting of three rows of large spots which are reddish-brown and outlined with black and white. These stand out vividly on a background of light brown. Russell's viper is one of the most dangerous of the Asian snakes and each year takes many lives. It is a very common reptile in some areas, a fact which may be accounted for by the huge broods it sometimes produces. In exceptional cases a female may give birth to five dozen babies. Adult vipers of this kind are really large reptiles and should not be cramped in small quarters. They feed well upon rodents; younger specimens will take frogs and lizards.

Russell's viper, *Vipera russelli*. Photo by G. Marcuse.

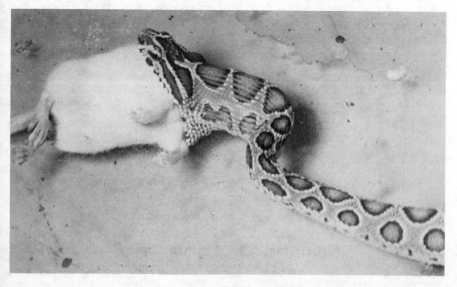

FAMILY CROTALIDAE

The pit vipers are closely related to the true vipers of the Old World, but most herpetologists accord them full family recognition under the family designation Crotalidae. One feature immediately identifies any member of this group: the presence of an orifice on either side of the head, between the eye and the nostril. This is a sensory organ and is believed to be used primarily for heat perception. Since many pit vipers feed exclusively upon warm-blooded animals, its usefulness in dealing with such prey at close range may be surmised. Serpents often seem unable to accurately direct their strikes at moving targets; the presence of heat detectors may assist in this as well as other ways. The larger pit vipers have an unsavory reputation and one which is well deserved, for they are among the most dangerous snakes.

TRIMERESURUS

Trimeresurus is a genus of tropical pit vipers of the Asian mainland and Pacific islands. They differ little from the tropical American *Bothrops*, and some herpetologists combine the many species under a single generic heading. The scientific listings of herptiles and other animals are in a constant state of change. This is often troublesome to the neophyte who wishes to look up a specimen in various books, but a closer familiarity with the subject soon acquaints the student with the synonyms that are used in describing species. In this book, snakes of these related genera are placed under separate headings: *Bothrops* for the New World species, *Trimeresurus* for those of the Old World.

Asian pit vipers, especially the island forms, once were difficult to come by. For a number of years now they have been imported in some numbers, though certain species are rarely to be found even in the preserved collections of the larger museums. Mainly, they are terrestrial snakes, although there are some kinds which have pre-hensile tails and spend most of their time in trees and bushes. One of these is the bamboo viper, *Trimeresurus gramineus*, a green snake of small size that makes a decorative exhibit in a cage containing branches. It feeds on frogs and small birds, sometimes descending from its arboreal perch to hunt along streams. A similar species is *Trimeresurus stejnegeri*, which grows to only two feet and adapts fairly well to cage life. The more terrestrial members of the genus

Bamboo viper, *Trimeresurus gramineus*. Photo by G. Marcuse.

are typified by the habu, *Trimeresurus mucrosquamatus*, a brown reptile with a series of darker blotches along its back and sides. A length of four feet is attained and food consists of birds and mammals. In its nocturnal search for rodents the habu has been known to enter human dwellings. The yellow-green habu, *Trimeresurus flavoviridis*, and the purple-spotted pit viper, *Trimeresurus purpureomaculata*, are occasionally available. Generally speaking, poisonous snakes of these and other kinds are more expensive to buy than the equally-common harmless types from the same areas. This is understandable, in view of the risk that is involved in their capture and transportation.

BOTHROPS

The jumping viper, *Bothrops nummifera*, is a thick-bodied and very pugnacious little snake of Central America. So much energy is expended in the strike of a three-foot reptile that it may actually leave the ground. Coloration is brownish, with dark rhomboidal spots along the back. The fer-de-lance, *Bothrops atrox*, is a greatly-feared snake of Central and South America. Specimens vary a great deal in color, but usually some shade of gray or brown prevails as the ground color and this is overlaid with light-edged triangles along the sides. These meet in the middle of the back, and the effect produced is that of a diamond-backed serpent. In some areas the fer-de-lance seems to grow not more than four feet, while in others specimens eight feet long have been found. Large litters are produced, four or five dozen being common. In captivity the fer-de-lance is a quiet snake in its demeanor; occasionally an individual will feed well and live for a long time. This is not the usual experience, however, for the majority of fer-de-lances are not as adaptable as the pit vipers of North America. Perhaps some of the trouble is concerned with the shock to the reptile of being captured. I have noted repeatedly that snakes which are incorrectly noosed or pinned with force to the ground during capture are much less likely to feed subsequently than those which are taken with a minimum of such disturbance. The jararaca, *Bothrops jararaca*; the urutu, *Bothrops neuwiedi*; and the jararacucu, *Bothrops jararacussu*, are allied to the fer-de-lance and some are very beautiful in their colors and markings. The palm vipers, *Bothrops schlegeli* and *Bothrops nigroviridis*, are slender greenish snakes which have taken up life in the trees. Some have horn-like developments over their eyes.

BUSHMASTER

The bushmaster, *Lachesis muta*, of the American tropics sometimes attains a length of twelve feet or more and is the largest viper in the world, from the standpoint of length. Specimens present a vivid and startling combination of pink and black when freshly shed. With fangs in excess of an inch in length and venom glands of huge capacity, the bushmaster is probably the most dangerous of the New World snakes. The bushmaster seems to be a rather uncommon species. The Instituto Butantan, a government agency of Sao Paulo, Brazil annually receives thousands of snakes. From these the venom is extracted and used in the production of sera for the treatment of snakebite. It is of interest to note that in a 62-year period of operation, the institute received nearly 800,000 snakes, both poisonous and nonpoisonous. Of this number, only 49 were bushmasters. Non-poisonous snakes numbered some 183,000, while poisonous snakes totalled over 590,000. This reflects a curious fact: although non-poisonous are found in greater numbers than poisonous snakes (the ratio being about five to one), the latter are more easily captured because of their tendency to stand their ground and actively defend themselves. A large crotaline snake is a very difficult animal to capture unhurt, especially in a jungle area. Noosed specimens struggle violently, and many undoubtedly incur internal injuries, particularly of the spine, during the process of capture. I believe that this may be a reason why the larger poisonous snakes of the tropics often fail to thrive in captivity. Unlike most American pit vipers, bushmasters lay eggs; reports have it that in some instances, at least, the eggs may be guarded by the female. Mammals and birds are eaten. Unlike most tropical snakes, bushmasters should be kept at the relatively low temperature of 70°. This is because they normally inhabit a very cool micro-habitat.

AGKISTRODON

Eastern Europe, Asia, and North and Central America have a variety of pit vipers, some very beautiful and interesting, belonging to the genus *Agkistrodon*. Some of the species bear living young; others lay eggs, which in some cases are brooded by the mother snake. About five feet when fully-grown, the hundred pace snake, *Agkistrodon acutus*, is a handsome species. It has a sharply-pointed, upturned snout and smooth scales. Triangular side blotches, quietly blended with dorsal rhombs, present a multicoloring of red, gray, brown, and black. Like many other snakes, it is very difficult to see when coiled among leaves. The Malayan pit viper, *Agkistrodon rhodostoma*, is another very pretty reptile, smaller than the preceding species and with keeled scales. It lays eggs that take only about a month and a half to hatch. Both the hundred pace snake and the Malayan pit viper are deceptively docile in captivity and will eat small mammals and birds.

In the United States, one of the better-known poisonous snakes is the copperhead, *Agkistrodon contortrix*. A good-sized snake of this species is about three feet in length. Tan is the prevailing ground

Copperhead, *Agkistrodon contortrix*. Photo by G. Marcuse.

color, and along the sides are triangular blotches of a deep chestnut color. These meet on the back, sometimes converging and forming an hourglass pattern. Copperheads are usually found in wooded, hilly areas that are broken up by expanses of rocky ledges. These are the hibernating places of the reptiles, where they may be found in large numbers in the spring and in the autumn, before they retire for the winter months. In the summer they disperse and may be found nearly anywhere, a favorite lurking place being old stone walls. Copperheads account for many bites among humans, but few if any of these terminate fatally, for the venom is not injected in a large quantity and is not very potent—compared, say, with that of the timber rattlesnake, a species of similar range and habits. Copperheads will eat both cold-blooded and warm-blooded animals and often show a preference for birds in the spring. In the summer many specimens will take only mice, while in the autumn the food of choice consists of frogs. These feeding idiosyncrasies are not invariable but nevertheless prevail among the majority of captives.

The water moccasin, *Agkistrodon piscivorus*, of the southeastern United States is a familiar reptile of swamps and river courses. Exceptionally, a six-foot specimen is found, but the majority of moccasins are about four feet. Those of the Carolinas and Georgia

Water moccasin, *Agkistrodon piscivorus*. Photo by F. J. Dodd, Jr.

are larger than the moccasins from Louisiana. "Cottonmouth" is the name often applied to these snakes because of their habit of posing with jaws widely agape before striking. Even the most ardent snake admirer would not call the water moccasin a pretty reptile; it is a dingy brown with obscure crossbands that may become visible only when the snake is wet. Babies are more brightly colored and bear a resemblance to copperheads in the boldness of their blotching. Of all the venomous snakes, perhaps there is none which makes a better adjustment to a life of confinement than the moccasin. Freshly-caught, it is a vicious reptile, but this attitude quickly gives way to one of quiet docility. Captive moccasins will eat almost anything in the way of animal matter. Fishes, frogs, salamanders, lizards, birds, mammals, and even other snakes are eaten with equal relish. Babies can be successfully reared on a diet of fishes alone. Water moccasins, which are among the least nervous of poisonous snakes, should be kept in plain wooden cages without sand or other accessories. Water should be provided in a small dish which does not readily tip.

The cantil, *Agkistrodon bilineatus*, of Mexico and Central America is another semi-aquatic *Agkistrodon*. It is a pretty dark reddish-brown or black reptile, attractively embellished with white lines about the head and outlining obscure blotches along the back. It does not grow as large as the cottonmouth, from which it seems to differ little in habits, though it is less hardy in captivity.

RATTLESNAKES

Rattlesnakes are found only in the Americas. They range in size from tiny species only slightly over a foot in length, whose rattles can hardly be heard, to massive creatures of six feet or more in length, with a weight of over fifteen pounds. The rattle itself is a horny, segmented tail appendage which may produce anything from a few spasmodic clicks to a loud, sonorous buzz. Some species make little use of this member, even when freshly caught, and one kind, discovered and named in recent years, seems to have lost the rattle entirely. With the exception of this species, the rattle is a mark of sure identification. Babies are born with a "button"—to this is added a segment with each shedding of the skin. This occurs several times in the course of a year, so it is not possible to tell the age of a rattlesnake by the number of rattles it possesses. Rattles frequently

Red rattlesnake, *Crotalus ruber*, showing detail of the head and rattle. Photos by G. Marcuse.

break, and this fact further disqualifies any assumption as to the age of a snake. Really large adults are seldom found with complete rattles.

The pigmy rattlesnake, *Sistrurus miliaris*, is found in fair abundance over much of the southeastern United States. It is a dusky gray or brownish snake with a series of darker blotches running the length of its back. The slender tail of a two-foot adult terminates in a diminutive rattle that can scarcely be heard at a distance of six feet. Pigmy rattlers differ from members of the larger genus *Crotalus* in having the tops of their heads covered with plates rather than granular scalation. Generally they are to be found in damp or actually wet situations, where they feed upon mice, frogs, salamanders, lizards, and occasionally smaller snakes. Babies are produced alive in broods which commonly number less than a dozen. They are only about six inches long and are difficult to rear, even if an adequate supply of the tiniest foods is available. In connection with the raising of the present species, as well as babies of some of the other small rattlesnakes, it might be mentioned that the little reptiles will often accept portions of larger animals, such as the legs or tails of lizards. From the accounts of bites which have been sustained it appears that the venom of this small rattler is a very potent one. If it were not for its small size and the minute amount of venom it is able to deliver, the pigmy rattlesnake would be a very dangerous snake indeed.

A larger relative of the pigmy rattler is the massasauga, *Sistrurus catenatus*, which (exceptionally) may reach a length of three feet. In one or another of its varieties this snake ranges over a wide belt from the Great Lakes area south to Texas and west to southeastern Arizona. The habits of the massasauga do not differ much from those of the pigmy rattler. In mixed collections of rattlers which I have received from various areas, I have noticed that the massasaugas are sometimes the most hostile, continually rattling when being transferred from cage to cage. They are also among the hardiest. I recall one shipment which arrived in the winter. It had been mishandled in transit and every rattler, with the exception of the massasauga, had contracted a respiratory illness to which it succumbed shortly. The massasauga was unaffected by the severe chilling.

Massasauga, *Sistrurus catenatus*. From Ditmars, *Reptiles of North America*.

In a large portion of the eastern United States, the timber rattlesnake, *Crotalus horridus horridus*, is the only poisonous snake, except where it may share its domain with copperheads. Mountain ledges are favorite haunts of the timber rattler, and portions of these ledges have deep crevices in which the species spends the winter months. In the spring, usually by the last week of April, the snakes emerge from their dens to bask in the sun. Often large numbers may be counted in a small area at this time. The reptiles mate, then each goes its own way in search of favorable feeding ground. In early fall there is a migration back to the dens, when they may again be found in numbers for a brief period before cold weather forces them to retire for the winter. Timber rattlers occasionally reach six feet, but three and a half is an average size. Two color phases occur—one a sulfur yellow with darker crossbands, the other brown, with more obscure markings. In some areas completely melanistic examples are not rare. Babies are always light in color; those of the darker phase start to change during their second summer, the process beginning at the head. In captivity timber rattlers survive over long periods. Mice are the favorite food and a rattler of average size can be kept in good health with a single large mouse each week.

The canebrake rattler, *Crotalus horridus atricaudatus,* is a handsome southern variety which grows to a larger average size than the timber. Some specimens are distinctly pinkish, with wavy crossbands of chocolate-brown. At present I have a specimen which was born in captivity and is growing rapidly. Though still less than three feet in length it is a fearless creature and quite remarkable in its aggressive disposition. In contrast to most rattlers, especially those born in captivity, this specimen has never tamed to the slightest degree. When the door of its cage is slid back, there is a quick rush to the point of disturbance—not the slow, sinuous glide of an animal interested only in food. If a dead mouse is offered with a pair of tongs, the mouse is bypassed by the snake in its attempt to imbed its fangs in the hand that is feeding it. For a snake with such a disposition it is unusual in that it feeds readily. No chances are taken with the reptile—I consider it one of the most dangerous poisonous snakes I have ever kept under observation.

The eastern diamondback rattlesnake, *Crotalus adamanteus,* and the western diamondback, *Crotalus atrox,* are formidable reptiles with long fangs and poison glands of large size. Both grow to huge size, over six feet, and the western species causes more deaths in the

Timber rattlesnake, *Crotalus horridus horridus.* From Ditmars, *Reptiles of North America.*

Eastern diamondback rattlesnake, *Crotalus adamanteus.* Photo by Ross Allen.

Tropical rattlesnake, *Crotalus durissus,* Central and South America. Photo by G. Marcuse.

Western diamondback rattlesnake, *Crotalus atrox*. From Van Denburgh.

United States than any other snake. With their handsome coloration and sullen demeanor, large specimens make spectacular exhibits, but often refuse to feed. It is best to acquire them as babies and raise them on a diet of mice, graduating to rats as the reptiles mature. These and other rattlers of North America do well if kept at a temperature of 75 to 80 degrees. When conditions are especially favorable rattlers will breed in captivity. Some have lived well over twenty years.

The hardiest rattlesnake and the one easiest to keep and feed is the prairie rattlesnake, *Crotalus viridis*. Several races, varying somewhat in size and color, occur throughout the West. They lack the beauty of some of the other species but more than make up for this in the ease with which they adjust to cage-life. Even fully-grown examples, captured but recently, seldom sound their rattles and feed without hesitancy upon mice.

Many other rattlers do fairly well in captivity. Especially attractive is the black-tailed rattler, *Crotalus molossus*, and the lighter phase of the red rattler, *Crotalus r. ruber*. Attempts to maintain the tiger rattler, *Crotalus tigris*, over long periods generally have met with little success. The same is true of the speckled rattlesnake, *Crotalus mitchelli*. All rattlesnakes give birth directly to their babies; babies are usually few in number, not over ten in the case of some species.

It is thought by some that rattlers can strike only from a coiled position. This is not true; rattlers can strike from nearly any position,

Prairie rattlesnake, *Crotalus viridis*. From Van Denburgh.

Black-tailed rattlesnake, *Crotalus molossus*. From Van Denburgh.

Red rattlesnake, *Crotalus ruber*. Photo by G. Marcuse.

Sidewinder, *Crotalus cerastes,* southwestern deserts. From Van Denburgh.

Willard's rattlesnake, *Crotalus willardi,* Arizona and adjacent Mexico.
From Van Denburgh.

even when crawling rectilinearly, though from this position the forward striking range would be but a few inches. How this is accomplished by an animal that is drawn nearly straight out, with no visible loop of neck or body, I am not able to say, but it can make exceedingly dangerous any attempt to hand-feed a supposedly tame specimen. Rattlers which have met death accidentally often retain reflexes which can cause the head to swing around and bite an object which touches the body of the expired reptile. Persons have been seriously poisoned in this way. Snakes which die from natural causes seem to lack this post-mortem reflexibility; nevertheless, caution is urged in handling even such specimens. Examining the head and mouthparts of a deceased snake should be a cautious procedure, for the fangs are needle-sharp and venom can be expressed from the glands with but slight pressure.

Some of the most experienced herpetologists and snake collectors have died from the bites of poisonous snakes. This chapter is best closed with the simple admonition: if you decide to keep one or more poisonous snakes, treat your material with the respect it deserves!

IX

Newts, Salamanders and Caecilians

AMPHIBIANS IN GENERAL

The newts and salamanders, along with the frogs, toads, and caecilians, comprise a group of animals which are known as amphibians. Herpetologists, both professional and amateur, concern themselves with the study of amphibians as well as reptiles, though fundamentally the two classes of animals are quite distinct. The unity of the two classes as a scientific discipline contributed to the coinage of the term "herptile," a word used frequently in this book and others in referring collectively to amphibians and reptiles.

I have never seen a really representative living collection of the world's amphibians, even in the best zoos and aquariums. As a group, they have been sadly neglected. We have a thorough knowledge of the life histories of some of the very common species, but of the vast majority we know little. While it is quite simple to gather an assemblage of the more common amphibians found in one's own area, it is a very different matter to obtain desired species from other places. Only a few amphibians are regularly carried in the stocks of dealers. The individuals which come in with reptile importations are frequently offered to prospective buyers on an unidentified basis. The prices of such specimens are generally low, and with luck it is possible to acquire some uncommon specimens. Many faded specimens of once-gorgeous frogs and salamanders repose in the preserving jars of museum study collections. Looking at them, one wonders what fascinating details of life history they would reveal under vivarium conditions.

Amphibians have much to recommend them to the keeper of herptiles. They will nearly always feed readily under captive conditions and do not require the high temperatures so necessary for the well-being of many reptiles. Nearly all do best in a moderately cool environment. Being less highly evolved than reptiles, they show little of the individual variation in temperament of the latter. For instance, one can say with some assurance that spotted salamanders will adapt well to captivity if their basic needs are provided. This could hardly be predicted with equal assurance of many kinds of lizards and snakes. Most amphibians show a degree of responsiveness to kind treatment. They learn quickly to associate the presence of their owner with a supply of food and will focus their attention upon him in alert expectancy. They do not like to be handled, however, and even very tame ones will try to escape when picked up. Salamanders and frogs have moist, slippery skin, and this makes them quite difficult to hold. Toads and newts usually have a drier skin and are less likely to be harmed by handling. The slimy skin secretion of amphibians is a protective covering that is similar to that of fishes. Aquarists and anglers know that dry hands will cause this skin covering to rub off and allow the entrance of infection. It is best not to handle frogs and salamanders frequently; if they must be picked up it should be done with wet hands. This, incidentally, adds to the difficulty of maintaining a firm yet gentle grasp. Also, it is well to remember that the skin secretions of some amphibians are poisonous and the hands should be washed thoroughly after being used to hold a frog, toad, salamander, or newt.

The salamanders present quite a variety in forms, sizes, and colors, as well as habits. Some are thoroughly aquatic, rarely, if ever, voluntarily leaving the water. At the other extreme are a number of species which spend their lives on land and become aquatic during a brief period only, when courtship and the depositing of eggs takes place. Yet others live entirely on land and do not go to the water even to deposit their eggs. A few ascend trees; others seem to spend most of their lives in burrows underground.

Salamanders are sometimes confused with lizards but can at once be distinguished from these reptiles by their smooth, scaleless skin. Like the other classes of animals, salamanders show enough diversity to be split up into several families. Some salamanders make excellent terrarium or aquarium animals, thriving and even breeding in captivity. Among the larger species one, at least, has lived fifty years in captivity; even more surprising is the great age attained by some of the smaller types. Several have approached or exceeded the twenty-five-year mark under very ordinary cage conditions.

Dryness and excessive heat are the great enemies of newts and salamanders. The importance of the heat factor has been stressed many times in the chapters on reptiles; in the present chapter and the one on frogs and toads, the stress must be placed on coolness, rather than heat. Because of this fundamental difference in their requirements, it is not a really easy thing to combine successfully a collection of amphibians and reptiles, unless the more tolerant of each class are selected. If individual cage controls are available, it is another matter, but the average private collector will not have an elaborate system of this kind. City apartment dwellers will often find it easier to care for amphibians than reptiles. The former are able to withstand cool nightly temperatures while the latter fare poorly if there is a drop to below 65 degrees. In my own home I solve the problem by keeping all reptiles in a constantly heated room and scattering the amphibians throughout other rooms, where the temperature can be kept relatively cool and allowed to drop even further at night.

Aquariums make the best homes for newts and salamanders. By means of a glass cover, a good humidity control can be maintained. They do not require a lot of light; most species prefer subdued lighting, and no salamander regularly suns itself. Thus, in the keeping of newts and salamanders, the reptile keeper's problem of providing sunlight is absent. Food requirements for salamanders and newts are not complex; they will be discussed under the headings of the various species.

MUDPUPPY

The most commonly kept of the larger, thoroughly aquatic salamanders are those of the family Proteidae, of which the mudpuppy, *Necturus maculosus*, is a familiar form and one that is used extensively in biological study. A large example may measure nearly eighteen inches and will require an aquarium of between twenty and thirty gallons capacity, with a water depth of eight to ten or more inches. Mudpuppies breathe by means of the bushy gills situated on both sides of the head; their oxygen requirements seem quite high, and for this reason it is well to provide the aquarium with an aerating unit of the type used by fish enthusiasts. When a mudpuppy is not receiving sufficient oxygen, the gills expand into plumes; while this may present an interesting and attractive picture in an aquarium, it is not a desirable one. Normally, the gill structures will be folded back and inconspicuous. Plain brown, sometimes with a dark mottling, the mudpuppy is not a beautiful animal, but it is interesting and will live over a long period if properly cared for. Earthworms, pieces of raw beef, and small fishes will be taken by captives. Breeding takes place in the fall; the eggs are deposited under, or attached to the undersurface of, a submerged log or flat rock. The female guards the eggs until they hatch some two months later. Young, when hatched, measure about an inch in length. These salamanders can withstand a great drop in temperature and remain active and healthy. In the wild state, they are frequently to be seen crawling under the ice of frozen lakes. In an aquarium they should never be over-crowded—I would consider two foot-long specimens ideal for a

Olm, *Proteus anguinus*. Photo courtesy American Museum of Natural History.

twenty-gallon container. Babies, or individuals of small size, can be kept in a smaller container. The water surface should not be closer than six inches to the top frame of the aquarium, which is best covered with a slightly raised sheet of glass, for the animals are able to escape from an uncovered tank that is filled close to the top. The water should be changed after the salamanders have been fed, to minimize fouling, a condition which the aquatic salamanders particularly dislike. No aquarium plants should be used in the tank housing mudpuppies; a few rocks firmly set in place to form a natural cave in the background may be used if one wishes to add a decorative touch. Nor should sand or gravel be used as a floor covering, for these add nothing to the comfort of the animals and make cleaning the aquarium more difficult. Aquatic salamanders are able to withstand the amount of chlorine present in freshly-drawn tap water and except, perhaps, in a few areas of the country, this should not present a problem. I would regard a temperature range of 50 to 60 degrees as ideal.

OLM

Closely related to the mudpuppy is the ghostly-white olm, *Proteus anguinus*, an interesting foot-long salamander found in the caves of southern Europe. Like the mudpuppy, the olm has red gill structures, and these gills present a beautiful contrast to the pink-white of the creature's body. The eyes are hidden beneath the skin—a condition often noted among animals which dwell in total darkness—but the creature seems nonetheless aware of what is going on about it and will readily find and devour the small worms and crustaceans which make up its diet. Eggs are deposited on the underside of stones and take about three months to hatch. In rare instances the female retains the eggs within her body until hatching and produces babies alive! The babies are miniatures of their parents, but possess rudimentary eyes. They require cool water, preferably not higher than 50 degrees, and should be kept in a darkened place. This may be accomplished to a degree by painting three or even four sides of the aquarium on the outside, leaving a small area of the front pane of glass unpainted so the occupants may be seen. An aquarium reflector equipped with a red bulb will afford fair visibility and discomfort the olms less than ordinary white light. Olms once were fairly common on the animal market, but today they are seldom listed by dealers.

In general, their care does not differ greatly from that of the mud-puppy, but smaller foods, in smaller amounts, should be given to them. Tubifex worms are a favorite item in the diet of captive specimens. It is a curious fact that if olms are kept constantly exposed to strong light they eventually turn black. With this species, it is said to be the male, rather than the female, which guards the eggs.

AMPHIUMA

The southeastern United States is the home of a huge elongated salamander called the Amphiuma, *Amphiuma means*, a species that lacks a good common name. "Congo eel" is the appellation applied in some areas of the South. The Amphiuma has a brownish-black dorsal surface and a lighter belly; its eyes are rudimentary, as are its legs, which are reduced to useless appendages less than an inch long in the case of an adult measuring three feet. Lakes, ditches, bayous, and streams are frequented by these salamanders. They are quite adapted to life in the water and seldom leave it except during the breeding season. Captives do well in a shoreless aquarium and will

Amphiuma, *Amphiuma means*. Photo by F. J. Dodd, Jr.

live for many years on a diet of raw beef pieces placed in front of them. Their aquarium, depending on the size of the inmates, should have water of several inches to a foot or more in depth. They should be able to reach the surface without swimming. Eggs are deposited in fairly dry situations under logs and stones near water. They may number only 150 and are guarded by the female, who remains coiled about them. Aquarium specimens are uncomfortable in bright light and will bite viciously if handled. Few salamanders make any attempt to bite, and those which do can usually produce nothing more than a series of superficial scratches. My first experience with an Amphiuma, some years ago when there was little information about them available in print, was something less than an agreeable one. I carefully lifted a fifteen-inch specimen from its aquarium to place it in an adjoining container while its permanent home was being cleaned. During the process, it swung its head about and fastened its jaws on the ring finger of my left hand. The bite seemed no more painful than that which could be produced by a small harmless snake and I did not become aware of its severity until I closely examined the wound. The flesh had been incised as though by a razor and only a tight compress would stop the flow of blood. Eventually it healed but the scar remains to remind me of the incident. Amphiumas are best moved about with a deep net. The family Amphiumidae has only one genus.

SIRENS

The siren, *Siren lacertina*, of the family Sirenidae, is another large aquatic salamander of the quiet waters of the southeastern United States. In body form it is somewhat similar to the eel-like Amphiuma, but it has weakly developed forelimbs, while rear legs are lacking entirely. Gill tufts adorn each side of the siren's rather angular head, and the over-all color of the amphibian is gray or dark greenish. Three feet may be reached by a large adult but the average length is about a foot shorter. Crayfish and worms may be the principal foods in the natural state, but in captivity a diet of lean raw beef, cut into slender strips, will maintain specimens in health over long periods. A shoreless aquarium is recommended, and this should be perfectly plain—devoid of foliage or sand, to make easier the frequent cleaning that is necessary. Almost nothing is known of the breeding habits, except that the species deposits eggs. I have always preferred to keep the larger aquatic gilled salamanders in a tank of their own, without mixing species. Even among individuals of the same species there is some biting, which often results in the destruction of the plumelike gills which are the principal adornment of these rather drab animals.

A smaller relative of the siren is the species known as *Siren intermedia*. A really tiny member of the family is the dwarf siren, *Pseudobranchus striatus*, with an average length of only five or six inches. The dwarf siren's habits are similar to those of its large relative, but dwarfs may be kept in small aquariums and fed on tubifex and white worms, as well as tiny bits of meat. Members of both *Amphiuma* and *Siren* genera can tolerate a degree of heat which would distress many other salamanders, but I would recommend a temperature not higher than 70 degrees.

GIANT SALAMANDERS

The giant salamanders belong to the family Cryptobranchidae, which has as its North American representative the hellbender, *Cryptobranchus alleganiensis*, a thoroughly aquatic river and stream type which exceptionally may reach thirty inches in length. Grotesque in the extreme, the hellbender is a broadly-flattened, wide-headed salamander with loosely-hanging folds of skin along its side. Its limbs are short and chunky and its tail is much compressed. In every way, this salamander appeals to the imagination as a primitive one—and such it actually is. Its close relative of the Orient, the giant salamander of Japan, *Megalobatrachus japonicus*, may reach a length of five feet and a weight of close to a hundred pounds. Giant salamanders are long-lived amphibians, possibly exceeding in this respect any other amphibian species. They live well even in deep aquariums where they must swim periodically to the surface for air. They are awkward in swimming, however, and in a private aquarium should have water of about twelve to eighteen inches in depth. The water must be changed frequently, especially if the aquarium is not large. In spite of their large size and slippery skin, hellbenders and giant salamanders can be easily handled if grasped behind the head with the rest of the body supported by the other hand. Eggs of the hellbender are deposited in running water in late summer and are guarded by the male. Upon hatching two to three months later, the gilled larvae are a little over an inch in length. At six inches, a

Japanese giant salamander, *Megalobatrachus japonicus*. Photo above courtesy American Museum of Natural History; that below by G. Marcuse.

Hellbender, *Cryptobranchus alleganiensis*. Photo courtesy American Museum of Natural History.

length which may be attained in less than two years, they have lost their gills and are replicas of the adults. The American and Oriental giant salamanders are frequently taken on hook and line. Their food consists of aquatic animals of a multitude of forms; captives are easily kept on a meat and fish diet. A filtering system in an aquarium of twenty to thirty gallons is of little value because of the grossness of the feeding habits of these amphibians and the large amounts of food they require. A running water system is much better. Single specimens of small size can be kept in a relatively small aquarium if the water is changed frequently.

The kinds of salamanders so far discussed can be kept in an aquarium which provides no means of leaving the water.

SALAMANDRIDS

The family Salamandridae provides the herptile keeper with some of the most attractive and interesting of the smaller vivarium animals. The Old and New World newts are members of this family and so, too, is the European fire salamander. North American newts start their lives as gilled larvae. Some kinds, when they have reached the age of three months, lose their gills, and come ashore for an interlude of land existence which may last three years or more, then return to the water for the balance of their lives. During the land stage they are reddish-orange in color and can frequently be found wandering in damp woods in broad daylight. Other kinds remain completely aquatic from the time they hatch, while still others are largely terrestrial and enter the water only to breed. Salamandrids, as the newts and salamanders of the present family are properly referred to, occur in Europe, Africa, and Asia, as well as North America.

The newts of Europe have for a very long time been studied in laboratories and private collections. Some of the species most frequently available are the smooth newt, *Triturus vulgaris*; the crested newt, *Triturus cristatus*; and the Alpine newt, *Triturus alpestris*. Mostly small amphibians, the largest kinds reach a length of only about seven inches. In the spring, when they go to the water to breed, the males take on beautiful colors that rival those displayed by the most beautiful fishes. They develop a crest along the back and tail; this is lost when the breeding season is over. Mating is preceded by an elaborate courtship, after which the male deposits a sperm mass which is taken up by the female in her cloaca, where fertilization

Palmated newt, *Triturus helveticus*, male, western Europe. Photo by
L. E. Perkins.

takes place. The eggs are then deposited on aquatic plant leaves and
abandoned. Recently hatched larvae are tiny creatures with bushy
growths of gills on both sides of the head. These shrink day by day;

Smooth newt, *Triturus vulgaris,* male above, female below. Photos by G. Marcuse.

Crested newt, *Triturus cristatus,* female above, male below. Photos by G. Marcuse.

Alpine newt, *Triturus alpestris,* male above, female below. Photos by
G. Marcuse.

finally the front legs make their appearance as stubs, followed by the growth of the rear limbs. At this stage the tiny newt dashes to the surface of their water to obtain air—it has already begun to devour tiny worms and crustaceans. Enchytrae and tubifex worms are good foods during this early period of growth. Parent newts should be removed from the aquarium when the egglaying has been completed. Otherwise, if the eggs are not devoured, the newly-hatched larvae certainly will be. Baby newts are reared without difficulty. Adults in the aquatic stage will eat almost any animal matter that is dangled in front of them with forceps. Chopped earthworms form a very satisfactory diet, but even pieces of finely-shredded lean raw beef will be eaten with relish.

The European newts do best in a vivarium which is approximately evenly divided between land and water areas. Water should be of six to ten inches depth and the land portion of the container should have flat stones or pieces of bark under which the adults can hide when they decide to leave the water. All aquariums or other containers housing newts should be kept securely covered. This can be accomplished with a framework of screening or a sheet of glass. If glass is used, it should be in two sections, with an opening between the halves to admit air.

Adult newts are comparatively easy to maintain because of the wide range of foods which they'll accept; here an adult newt is swallowing a tadpole. Photo by H. Pfletschinger.

Like other herptiles, newts should never be crowded. It is often possible to obtain very large catches in the field, but only a selected few should be brought home. A five-gallon aquarium will comfortably house a pair of newts. If breeding is to be attempted, a larger size is preferable. Newts are perhaps the easiest of all herptiles to successfully breed and rear in captivity. An ideal water temperature for the European newts is one which does not go over 60 degrees. Temperatures much lower than this are tolerated without adverse results.

Notophthalmus viridescens, the common newt of the eastern half of the United States, has an adult length of about four inches. Greenish-brown in color, it is not as attractive as some of the exotic kinds, but is readily available and lives well in an aquarium under the conditions described for the European species. Like them, it will breed in an aquarium, which activity can take place during the fall, winter, or spring. Along the western coast of the United States are two large species known variously as rough-skinned newts, *Taricha granulosa,* and California newts, *Taricha torosa.* The various species and varieties have a dorsal surface that runs from reddish-brown to black, while the belly may be orange or yellow or, in one very attractive form, scarlet red. They are hardy amphibians which, in the natural state, spend much of their time on land in damp places under stones and logs. They can be caused to adopt a completely aquatic existence if deprived of a landing place in their aquarium; they are perhaps most interesting when maintained in this manner. Most learn to recognize their keeper and can be hand-fed on small pieces of meat and worms.

Though a member of the same family and closely related to the newts we have discussed, the fire salamander, *Salamandra salamandra,* is quite different in appearance, being robustly built and positively striking in its gorgeous livery of black and yellow. Most persons who keep herptiles have their favorites; among the tailed amphibians, this species is my favorite. A large fire salamander may be over six inches long, but it normally is not an active animal and will do well in a small terrarium which is kept moderately damp and provided with stones and pieces of bark. Not more than a pair should be kept together, for fire salamanders tend to congregate if kept in numbers, and this habit is believed to give rise to fungoid conditions of the skin. Kept alone, or with a single companion, a fire salamander will live for many years under the most simple of terrarium conditions. I once kept a specimen for five years in a two-

Fire salamander, *Salamandra salamandra*. Photo by G. Marcuse.

gallon aquarium which was provided with a base of damp sand. The only other furnishings were a flat-topped rock over which was arranged a piece of bark, forming a hollow between it and the rock. The cage was kept in the coolest part of the house and the salamander was hand-tendered a strip of lean raw beef once each week. This was followed by a rinsing of the cage and gravel under cold tap water. Covering the cage were two pieces of glass, separated in the middle to form a quarter-inch opening to allow a circulation of air. The handsome creature was discomforted by heat in excess of 65 degrees and at such times would prowl about. At other times it would invariably be found in its resting place beneath the portion of tree-bark. It became sort of a conversation piece; European visitors would recognize the animal at once.

The breeding habits of the fire salamander are interesting. The species normally gives birth to living young in shallow water some ten months after the adults have mated on land in June or July. The babies, numbering anywhere from a few to several dozens, have gill structures and remain in the water until the gills are absorbed, when they come ashore to assume a terrestrial life.

Other exotic salamandrids which are imported with some frequency are the colorful and voracious red-bellied newt, *Cynops pyrrhogaster*, of Japan, and the ribbed newt, *Pleurodeles waltl*, of Spain and North Africa. Red-bellied newts have a great tolerance of temperature changes and are among the easiest of the salamanders to keep. They are rather stout and chunky little creatures, when in good health, and squabble much among themselves over pieces of meat that are put into their aquarium. Their backs are very dark brown or black, while their stomachs are a bright red, in striking contrast. The ribbed newts live well also, with a minimum of care. One of their peculiarities is the tendency of the ribs to pierce their skin and protrude as tiny knobs along the sides of the adult specimens.

Ribbed newt, *Pleurodeles waltl*. Photo by G. Marcuse.

MOLE SALAMANDERS

North America has the distinction of being the home of more kinds of salamanders than any other continent. The family Amby-stomidae, composed of the so-called mole salamanders, creatures resembling the fire salamander in the stoutness of their configuration and often of pretty coloration, is one of the largest. Mole sala-manders are, for the most part, secretive amphibians which spend much of their lives underground. If they are seen at all it is likely to be at breeding time, when enormous numbers congregate in suitable ponds and other still waters for a brief period of courtship and the depositing of eggs. Unlike most burrowing animals, which only too often will sicken and die if not allowed to follow their natural habits, the mole salamanders will adapt to terrarium conditions which cater only in part to their tendencies to hide. This can be accomplished with a thin layer of aquarium gravel, rather than soil, for a floor covering, and the provision of hiding places in the form of propped-up flat stones and large segments of rotten tree bark. Of course, a more conventional terrarium set-up, with plants and soil, is suitable also, but it will be impossible at most times to observe the sala-mander inhabitants of such an arrangement. There seems little to be gained in the keeping of any animal which can never be seen.

Over the eastern half of the United States, the spotted salamander, *Ambystoma maculatum*, is a common amphibian. With its speckling of yellow on a blue-black ground color, it is a pretty denizen of the woods. Eight to nine inches is the size range of the largest adults. Spotted salamanders would be very conspicuous herptiles if it were not for their secretive habits. During warm, rainy nights in early spring they migrate to ponds in large numbers and may even cross highways in their march to a favored breeding pool. Eggs are de-posited in large masses which measure about three inches in dia-meter and are attached to submerged twigs or plants. They hatch in three to six weeks, depending on the prevailing temperatures of the water. When the larvae hatch they are tiny gilled creatures, but growth is rapid and by fall their legs have developed and the gills have been lost. By this time the little salamanders will be over two inches in length and ready to take up a land existence, returning to the water in the second spring after their birth, when they will be young adults and ready themselves to carry on the reproductive process. During their larval stage the babies, like those of many

Spotted salamander, *Ambystoma maculatum.*

herptiles, seem to differ much in natural vitality; some grow quickly and prey upon their weaker members. This is a natural thing and little can be done to prevent it in an aquarium, though it can be minimized by the sorting of specimens by size. From a single egg mass which may contain a hundred or more eggs, normally only a small percentage of the salamanders will ever reach adulthood. Tubifex and white worms, as well as daphnia and other tiny crustaceans, form a convenient food upon which to raise the larvae. Transformed individuals feed readily upon earthworms and soft-bodied insects; those which I have kept would readily take meat from forceps or the tip of a straw when it was moved about directly in front of them. Like most other herptiles, these salamanders are able to go without food for long periods, but they become terribly emaciated during such prolonged fasts. Inadvertently, a small specimen was once left in a plastic collecting bag with moss and wood pulp for a period of several months. When discovered it was very thin, but active and in apparently fair health. It was carefully nursed along with tiny bits of raw beef and in the ensuing weeks regained the normally rotund appearance of the species.

Some of the other mole salamanders are very attractive herptiles. The marbled salamander, *Ambystoma opacum*, is a beautiful animal, black with white or silvery crossbands. It is fully grown when four to five inches long and differs from the spotted salamander in laying its eggs on land in the fall of the year. These are deposited singly, in a depression under a rock or fallen log, and the female stays with them during the period of incubation. In some cases, hatching may not occur until spring. The marbled salamander has much the same range as its spotted relative, but in contrast to the latter may often be found in fairly dry situations. It lives well in captivity, making a very decorative inmate of the terrarium.

Axolotls, *Ambystoma* sp. Photo by L. E. Perkins.

Crested newt, *Triturus cristatus.*

Alpine newt, *Triturus alpestris.* Photo by S. Frank.

Axolotl, *Ambystoma* sp., leucistic strain. Photo by L. E. Perkins.

Another familiar ambystomid is the tiger salamander, *Ambystoma tigrinum,* a large species that is widely distributed in North America and shows great variation of color and markings over its broad range. Under certain circumstances, the larvae of the tiger salamander, and other species as well, fail to lose the gills and remain permanently aquatic animals. In Mexico they are called axolotls, and this name has carried over into English usage. Axolotls may reach a very large size, corresponding with transformed individuals of the same age. A white or leucistic strain is frequently kept in aquariums and makes a quite handsome display animal.

There are many other kinds of mole salamanders, all of them interesting and attractive. The species I have kept have been uniformly hardy under terrarium conditions, and I would say that the mole salamanders are the most responsive and easily kept of the New World salamanders. Observation of captive individuals has extended over long periods, and the life span of mole salamanders may be in excess of twenty-five years. Included in the family group is the largest known land salamander in the world—the western giant salamander, *Dicamptodon ensatus,* a creature which reaches a length of at least twelve inches and is able to devour fair-sized vertebrate animals as well as insects and earthworms.

PLETHODONTIDS

The largest family of salamanders in the world is the Plethodontidae, a group of aquatic and terrestrial species which has its headquarters in the Appalachian Mountains of the eastern United States but has forms which extend the range to the western part of the country and tropical America. These salamanders have no lungs, respiration taking place through the delicate skin. Size range among the varied types runs from an inch to eight inches or slightly more. Most are very secretive and hide during the day, coming out at night to hunt for food. Like many of the lizards, the plethodontids have fragile tails, and this should be borne in mind when it is necessary to handle them. They do best if handled very little and kept in a cool environment. They are extremely dependent upon moisture, quickly dying from dessication in its absence. For this reason, specimens which escape from their cage seldom survive. Among such a large group there is, naturally, some diversification of habitat preference among the terrestrial kinds. But most will do well in a damp terrarium with an abundance of hiding places. Earthworms and insects constitute an adequate diet; in the case of very small salamanders, tubifex and white worms form an acceptable diet. A few climb to some extent while others spend their entire lives in underground streams. The majority make their homes close to brooks and ponds, or in swamps. In the eastern United States, an ideal place to look for these salamanders is under stones near swiftly-flowing mountain streams where there is a heavy overhang of tree cover. Such places are often cool on even the hottest days, and coolness is one of the determining factors in the abundance of these small animals in such areas.

The commonest herptile in many places is the red-backed salamander, *Plethodon cinereus*, a species which occurs in two color phases. One is plain black or gray, flecked with lighter markings, while the other has a broad red band the length of its back. Like most others of its family, this salamander is never found wandering about in the daytime. Sometimes six or more individuals will be uncovered when a log is overturned. In regard to its moisture requirements, the red-back is less fussy than most plethodontids and is sometimes found far from any permanent body of water, though never in any place which completely lacks moisture. Four to five inches is the average size of adults; the babies, which do not go

Marbled newt, *Triturus marmoratus,* southwestern Europe. Photo by
J. K. Langhammer.

Common newt, *Notophthalmus viridescens,* eft. Photo by F. J. Dodd,
Jr.

Broken striped newt, *Notophthalmus viridescens dorsalis,* Georgia and Florida. Photo by M. F. Roberts.

Rough-skinned newt, *Taricha granulosa.* Photo by H. Hansen, Aquarium Berlin.

Red-backed salamander, *Plethodon cinereus*. Photo by F. J. Dodd, Jr.

through a larval stage, hatch from eggs which are deposited in damp terrestrial situations. Captives live quite well in a terrarium and are able to tolerate more warmth than their relatives of mountain-brook habitats.

The prettily speckled slimy salamander, *Plethodon glutinosus*, grows to nearly eight inches and has acquired its common name from the skin secretion which rubs off when the animal is handled. Its habits are similar to those of its smaller cousin, the red-back, but because of its larger size the slimy salamander is not so likely to get lost in a large terrarium. Also, it is able to devour earthworms of fair size, which may simplify the feeding problem. In general, the salamanders of the genus *Plethodon* are less frightened by humans than the species which live in or near streams. Often they can be tempted to accept pieces of raw beef from the end of a straw. In the hand-feeding of salamanders and frogs a straw is to be preferred over forceps. There is a natural quivering at the tip which simulates the movement of an insect, and this quivering may prompt the appetite of an amphibian which would refuse a morsel offered with forceps. Another advantage to the use of a straw is the ease with which a bit of meat may be snapped up by a shy animal. If a piece of meat is offered with forceps and the animal is unable immediately to free it from the grip of the instrument, further interest may not be shown.

The lungless salamanders are mostly sleek and graceful amphibians, but rather plainly colored or obscurely striped. A few species, however, are strikingly beautiful. One of these is the red salamander, *Pseudotriton ruber*, of the eastern states, chiefly in mountainous areas. The species reaches a fair size, seven inches or slightly more, and is an over-all brilliant red with jet black spots profusely scattered over the back in vivid contrast. In my early collecting days one of my first big field discoveries was a colony of these handsome salamanders in a spring-fed swamp in New York. The owner of the land kindly lent me some hip-boots, and with these I was able to explore likely hiding places in the knee-deep moss and mud. A breeding congress

Red salamander, *Pseudotriton ruber.* Photo courtesy American Museum of Natural History.

Fire salamander, *Salamandra salamandra*. Photo by G. Marcuse.

Tiger salamander, *Ambystoma tigrinum*. Photo by H. Hansen, Aquarium Berlin.

Slimy salamander, *Plethodon glutinosus*. Photo by F. J. Dodd, Jr.

of garter snakes inhabited the area—this was exciting enough to a youthful herpetologist, but far more important was the discovery of several of these really gorgeous salamanders. Two were brought home and lived for some time. They would have survived longer, I realize now, if they had been kept cold and provided with moss and pieces of bark under which to hide.

Some salamanders move quickly when uncovered and are exceedingly difficult to catch and hold. The dusky salamander, *Desmognathus fuscus*, is one of these. A collector may work his way along a shaded mountain brook, turning over rocks and logs, and find perhaps fifty of the agile amphibians in a few hours. Generally, though, only a small percentage will find their way into the collecting bag. Dusky salamanders are mostly plain brown creatures with darker stripes and spots; there are many species and varieties in the genus and one kind, the black-bellied salamander of Georgia and the Carolinas, grows to the impressive length of eight inches. Known scientifically as *Desmognathus quadramaculatus*, the black-belly occasionally ventures into the open during daylight hours.

Mountain salamander, *Desmognathus ochrophaeus*, Allegheny Mountains. Photo courtesy American Museum of Natural History.

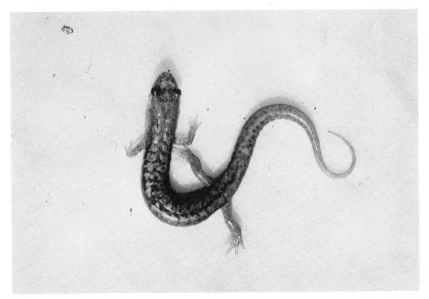

Spotted salamander, *Ambystoma maculatum.* Photo by J. K. Langhammer.

Dusky salamander, *Desmognathus fuscus.* Photo by F. J. Dodd, Jr.

Longtailed salamander, *Eurycea longicauda*, eastern United States. Photo by J. K. Langhammer.

Cave salamander, *Eurycea lucifuga*, central United States. Photo by J. K. Langhammer.

Western North America, particularly the coastal areas of Washington, Oregon, and California, has an interesting salamander fauna. The ensatina, *Ensatina eschscholtzi*, with its vividly blotched varieties, is a very handsome salamander, dark brown or black with stipplings of bright orange or yellow. Large specimens may run to six inches in length; they live well in a damp woodland terrarium but are not often available commercially because it is only rarely that they are found in any numbers.

The slender salamander, *Batrachoseps attenuatus*, and its relatives are diminutive kinds with elongated bodies and tiny legs. They rarely grow larger than four inches and are blackish, often with a lighter dorsal stripe. Eggs are deposited on land and the babies do not go through a larval stage.

Climbing salamanders (genus *Aneides*) are a small group of plethodontids, some species of which are noted for their inclination to climb trees. The arboreal salamander, *Aneides lugubris*, is often encountered in live oak trees at a great height. Most salamanders are voiceless, but members of the present group often emit a squeal when picked up. They have strong jaws and sharp teeth and do not hesitate to defend themselves by biting. Needless to say, with such a small creature—adults average only about four to five inches—only super-

Two-lined salamander, *Eurycea bislineata,* eastern United States. Photo courtesy American Museum of Natural History.

ficial scratches can be inflicted. Climbing salamanders are usually some shade of tan or dark brown. They have tails which are prehensile to a degree and, as might be imagined from their arboreal habits, require somewhat less moisture than the earth-bound plethodontids. A single species of the genus lives in the eastern part of the United States. This is the green salamander, *Aneides aeneus*, whose coloring is quite unique among the members of its family. It frequents the narrow crevices of cliff faces and a piece of wire or some other tool is often a necessary adjunct to the collecting of specimens.

The web-toed salamanders (genus *Hydromantes*) have a curious distribution, the several California forms having their nearest relatives in southern Europe. These salamanders have very long tongues which can be shot out to pick up the insects which come within range. Their webbed feet enable *Hydromantes* species to ascend steep rock surfaces of their mountain and cave homes. The Mount Lyell salamander, *Hydromantes platycephalus*, and its related species have very restricted ranges and habitat preferences. They are not likely to be encountered on any ordinary field trip, but if the prospective collector will learn all he can of their habits and locality records, and picks the right time of year for his search, he is more than likely to return with some specimens.

Italian cave salamander, *Hydromantes italicus,* Italy. Photo courtesy American Museum of Natural History.

Clawed frog, *Xenopus laevis*. Photo by Dr. Herbert R. Axelrod.

Fire-bellied toad, *Bombina orientalis*. Photo by W. Mudrack.

Surinam toad, *Pipa pipa.* Photo by H. Schultz.

Fire-bellied toad, *Bombina orientalis.* Photo by W. Mudrack.

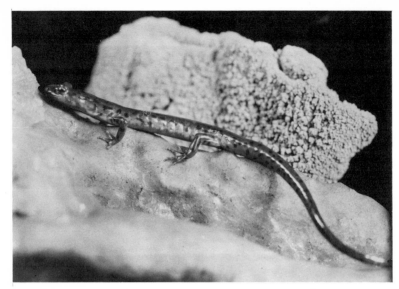

Cave salamander, *Eurycea lucifuga,* central United States. Photo courtesy American Museum of Natural History.

Georgia blind salamander, *Haideotriton wallacei,* Georgia and Florida. Photo by F. J. Dodd, Jr.

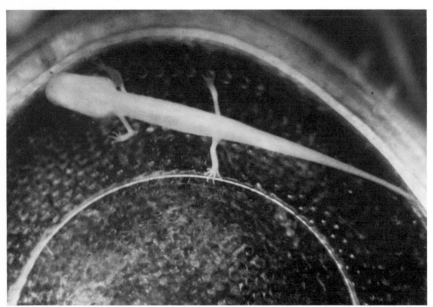

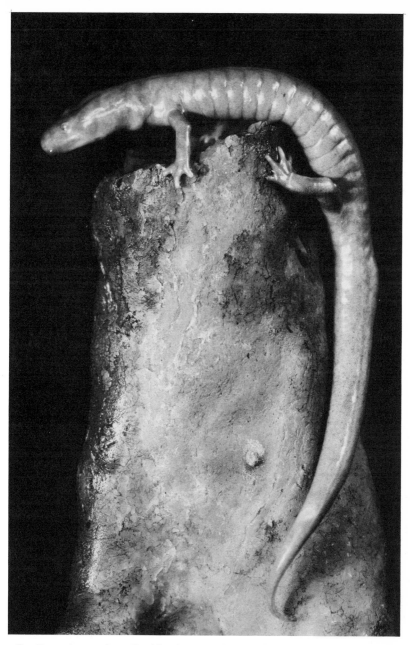

Grotto salamander, *Typhlotriton spelaeus,* Ozark Mountains. Photo courtesy American Museum of Natural History.

Couch's spadefoot, *Scaphiopus couchi,* southwestern U.S. and Mexico. Photo by F. J. Dodd, Jr.

Megophrys nasuta, southern Asia. Photo by J. K. Langhammer.

Western spadefoot, *Scaphiopus hammondi,* western United States.
Photo by J. K. Langhammer.

There are many other salamanders which make excellent cage animals, but the habits of some are all but unknown. Careful observations of even the common species may enhance our knowledge. In general, it may be said that the smaller and more secretive the animal, the less we know of its life history. Since most salamanders fit very well the description of being both small and secretive, it is not surprising that there is much to be learned about them.

CAECILIANS

The caecilians of the order Gymnophiona, family Caeciliidae, form one of the strangest groups of amphibians. They are highly specialized, wormlike burrowers or aquatic creatures with no trace of limbs. As a group they are the least known of the amphibians. Some are known to be egg-layers while at least one form produces its young alive. The few caecilians which have been kept in captivity have done indifferently well in a burrowing medium of moss or soft soil. One genus, *Typhlonectes*, is believed to be thoroughly aquatic. Many of the terrestrial forms coil about their eggs during the period of incubation. Some species have fed well under captive conditions upon earthworms. The group is one which is worthy of much study.

X

Frogs and Toads

ANURANS IN GENERAL

The frogs and toads of the world easily outnumber the salamanders and newts by more than ten to one. Each year some previously undescribed kinds are given technical names and placed in our checklists. Many species are known to us only from preserved specimens in museums. There are gaps in our knowledge of even the commoner species, and many of these gaps can be filled by the observations of keen herptile enthusiasts. None of the frogs and toads grows to really large size; even the giants of the group have a body length of less than a foot. Therefore, they do not present the housing difficulties which may be encountered in the keeping of the larger members of other groups of herptiles. When collecting in the field, one will often come across a frog or toad in a place that seems to support no other herptile life. As a group they have invaded even the Arctic Circle.

Collectively, the frogs and toads are often referred to as anurans. From the standpoint of the vivarium-keeper the various anurans can be conveniently grouped according to their habitat preferences. Such a way of splitting them up corresponds roughly with their technical family classifications, for the latter are based on structural details and these, in turn, are linked with modes of life. There are burrowing types which spend most of their lives underground, completely aquatic species which never leave the water, surface-dwelling forms which spend much of their time in or near water, terrestrial types which require some moisture but enter the water only to breed, and

South American bullfrog, *Leptodactylus pentadactylus*. Photo by van den Nieuwenhuizen.

Barking frog, *Eleutherodactylus sp.* Photo by F. J. Dodd, Jr.

Horned frog, *Ceratophrys cornuta.* Photo by Dr. Herbert R. Axelrod.

Horned frog, *Ceratophrys calacarata.* Photo by F. J. Dodd, Jr.

finally arboreal types which have varying degrees of specialization for life in trees and bushes. Few amphibians have successfully invaded the desert, and none lives in the sea. No frog or toad is known to have a poisonous bite, but the skin glands of many kinds produce exceedingly poisonous secretions. Examples are the poison arrow frogs and the giant toad. More than one dog has died from the effects of foolishly mouthing a giant toad. Certain South American frogs can bite painfully with large, tooth-studded jaws, but the vast majority of the tailless amphibians are harmless and beneficial animals, benevolent of mien and with dispositions matching their looks. Some of the tropical frogs have a beauty of coloring which rivals that of the butterflies and moths which flutter about them in their jungle homes.

AFRICAN CLAWED FROG

The very aquatic tongueless frogs of the family Pipidae are among the most familiar of the exotic amphibians which are offered for sale in pet stores and aquariums. A species often imported is the

Pair of dwarf water frogs, *Hymenochirus curtipes*, male at left. Photo by B. Haas.

Amplexus in *H. curtipes*. Photo by B. Haas.

Young larvae of *H. curtipes*. Photo by B. Haas.

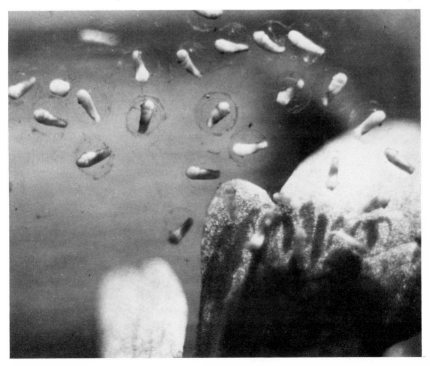

443

American toad, *Bufo terrestris americanus;* mating (above), albino (below). Photos by J. K. Langhammer.

Colorado River toad, *Bufo alvarius*. Photo by J. K. Langhammer.

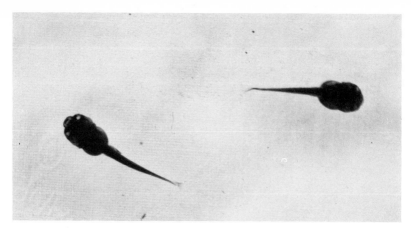

Tadpoles of *H. curtipes.* Photo by B. Haas.

Mother and young *H. curtipes.* Photo by B. Haas.

very small *Hymenochirus curtipes*. Several other very similar species are also often imported. They are gracefully-swimming little animals that can be kept in good health for years and even bred in a fairly large aquarium. The much larger *Xenopus*, often used medically for pregnancy tests, is also commonly available. Of the several species, *Xenopus laevis* is probably the most commonly imported. While specimens of *Hymenochirus* seldom greatly exceed one inch in length, adult *Xenopus* are commonly five or six inches long.

Clawed frogs are not colorful, but their interesting habits make them worthwhile additions to any herptile collection. Often these aquatic frogs are kept in rather deep aquariums, but a better arrangement is one where the depth of the water does not exceed four or five inches. A water temperature of 70 to 75 degrees is suitable, and food should consist of small animal matter such as white and tubifex worms, chopped earthworms, and even scraped lean beef. A layer of ordinary aquarium gravel makes a good floor covering for the tank housing clawed frogs—perhaps mud would be better, but it certainly would do little to enhance the appearance of the aquarium. The frogs spend much of their time swimming over the bottom, using their front feet to scoop into their mouths such edibles as may be found. Captives become quite tame and will swim to the surface of their tank and take food from one's fingers. Frequently, contented

Large clawed frog, *Xenopus laevis*. Photo by G. J. M. Timmerman.

Spiny toad, *Bufo spinulosus,* South America. Photo by H. Hansen, Aquarium Berlin.

Giant toad, *Bufo marinus.* Photo by Dr. Herbert R. Axelrod.

Common toad, *Bufo bufo*. Photo by H. Hansen, Aquarium Berlin.

Tadpole of *Xenopus laevis.* Photo by G. J. M. Timmerman.

specimens will protrude their heads from the water and chirp, especially in the evening. They never leave the water voluntarily and on land are all but helpless.

Clawed frogs often breed in aquariums, attaching their several hundred eggs to aquatic vegetation. If this happens, the adults should be removed at once to prevent them from devouring their eggs or offspring. The eggs normally hatch in less than a week; the tiny tadpoles will remain clinging to aquatic plants for a few days, absorbing the egg yolk. Shortly they become free-swimming and

Detail of foot of *Xenopus laevis.* Photo by G. J. M. Timmerman.

start feeding on protozoans. The large green algae masses found in stagnant waters will provide the growing creatures with a proper diet, but care must be taken not to introduce any predaceous insects. Perhaps a better aquarium diet is dried and powdered egg. Tadpoles normally swim in a head-downward position. From the time of hatching until metamorphosis into tiny froglets will take about two months. The tadpoles of *Xenopus* differ from those of *Hymenochirus* by having two long tentacles or antennae growing from the head.

SURINAM TOAD

A weird-looking member of the family to which the clawed frog belongs is the Surinam toad, *Pipa pipa*. The interchangeability of the terms "frog" and "toad" as parts of popular names should be noted here. Though they belong to the same family and are very closely related, *Xenopus* is commonly referred to as a frog, while *Pipa* is called a toad. Surinam toads grow to a larger size than clawed frogs and live equally well in aquariums, but do not often breed. Their appearance is bizarre in the extreme. A much-flattened body appears rectangular in outline when viewed from above; the head is triangular, terminating in a pointed snout. The hind feet are broadly webbed, while toes of the forefeet end in starlike tips. The South American rivers inhabited by Surinam toads are very muddy and the toe tips, as well as fleshy appendages about the mouth, doubtless prove of assistance in locating food. There is little need for eyes in such an environment, and the Surinam toad's eyes have been reduced to tiny dots. The female toad carries her eggs on her back, where they are placed by the male after fertilization. The entire larval development takes place on the back of the mother; when the babies are fully developed they emerge from the skin recesses in the back of the female, where they have been for several months, and swim off to live their own lives. Babies and adults alike are carnivorous and should have a water temperature of about 75 degrees.

DISCOGLOSSIDS

The fire-bellied toad, *Bombina bombina*, belongs to the family Discoglossidae, a small group of aquatic forms native to Europe and Asia. Fire-bellied toads have rather plain grayish backs, but their underparts are beautifully colored in red or orange. Stagnant pond and ditch waters are their usual habitats, and in captivity an aquarium

Crested toad, *Bufo superciliaris,* Africa. Photo by H. Hansen, Aquarium Berlin.

Atelopid, *Atelopus cruciger*, South America. Photo by J. K. Lang-hammer.

with a few inches of water and a large, very rounded stone which protrudes above the water surface are their essential requirements. Floating plants and a layer of sand on the bottom may be used, if desired. As a substitute for this kind of an arrangement an aquarium which is divided between water and land areas may be used. Fire-bellies spend much of their time floating leisurely in the water, with just their heads protruding, but these anurans do occasionally like to crawl out on land. They will accept earthworms, insects, and even pieces of raw beef.

The related yellow-bellied toad, *Bombina variegata*, has similar habits and is found in southern Europe. *Bombina orientalis* is a particularly beautiful mountain stream dweller of Asia. All of the *Bombina* species have a poisonous skin secretion which makes them immune to depredation by most animals. The well-known European midwife toad, *Alytes obstetricans*, is a discoglossid, but except in the matter of its breeding habits is not as colorful or interesting as the *Bombina* species. After mating on land, the male carries the eggs about, attached to the rear of his body, until they are ready to hatch. He then goes to the water, and the larvae emerge and fend for themselves.

Painted frog, *Discoglossus pictus*, southern Europe and northern Africa. Photo by G. Marcuse.

Midwife toad, *Alytes obstetricans.* Photo by W. Lierath.

SPADEFOOT TOADS

Pelobatidae is the name of the family to which the spadefoot toads and their relatives belong. Representatives of the family are found in Europe, Asia, Africa, and North America. The spadefoot toad of Europe, *Pelobates fuscus,* is strikingly reminiscent of the North American spadefoots (*Scaphiopus* species). The skin of spadefoot toads is much smoother than that of the more familiar garden toads of the genus *Bufo.* Their eyes are curious in that the pupils are vertically elliptical when exposed to light, but become round in the dark. If nothing was known of their habits it would be easy to guess, from their appearance, that they were nightroving amphibians. Even in places where they are common, however, it is not usual to find many about except during the breeding period, which in the United States follows warm rains in the spring and summer.

I have found spadefoots rather difficult to maintain satisfactorily in a terrarium. They fare poorly if kept without hiding places or earth in which to burrow. Yet if provided with such a duplication of their natural environment they remain out of sight and seldom show much interest in food. Such habits in captivity probably correspond

Spring peeper, *Hyla crucifer*. Photo by W. Mudrack.

Bell frog, *Hyla gratiosa,* spotted phase, southeastern United States. Photo by F. J. Dodd, Jr.

Poison arrow frog, family Dendrobatidae. Photo by W. Mudrack.

Megophrys nasuta, an unusual member of the family Pelobatidae from southern Asia. Photo by Dr. Otto Klee.

with those of wild specimens which may remain in underground burrows for weeks or months. In contrast, however, to the specimens which are dug out of their burrows in the wild state, captives become emaciated in a relatively short time. An aquarium with several inches of soil, a sunken water container, and a covering of moss or dead leaves and pieces of bark seems to make the best home for spadefoots. One has to rate the spadefoots among those frogs and toads that do not adapt well to artificial conditions. In their many species they are inconspicuously-colored little creatures, usually a shade of brown or gray, sometimes with darker markings on the back.

BARKING FROG

The family Leptodactylidae embraces a tremendous array of frogs whose headquarters are the American tropics. Curiously, in the Old World they are confined to Australia. Viewed as a group, their breeding habits are as varied as the animals themselves. Some lay their eggs in the water; others in frothy masses on land, from which the tadpoles are washed down into ponds by rain; other species lay on land and stay nearby until they hatch fully developed babies which have completed their metamorphosis within their eggs. The frogs of this family range in size from very tiny species to large ones.

South American bullfrog, *Leptodactylus pentadactylus*. Photo by G. Marcuse.

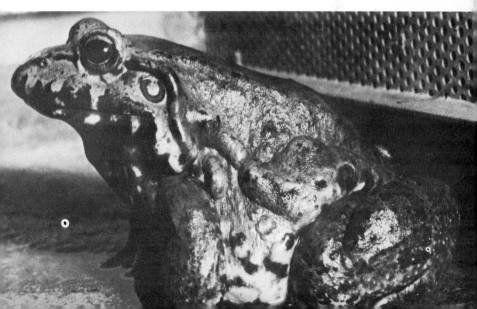

Bell frog, *Hyla gratiosa,* green phase, southeastern United States. Photo by W. Mudrack.

Pine barrens tree frog, *Hyla andersoni,* New Jersey to northern Florida. Photo by J. K. Langhammer.

Eastern chorus frog, *Pseudacris triseriata.* Eastern United States. Photo by W. Mudrack.

The barking frog, *Eleutherodactylus latrans*, occurs in the southwestern United States and northern Mexico, where it frequents rocky areas. It is a secretive species and remains hidden in fissures and under rocks during the day, coming out at night, when its call, resembling the bark of a dog, can often be heard during rainstorms. Barking frogs reach a length of only about three inches and are grayish in color, often clouded with lighter or darker blotches. The breeding season of this species runs from late winter to May; the eggs, often numbering fifty, are laid on land, separated from each other, and are often if not invariably guarded by the male. Completely terrestrial, the barking frog should be kept in an aquarium with a damp sand base and a scattering of fair-sized rocks in the background. The rocks may be formed into a cavelike structure, care being taken that each rock is firmly placed and cannot be readily shifted. It is amusing to watch one of these frogs progress from one place to another in a curious and deliberate walk. The food of the barking frog consists mainly of insects and spiders.

SOUTH AMERICAN BULLFROG, MOUNTAIN CHICKEN

The South American bullfrog rivals or may even exceed our native bullfrogs in size. Its scientific name is *Leptodactylus pentadactylus* and it is one of the kinds which deposit their eggs on land, covered with foam. The larvae undergo part of their development within the frothy mass but complete it in the water. A large adult may measure nine inches and is colored handsomely in tan or brown, suffused with orange. Another beautiful though somewhat smaller leptodactylid species is called the mountain chicken, *Leptodactylus fallax*. Nearly all of the really large frogs will not hesitate to eat any smaller ones which may be confined in the same cage, including even those of their own species. It is important, therefore, not to mix frogs of very unequal sizes.

HORNED FROGS

The horned frogs of the genus *Ceratophrys*, in some of their forms, are beautifully adorned and highly aggressive creatures that make handsome vivarium inmates. Some grow to a length of eight inches and have an immense body bulk. All of the horned frogs have enormous mouths and are highly predatory, the food of some consisting almost solely of other frogs. Large specimens will attack anything which threatens them; they can inflict painful bites, holding on with bulldog tenacity. Even the tadpoles of the horned frogs are highly carnivorous. In our studies of herptiles we cannot fail to note the frequency with which a multiplicity of unusual characteristics occurs within a species or group. The horned frogs are outstanding in almost every respect. Some of the species are small, but several grow to huge size and have beautifully blended colorings of reds, tans, browns, greens, and blacks. On a plain background these frogs are most conspicuous, but on the jungle floor, among leaves and debris, they can hardly be seen. They move about but little, preferring to lie in ambush for the unwary snakes, lizards, mice, and other vertebrates which come within range of their powerful jaws. Some species have prominent hornlike developments over their eyes, adding further to their bizarre appearance. The horned frog of the Amazon, *Ceratophrys cornuta*, is one of the largest species; *Ceratophrys dorsata* of Brazil is another. The kind we find most often in dealers' cages is the Colombian horned frog, *Ceratophrys calcarata*, a rather quiet and demure species if, indeed, we can use these terms to describe any of the horned frogs. Forest frogs of this genus do not require a water pool in their cage. A sand or soil covering may be used for the floor, and this may be overlaid with moss and dead leaves. The *Ceratophrys* species described above and most other tropical species should be kept in a cage temperature range of 70 to 75 degrees. Lowland types require a higher temperature than those from elevated regions.

BUFONID TOADS

When one speaks of toads it is usually one species or another of the family Bufonidae that comes to mind. These are the common garden-variety toads that are so numerous nearly everywhere. Every continental land mass except Australia has native toads of this family. *Bufo* is the most important genus in the family, and it alone has more than 250 distinct kinds of toads. Though varying greatly in size from tiny species like the oak toad, *Bufo quercicus*, to huge ones like the giant toad, *Bufo marinus*, all of the *Bufo* species are very much alike in over-all appearance. They have heavy bodies and cannot make the long leaps of the more agile frogs. Their skins are dry and in many species very rough, giving the appearance of being wart-covered. Toads cannot, of course, cause warts if handled. But the skin glands do produce a poison which can be very irritating to mucous mem-

Hyla smithi. Photo by F. J. Dodd, Jr.

Dumpy green treefrog, *Hyla caerulea,* Australia. Photo by G. Marcuse.

Australasian green treefrog, *Hyla infrafrenata.* Photo by Dr. Otto Klee.

American toad, *Bufo terrestris*. Photo courtesy American Museum of Natural History.

branes and fatal if swallowed in sufficient amount. For this reason toads are molested only by animals which have special ways of dealing with them. The hognose snakes eat toads; in fact, these snakes feed upon little else, but most kinds of snakes which regularly eat frogs will ignore toads. Toads, like other amphibians, require moisture but will not dry out and die as quickly as most other amphibians if deprived of it. A moderately damp terrarium or box with a floor covering of soil will comfortably house one or more toads. If the animals and their surroundings are sprinkled daily with water it is not necessary to provide a pool. I believe, however, that it is better to have one in the cage, sunk flush with the soil or gravel. This enables the amphibians to absorb the proper amount of moisture. Except in the breeding season, toads of the genus *Bufo* are seldom found actually in water. They are terrestrial amphibians, and the members of the family which are aquatic or arboreal have been placed in other genera. The toads of North America and Europe are rather drab creatures when compared to some of their tropical relatives. Though no toad is as colorful as some of the more beautiful frogs, certain tropical species have handsome blends of tans, browns, and black.

Fowler's toad, *Bufo woodhousei fowleri*. Photo courtesy American Museum of Natural History.

Over the eastern half of the United States the American toad, *Bufo terrestris*, is perhaps the most often encountered herptile. In many books it is referred to as *Bufo americanus*, the name *terrestris* being reserved for the southern variety, which differs in minor details from the northern population. Currently, however, both southern and northern populations are regarded simply as geographical variations of a single species: *terrestris*. This is mentioned only to point out to the neophyte herpetologist the fact that scientific names change from time to time, as the study of relationships progresses. Serious students take such changes in stride, but they can be confusing to the beginner. Unless one has access to the latest technical writings in all of the major languages it is impossible to keep completely up-to-date. The habits of the American toad are similar to those of other species. It emerges from hibernation in early spring and travels by night to the pond where breeding will take place. The males arrive first and their trilling becomes a sound of the spring night. When the females arrive on the scene, mating and egg-laying take place. The eggs are deposited in long strings and commonly number several thousands from a single female. Hatching takes place in about a week, and tadpoles frequent the shallow shore waters in enormous numbers. Those

Marsupial frog, *Gastrotheca marsupiata.* Photo by Dr. Otto Klee.

Nesting treefrog, *Agalychnis dacnicolor,* Central America. Photo by J. K. Langhammer.

Burrowing treefrog, *Pternohyla fodiens,* Mexico. Photo by F. J. Dodd, Jr.

Mexican tree frog, *Smilisca baudini*, Central America. Photo by F. J. Dodd, Jr.

which survive the onslaught of predators transform into tiny toads in a few weeks and for awhile thereafter remain close to the pond where they were born. Eventually each goes its own way and reaches maturity in two to three years.

Nearly all of the many kinds of bufonid toads live well in captivity. Records of some that have survived twenty or more years are not uncommon. Toads, and other anurans as well, require food at more frequent intervals than most reptiles. Generally speaking, they will not accept other than living food, though pieces of meat which are put in motion before them will sometimes be accepted by specimens which are accustomed to vivarium life. An exception to the rule of feeding naturally only upon live creatures has been brought to light in a number of articles 'which state that wild *Bufo* specimens will sometimes recognize as food and devour such unlikely items as canned dog food. The veracity of these reports can hardly be questioned, but in the vivarium toads will not show any interest in nonmoving creatures or objects. It would, indeed, be convenient if we could feed them dog food, upon which many turtles seem to thrive. Toads which are accustomed to hibernating may stop eating in the fall. The instinct is so strong that even in a warm room they tend to remain in seclusion during the winter months, but usually they can be induced to accept worms or insects. An alternative can be had in allowing the creatures to go into actual hibernation. This can be accomplished if the animals have been well fed during the summer and have accumulated enough fat to carry them over a period of several months. Their cage should be filled nearly to the top with wood pulp, leaf mold, or moss and placed in a room or other situation where the temperature will remain around 40 degrees. The hibernating medium should be sprinkled occasionally but not allowed to become soggy. Some, though not much, ventilation is necessary. I have at times allowed herptiles to hibernate over the winter months but no longer make any attempt to do so, for I do not believe it will appreciably benefit the animals or increase their captive lifespan. This will be disputed by some vivarium keepers, who will insist that herptiles from cold winter climates do benefit by a period of rest in captivity. I can only answer that nearly all of the longevity records were established by herptiles which were not permitted to hibernate. Of course, if it is not possible to keep herptiles warmed during the winter, they must be allowed to go into hibernation. Any reptile or amphibian which has not been feeding regularly or is not in really top shape is unlikely to survive a period of hibernation.

Toads' eggs can be hatched and the tadpoles brought through transformation in an aquarium. Perhaps the best way of doing this is by bringing a portion of the natural pond home, along with the eggs. This can be done with wide-mouthed glass or plastic gallon containers. Gently scoop up and place some of the eggs in one of the jugs which has been half-filled with surface water from the pond. In another jar place generous quantities of the leaves, twigs, and debris from the bottom of the pond. Fill the remaining containers with plain water. In an aquarium or other container at home, the process can be reversed. First add the water to a suitable depth,

Green toad, *Bufo viridis*. Photo by Van Raam.

Arum frog, *Hyperolius horstockii,* southern Africa. Photo by W. Mudrack.

African treefrog, *Hyperolius fusciventris*, Africa. Photo by W. Mudrack.

Golden mantella, *Mantella aurantiaca*, Madagascar. Photo by W. Mudrack.

Black-spined toad, *Bufo melanosticus,* Southeast Asia. Photo by G. Marcuse.

usually not more than six or eight inches. Introduce the bottom debris, including any slime-covered rocks, and allow the silt to settle. Then pour the eggs into the container. In the absence of pond water any soft or slightly acid water may be used. When the eggs have hatched, keep only a few of the larvae—they will have a much better chance of living if not overcrowded. The water must not be allowed to become contaminated; a frequent change may be necessary to avoid this, especially if the aquarium is a small one.

Most frog and toad tadpoles are herbivorous, while the larvae of salamanders are carnivorous. Suitable foods are such items as boiled lettuce leaves, spinach, pond algae, pieces of hard-boiled egg, dried daphnia, and small amounts of canned dog food. The diet of the babies should be varied to insure proper growth and a small daily feeding is much better than a larger one at less frequent intervals. Make sure the food is quickly cleaned up and not allowed to decompose.

Argentine toad, *Bufo arenarum,* South America. Photo by G. Marcuse.

Most tadpoles will transform into tiny frogs or toads in periods ranging, with the species, from a few weeks to a few months. First the back legs make their appearance, then the front ones. By this time the aquarium must have a shore or landing place where the baby amphibians can leave the water. Then comes the problem of supplying live food in sufficient quantities to satisfy the appetites of the youngsters. The white worms known as enchytrae can be used in part for this purpose, but even better are the multitudes of tiny creatures found in the lower leaf debris of damp woods. When a small amount of this is placed in the vivarium it can be confidently assumed that the tiny toads or frogs will find and devour whatever small living creatures it may contain. Salamander larvae may be cared for in much the same manner, the chief difference being that they will require animal matter during their development. Brine shrimp, finely-ground earthworms, crushed snails, canned dog food, bits of fresh raw meat, and white worms are a few of the food items accepted

Leopard frog, *Rana pipiens*. Photo by F. J. Dodd, Jr.

Pustulose frog, *Rana pustulosa*, Central America. Photo by F. J. Dodd, Jr.

Burrowing frog, *Rana adspersus,* middle and southern Africa. Photo
by J. K. Langhammer.

by developing salamanders, and also by spadefoot toad larvae and the young of certain other carnivorous baby anurans. Amphibian larvae have been little described and it is often next to impossible to determine what species of frog, toad, or salamander one has on hand until transformation takes place. Salamander larvae differ from those of the anurans in sprouting the front legs first.

The toads of the United States that are likely to be available are such species as Fowler's, *Bufo woodhousei fowleri*; Colorado River, *Bufo alvarius*; western, *Bufo boreas*; oak, *Bufo quercicus*; and the American green toads, *Bufo debilis* and *Bufo retiformis*. European species are the common toad, *Bufo bufo*; the European green toad, *Bufo viridis*; and the natterjack toad, *Bufo calamita*. The very large Blomberg's toad, *Bufo blombergi*, from South America is an especially handsome creature, reaching a length of eight to ten inches. Equally large, though not nearly so colorful, are the South American populations of the giant toad, *Bufo marinus*. The last species will devour nearly any living creature which it can cram into its capacious maw. This includes such vertebrates as mice, small rats, and sparrows. Occasionally some very attractive toads from Asia and Africa are

Blomberg's toad, *Bufo blombergi*. Photo by G. Marcuse.

imported. Generally the prices of imported toads are not high, and I have often thought that a good collection of the many different *Bufo* species would afford an interesting example of the variation in size and colors that may take place within a single genus of animals.

POISON ARROW FROGS

The extremely colorful and rather active little South American frogs of the family Dendrobatidae are often imported. The strawberry poison arrow frog, *Dendrobates pumilio*, is red and black; other species in the genus have vivid black and yellow markings. One to two inches represents the maximum growth attained by these decorative frogs. They are among the most handsome members of any collection of herptiles, and if they have a disadvantage it is in their feeding habits—they require the tiniest of insects, which may sometimes be hard to procure. A moss-covered terrarium with a few branches or strong-leaved plants makes a suitable home for *Dendrobates* and the related *Phyllobates*. They are forest frogs, rarely entering the water, but requiring humid surroundings and a temperature of 70 to 75 degrees. The male frog carries the eggs about on his back

Crested toad, *Bufo typhonius*, Brazil. Photo by H. Schultz.

Rana erythraea. Photo by Dr. Otto Klee.

Poison arrow frog, *Dendrobates* sp. Photo courtesy American Museum of Natural History.

until they have hatched and the larvae have reached a fairly advanced stage of development. He then enters the water, allowing the tadpoles to swim free and finally metamorphose. The poison arrow frogs, of some species at least, have a very toxic skin secretion which has long been used by the Indians in the poisoning of their arrows to produce quick death in a mammal or bird. Some care should be used to see that this skin secretion does not get into the eyes or mouth after handling a frog. The little frogs are so delicately formed and fragile that it is perhaps best not to handle them at all, except with a net when it is absolutely necessary. They live quite well in confinement if properly cared for but it is likely that they do not have a very long natural span of life.

TREEFROGS

I am not very much in favor of displaying herptiles in so-called "natural environment" arrangements if they will live just as well in simple cages with a minimum of accessories. Some herptiles, in fact, do very poorly in cages which attempt to duplicate the natural habitat of their inmates. Other herptiles demand an imitation of their natural home, to some degree at least, or they will fail to thrive. Or if

Gray treefrog, *Hyla versicolor*. From Dickerson, *The Frog Book.*

they do live they will show few of their characteristics. Such are the treefrogs of the family *Hylidae*. Treefrogs are agile and long-limbed; they have toe pads which enable them to ascend smooth vertical surfaces. Many have a pronounced ability to change color. They number in their clan some of the smallest frogs as well as species which reach a length of at least five inches. In their various greens and browns, many are delicately handsome and some do exceedingly well in captivity if provided with an adequate supply of insects and other small invertebrates. They are found on every continent but reach their maximum abundance in Central and South America. The United States has a fair number of species.

The gray treefrog, *Hyla versicolor*, is a widespread and fairly common species over much of the eastern half of the United States. It is about two inches when fully grown and may be brown, green, or gray—the color changing according to the mood of the animal and environmental factors. Usually this treefrog is found on the trunk or branches of trees which are close to water. In its grayish color phase it is almost impossible to see when clinging to the bark of a tree. The usual time for breeding and egg-laying is early June; the eggs are attached singly or in small groups to the stems of pond vegetation.

Phyllomedusa rohdei, Paraguay. Photo by Van Raam.

They hatch in a few days and the tadpoles are easy to identify because of their distinctive golden color and red tail. The change to the adult form occurs during the summer, at which time the half-inch froglets leave the pond and take up residence in trees and bushes. Gray treefrogs are hardy terrarium inmates and like other species of their kind can be made to feel at home in a well-planted terrarium with a floor covering of soil and moss, some hardy broad-leaved foliage, and perhaps a portion of a tree limb.

The green treefrog, *Hyla cinerea*, is another attractive species that is very streamlined in over-all appearance and has a somewhat pointed head. It occurs chiefly in the southeastern United States and the Mississippi Valley. The spring peeper, *Hyla crucifer*, is less than an inch in length when mature but does well in a damp terrarium if kept well supplied with tiny insects and worms. It is perhaps the most abundant treefrog over its wide range in the eastern United States. The European treefrog, *Hyla arborea*, is a chunky little species that is less active than many of its New World relatives. It has long been recognized as an excellent terrarium animal by European herpetologists; that is probably one of the reasons why we seldom find it offered for sale in the United States.

Spring peeper, *Hyla crucifer*. Photo courtesy American Museum of Natural History.

Pacific treefrog, *Hyla regilla,* Pacific coast of United States. Photo by L. Van der Meid. ·

European treefrog, *Hyla arborea.* Photo by Muller-Schmida.

Golden treefrog, *Hyla aurea*, Australia. Photo by G. Marcuse.

Tropical and semi-tropical regions have treefrogs of huge size and all the attractive coloration of their smaller cousins. The Australasian *Hyla infrafrenata* is a beautiful green species that reaches many times the size and bulk of our more familiar treefrogs of Europe and North America. Giant treefrogs of this and other species require sturdy foliage in their terrariums to support their considerable weight. One such giant, the Cuban treefrog, *Hyla septentrionalis*, is an immigrant which has become successfully established in Florida and the Keys. It may reach a length of five inches but lacks the beautiful coloring of some members of its family.

Some of the less well known members of the treefrog family are those of the genera *Phyllomedusa*, *Gastrotheca*, and *Agalychnis*. Some are most remarkable in appearance or habits. *Gastrotheca*, for example, carries her eggs on her back concealed in a sort of pouch, and members of this genus are often called marsupial frogs. Depending upon the species, the young may emerge from the pouch as tadpoles and finish their larval stage in water, or complete transformation may take place within the pouch.

Marsupial frog, *Gastrotheca marsupiata*. Photo by G. Marcuse.

Agalychnis dacnicolor, Central America. Photo by F. J. Dodd, Jr.

Flying frog, *Rhacophorus* sp., eastern Africa, family Rhacophoridae. Photo by G. Marcuse.

African treefrog, *Hyperolius* sp., a member of the large African and Asian family Rhacophoridae, related to the ranids. Photo by Van Raam.

TRUE FROGS

The true frogs of the family Ranidae are what we might call typical frogs; a description of them is hardly necessary. *Rana* is the largest genus of the family and contains over 250 species, distributed on every continent. It includes such familiar amphibians as the edible frog of Europe, *Rana esculenta*, and the bullfrog of North America. Mostly, the ranid frogs stay close to water; when alarmed, they plunge in and swim to the bottom, taking refuge among aquatic plants or bottom debris. Many are tremendous leapers and are able to cover great distances in a single jump. Though many are rather prettily marked, none shows the beauty of coloration found among members of certain other families of frogs. The typical frogs live quite well under terrarium conditions which allow them to enter or leave the water at will. They can be kept over long periods in shallow water without a landing place, but they cannot survive long in a situation where water is not abundantly available. Some of them remain very nervous for a time after capture and may injure their snouts severely in frantic leaps against the sides or covers of their cages. This wildness persists longer when numbers are housed

Golden mantella, *Mantella aurantiaca*, Madagascar, related to the ranids. Photo by Muller-Schmida.

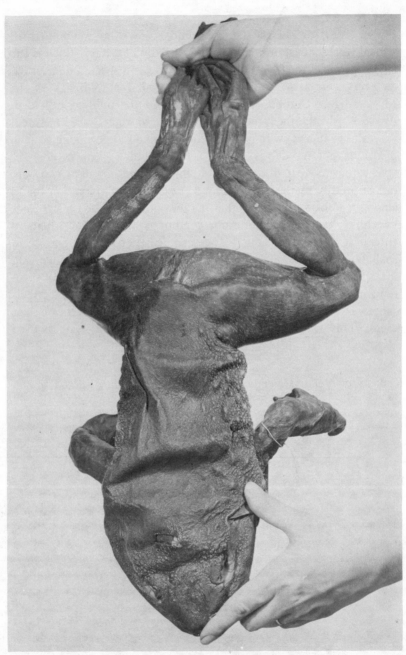

Goliath frog, *Gigantorana goliath,* preserved example to show size.
Photo courtesy American Museum of Natural History.

Burrowing frog, *Rana adspersa*, middle and southern Africa. Photo by G. Marcuse.

together. This may be a good time to mention that nearly all amphibians live better when kept alone or with just one or two others of their kind. Large frogs readily devour small ones and the bullfrog, particularly, is a notorious cannibal.

During the early days of their captivity, frogs should be disturbed as little as possible. Their cages may be partially covered to prevent outside disturbance at this time. They tame rather quickly if kept alone or in pairs and soon reach the point where they will accept food from the hand. Nearly all invertebrates of a suitable size fall prey to frogs, and even such vertebrates as mice and reptiles may be eaten by the larger species. The largest frog in the world belongs to this family. It is called *Gigantorana goliath* and is found in Africa. Large adults may be close to twelve inches in body length. Another unusual African species is the hairy frog, *Astylosternus robustus*, the males of which develop slender filaments of flesh resembling strands of hair along the sides of their bodies during the breeding season.

The North American bullfrog, *Rana catesbeiana*, is a common species and one which has been introduced into places where normally it would not occur. Its large size combined with the fact that it is edible have caused it to be hunted extensively, and in some areas its numbers have considerably diminished. This has brought about laws which regulate the capture or possession of the species in some states. Bullfrogs in their adult stage are rather solitary creatures and often a small pond will form the home area of only a single large adult. The sexes are easy to distinguish because the tympanum or ear opening of the male is much larger than that of its mate. With the latter, it may be about the same size as the eye, while in the male it considerably exceeds this organ in diameter. Nearly all frogs are vociferous, but the resounding boom of the bullfrog in a quiet woodland pond just before a shower or at breeding time in the spring or early summer is one of the noises the naturelover delights in. Egg masses of the bullfrog are deposited at the surface of quiet water, and a single laying may contain very many thousands of frogs-to-be. The tadpoles hatch in about a month and the babies may remain in the larval stage for two years and attain a length of six inches. When transformation finally takes place the babies are not the tiny creatures one might expect. Instead, they are nearly three inches in body length when the tail is finally lost and they take up a partial land existence. Because of their size and the wide variety of foods they will accept, baby bullfrogs are easily reared in a terrarium. Their life expectancy is well over ten years.

Bullfrog, *Rana catesbeiana*. Photo by G. Marcuse.

Large frogs, like this bullfrog, are often carnivorous. Photo by G. Marcuse.

Adult bullfrogs are extremely wary and are not often caught in the daytime. At night, in the beam of a flashlight, they seem unable to sense danger and are easily taken. Though bullfrogs may reach a very large size, they are completely inoffensive as far as humans are concerned. They never attempt to bite but will kick so vigorously that it is difficult to hold a large specimen. This is best accomplished by grasping the amphibian about its waist, with the legs extended. In this position even the largest specimen is helpless. A bullfrog is one of the best anurans to keep and study in a terrarium. It loses its natural shyness and a single individual of large size can be housed comfortably in an aquarium which measures eighteen inches in length. Bullfrogs and other species of its genus do well on a diet of earthworms.

The green frog, *Rana clamitans*, is often confused with the bullfrog but is a much smaller animal. It is closely related, however, and from a distance it is difficult to determine whether one is looking at a fully-grown green frog or a half-grown bullfrog. Both are greenish with lighter underparts, but the green frog has a fold of skin along its side, distinguishing it at once from its larger relative, whose sides are smooth. Its habits are similar but it is more gregarious than the bullfrog, and sometimes large numbers of green frogs may inhabit a pond.

Green frog, *Rana clamitans.* Photo by M. F. Roberts.

The pickerel frog, *Rana palustris*, is often found in great numbers in or near small bodies of water in the eastern United States. Tiny irrigation ditches are a common habitat, and though these frogs are quick to take alarm and dive to the bottom, they have little hope of escape, at least from humans, in such places. The species is attractively spotted and the undersurfaces of its rear limbs are orange-yellow in color. It is noted for its toxic skin secretion, which causes the species to be rejected by many frog-eating animals. It is not wise to house pickerel frogs with other animals. Even on collecting trips it is best to segregate these frogs from other species, because the other species are likely to succumb to the effects of the poison which the pickerel frog exudes.

Another spotted frog is the leopard frog, *Rana pipiens*. Superficially, it resembles the foregoing species, but has more rounded spots and its legs lack the bright orange coloration of the related species. Its range, in its many varieties, covers nearly the whole of the United States. It is the species often used as fish bait and in biology classrooms and can be purchased very cheaply from biological supply houses. In the terrarium it does well, but some individuals tend to retain an excitable disposition and dash themselves against the glass of their cages when disturbed. Though their ranges coincide in the East, on field trips I have not noted the leopard and pickerel frogs living together.

Leopard frog, *Rana pipiens*. Photo courtesy American Museum of Natural History.

Pickerel frog, *Rana palustris*. Photo courtesy American Museum of Natural History.

Indian bullfrog, *Rana tigrina*, southern Asia. Photo by L. E. Perkins.

Moor frog, *Rana arvalis,* north and central Europe, western Asia. Photo by G. Marcuse.

A pretty ranid frog is frequently found in damp woods, not close to any permanent water. It is the wood frog, *Rana sylvatica,* light tan in color with dark brown blotches behind the eyes. Wood frogs change color to a considerable extent and in places with a very dark ground cover the frogs themselves may be dark brown in over-all coloration. In length it does not often exceed three inches. A damp, not wet, terrarium makes a good home for one or more wood frogs. If kept moist with a fine spraying daily the species does not require a pool in its cage. Insects and earthworms are the principal fare of captives.

The red-legged frog, *Rana aurora,* is a species of our western coast and is the largest native frog of that area, growing to at least five inches. Rather pretty, this species usually has a reddish overcast to its skin; the undersides of its rear limbs are bright red. Unlike many of its relatives, the present species is somewhat delicate in confinement and offers interesting possibilities to those who would like to experiment with ways of maintaining it over long periods. Possibly a very cool environment is the answer to keeping red-legged frogs in good health. One specimen lived over ten years, but the majority do not live this many months.

Common frog, *Rana temporaria*, Eurasia. Photo by H. V. Lacey.

Many imported ranids live very well in terrariums, but are rarely available on the animal market. In nearly every country the larger species are sold as food and may be purchased in local market places. Ranid frogs will not withstand high temperatures, so the shipping of specimens from tropical places is more than likely to prove discouraging.

NARROW-MOUTHED TOADS

The narrow-mouthed toads of the family Microhylidae are mostly small and very secretive animals that live in nearly all the warmer portions of the globe where there is sufficient moisture. A few kinds are arboreal or terrestrial, but the majority seem to spend most of their lives in burrows or otherwise hidden from observation. As with the majority of anurans, we know little of their life histories. The eastern narrow-mouthed toad, *Gastrophryne carolinensis*, is a smooth-skinned, dark brown or gray amphibian with a markedly pointed snout. In a terrarium it seldom ventures into the open, and often an entire display will have to be torn apart to find a specimen that has burrowed deeply. Wild specimens are found with some frequency on rainy nights or, in dryer weather, under stones or logs

Eastern narrow-mouthed toad, *Gastrophryne carolinensis.* From Dickerson, *The Frog Book.*

Marsh frog, *Rana ridibunda,* central Europe to western Asia. Photo by G. Marcuse.

Sheep frog, *Hypopachus cuneus,* southern Texas to Mexico. From Dickerson, *The Frog Book.*

in damp places. These frogs feed on the tiniest of insects; some members of the family appear to eat nothing but termites and live within the nests of these insects. The African *Breviceps* species are members of this family; at least some among them deposit their eggs on land. The entire development of the larvae takes place before hatching. *Kaloula* of Asia is sometimes imported and seems a little less secretive than other narrow-mouthed anurans.

At one time or another I have kept representatives of the majority of families of frogs and toads. All were interesting and some lived for considerable periods. I do not think that any of the many kinds I have kept made better vivarium inmates than the toads of the genus *Bufo.* I would also rate the bullfrog highly in this respect. Some of the treefrogs are not unduly secretive and make decorative, interesting, and often long-lived terrarium inhabitants. Herpetologists, like other workers in scientific fields, have their specialties—favorite animals, if you will. Fewer seem to have studied the tailless amphibians than other kinds of herptiles and as a consequence we know next to nothing about the life histories of most species. Frogs and toads, as well as another amphibian group, the caecilians, offer an inviting field of study at professional or amateur level.

XI

Collecting Herptiles

Probably few herptile keepers confine their attention to a single animal. Most have several specimens and many have extensive collections. Some have only snakes or turtles, while others have a more varied assortment of the many types. There are living in the world today close to 10,000 recognized species of reptiles and amphibians. No one, in a single lifetime, could possibly hope to have under observation more than a tiny percentage of the living forms. Young people, in particular, tend to acquire and keep whatever comes along and learn as much as possible about the various class and family members. Often this type of interest gradually evolves into a specialty. There is little accounting for the likes and interests of humans, and the herptile collector may decide to concentrate on salamanders, or perhaps lizards, or even a single genus in some family. There is little doubt that at the present time more people keep turtles and tortoises than any other herptiles. This may be due, in part, to these reptiles' ready availability both in the wild state and in the cages of dealers.

Whether one decides to develop a specialty or maintain a general collection there is a word of advice which should be well-taken: limit the numbers of individuals in your collection to a reasonable figure. The care of a large collection of reptiles requires not only considerable expenditure of time and effort but also can be very expensive as well. The observation of a few individuals over a long period can be more rewarding than keeping a large collection whose members are suffering from varying degrees of neglect. My own special interest is snakes, and I try never to have more than a dozen individuals on hand at any given time. The cleaning and feeding of a collection of this scope can easily occupy one evening a week. Special problems arise from time to time, and they can occupy much of one's spare time.

BUYING HERPTILES

There are many dealers in the United States who offer herptiles for sale by mail order. With some, this is an adjunct to a bird, mammal, or aquarium fish business. Others make a specialty of local and imported herptiles and maintain fairly large stocks, especially during the warmer months of the year. Some issue monthly or bimonthly bulletins which describe what is on hand; the bulletins may be in addition to a printed listing of stock available at nearly all times. Often a price bulletin subscription service is offered; such a subscription will provide an influx of interesting mail for the herptile enthusiast. It is a way, too, of keeping abreast of the going prices on the commoner imported reptiles and amphibians.

Prices, particularly of imported specimens, may seem high to the novice herpetologist, but it must be recognized that the dealers suffer losses in the importation of herptiles as well as in their own compounds after arrival. Herptiles have to be fed and kept clean and, in cool climates, artificially heated. They have to be advertised or they will not be sold. Nearly all dealers guarantee the live delivery of the herptiles they sell by mail. All of these items affect the price tag on a reptile or amphibian. Like everything else we buy, the prices of herptiles have been rising steadily over the years, and there seems little likelihood that this trend will ever be reversed. It is amusing to compare a reptile price list of twenty years ago with those of today. The selling prices of many of our commoner native species have more than quadrupled. Dealers in reptiles may be honest or otherwise. Those who are "otherwise" commonly do not last long in the business because word of them soon gets around. Often a price list will describe an animal of particular interest, and the collector may wish to learn more about it before laying his money down. A telephone call to the dealer may be well worth its price to determine the actual condition of the animal, its sex, whether it is feeding, and so forth. Most dealers do not have the time, and many are ill-fitted temperamentally besides, to enter a mail correspondence about a reptile or amphibian.

The New York Zoological Park, Bronx, New York 10460 publishes a leaflet which gives the names and addresses of dealers in amphibians and reptiles. Inquiries should be sent to the Reptile Department. Another such list is published by Ross Allen's Reptile Institute, Silver Springs, Florida 32688. Many large pet shops now carry native and exotic reptiles, and even department stores frequently have them in stock. The advantages of buying locally when possible are obvious. The animals may cost more, but one can see what he is getting and often determine whether it is feeding, and there are no transportation expenses. In purchases by mail the last item is nearly always borne by the consumer.

There are many ways of getting in touch with other persons who are interested in herptiles, and often pleasant and mutually beneficial friendships develop. Herptile clubs that offer interesting possibilities for the exchange of ideas and specimens, as well as companionship on field trips, have been formed in many communities. Your nearest museum or zoo will often be able to provide the addresses of such clubs or put you in contact with individuals who have interests similar to your own.

On field trips you will occasionally encounter very large populations of herptiles. While the depletion of these populations by collecting is decidedly ill-advised, from the standpoint of conservation, there can be little objection to the taking of a few extra individuals for other herpetologists. The interest in herpetology would not be making the progress it is making it if were not for the availability of live material to study in private collections.

SHIPPING HERPTILES

Correspondence with collectors in other areas is another way of obtaining specimens not found locally. Mutually profitable exchanges may be made by mail or express. In the United States, post offices do not knowingly accept snakes for transportation through the mails, but other small herptiles may be sent in this manner. For the domestic shipment of snakes, as well as the larger lizards, turtles, and crocodilians, air express is generally used. Before packing any specimens for shipment it is well to obtain the advice of someone who has had experience in their shipment. Snakes are generally enclosed in bags, then packed loosely in wooden boxes with shredded newspapers. Cloth bags are better than plastic ones for reptiles, but in the case of amphibians plastic bags will conserve the needed moisture better than cloth ones. Air parcel post should be used for mail shipments if the distance is more than a few hundred miles. Fresh sphagnum moss makes an excellent packing material for the bags containing aquatic turtles, crocodilians, and all amphibians. Most snakes should be kept dry in transit. When you buy something from a dealer by mail, note carefully his packing methods. If shipments are carefully packed and plainly labelled as to contents, with the notation "Do not overheat or freeze," surprisingly few losses occur in transit. I am strongly opposed to the winter shipping of reptiles and amphibians, particularly tropical kinds, to or from cold climates. Chills almost inevitably occur, and the results of them may not become manifest for days or weeks after the specimens have arrived at their destination. Styrofoam shipping containers minimize the possibility of chills.

FIELD TRIPS

Herptile enthusiasts should at least occasionally take to the field for first-hand observation and collecting of reptiles and amphibians in their natural haunts. The equipment required for such excursions need not be elaborate or expensive. Nor are trips into remote heavily forested areas essential. As one travels along in a car, many likely spots at the side of the road may be spotted and investigated. Friends are often amazed by the few pieces of equipment I take into the woods on collecting forays. Generally, everything I need can be carried without creating even a bulge in my pockets.

Unless poisonous snakes are concerned, I rarely carry a stick or noosing pole. Except in the case of poisonous reptiles, the hands form the best collecting tools. Aquatic types may require the use of a net or seine, while poisonous kinds must be handled with staffs or tongs. Some lizard species are not readily caught without the aid of a noose. But the majority of all herptiles may be caught easily with the hands alone. In the United States, the poisonous snakes, Gila monster, large snapping and softshell turtles, and *Amphiuma* salamanders are the herptiles most capable of producing serious injuries to the collector; they have been listed in the order of importance in this regard. The many other species are capable of producing little more than superficial scratches with their jaws or teeth. (Probably few collectors will have the opportunity or inclination to capture the large sea turtles, which can produce injuries with both jaws and flippers.)

Dry, rocky terrain usually provides good habitat for many species of lizards, snakes and some tortoises. Photo by O. Stemmler.

The herpetologist soon becomes familiar with the herptile fauna of his own area and the places where certain species are most likely to be found. A number of pamphlets and books dealing with the herpetology of the individual states can be useful in collecting specimens in unfamiliar areas. Zoo and museum curators and their staffs, if convinced that the amateur is serious, can offer good clues to likely habitats of desired specimens. The preserved study collections of museums can offer valuable collecting data which can be put to use in the field.

Herptiles of various species have very specific habitat preferences, and a thorough knowledge of them is essential if there is to be any fruitful collecting. Nearly all reptiles and amphibians tend to form colonies: where one of a kind is found, there are likely to be more Only rarely does an individual turn up far removed from others of its

Southern bayous and other bodies of water are good collecting areas for many aquatic snakes and other species which like wet habitats. Photo by R. E. Watts.

Tropical habitats are many and varied, often within the distance of a few yards. Photo by Dr. Herbert R. Axelrod.

kind. Some herptiles are rated as being excessively rare, but this description is based on the scarcity of captured specimens. Excessive rarity is probably more often apparent than real, for no animal continues to perpetuate itself when its numbers have been reduced to a critical minimum. Many species once considered rare are now known to be very common, a fact discovered by the careful field study of habitat preferences. Reptiles and amphibians may or may not diminish in numbers in areas of heavy human population. In fact, people quite often will unwittingly bring about an increase in herptiles. The experienced collector knows that a trash heap will often reveal more reptile life than a similar spread of favorable rocks in a clean woodland. The polluted waters with which we are now so much concerned are another matter. Frogs and salamanders disappear from polluted waters first, being followed by the turtles and other aquatic reptiles.

Fortunately for the reptile hunter, he has few laws to contend with in the pursuit of his quarry. But there are some restrictions that must be observed if conflict with the law is to be avoided. It is well to familiarize oneself with local and state ordinances before embarking on a collecting trip. Marine turtles and crocodilians are under protection in some places, and the poisonous Gila monster is protected in Arizona, its area of principal abundance within the United

In areas which lack otherwise suitable habitat, amphibians are often abundant in or near small ponds or water tanks. Photo by Dr. Herbert R. Axelrod.

States. Horned lizards are also protected in Arizona and Texas. There are laws governing the capture of tortoises in Texas, and several states protect wood turtles, box turtles, sliders, and diamondback terrapins. Frogs used as food are protected in many states, at least during the breeding season. All animals, including herptiles, are protected in most state parks and in all national parks and monuments. Check with the ranger or security officer before collecting in these preserves. Salamanders are not specifically protected in any state, although several species and populations are included in recent lists of endangered wildlife; presumably such species will eventually have protective legislation. As a general rule, snakes are not protected even though they are certainly the most beneficial of all herptiles. Arizona is considering the protection of all its herptile fauna, however, and Florida has recently passed several restrictions on collecting. Mexico, once the week-end collecting utopia of many southwestern herpetologists, now has strict laws to protect all of its fauna.

Collecting on private or posted property is another matter to be considered. Many owners willingly grant permission for such activities; others will not. The more enlightened land owners may be aware of the value of snakes as rodent destroyers and accordingly be reluctant to have them removed from their property. Before collecting poisonous snakes it is well to be aware that accidents which may result, if due to the knowing and willful handling of such creatures, may not be covered by the terms of an insurance policy.

The element of luck seems to play a part in determining whether a field trip will prove productive. Under seemingly ideal weather conditions, at the best time of the year, one often searches in vain for herptiles which are known to be common in the vicinity. Then, on a day when everything seems wrong, a good catch will be made. The weather preceding the day of collecting may have a bearing on this. When large numbers of reptiles or amphibians are found, it is not a good policy to take more specimens than are required. Remember that herptiles do well if kept in pairs or trios but that they seldom thrive if large numbers are caged together. By taking only a few specimens and leaving the habitat as undisturbed as possible, the collector realizes that he has a good chance of finding others in the area at some future time, if they are needed. A day of careless collecting in a small area can all but destroy a colony of herptiles. For the same reason, careless dissemination of information as to the where-abouts of favorable collecting sites is not be to approved. For this reason, the novice may find it difficult to obtain information from zoo and museum curators, unless he can convince them that he is earnest in his study and will take only a limited number of specimens. Little reliance can be placed on the information given by rural residents. Names of herptiles may be inaccurate, descriptions vague, and estimates of numbers of individuals completely unreliable. There are some rather famous collecting sites in the United States, and during favorable times of the year they may attract herpetologists from far and near. In some of these places, the reptiles concerned are, at best, not abundant forms; how long they may be able to withstand such annual onslaughts is a matter for concern.

FIELD EQUIPMENT

The most essential items in the equipment of a field collector are a series of cloth and plastic bags. The bags may vary in size from about twelve by eighteen inches to the size of a large pillow case. The plastic ones should be capable of holding water, and the cloth ones should have seams which cannot be forced open under considerable pressure. All bags should be examined to make sure they are free of cuts or holes. When not in use these bags can be conveniently folded and put in pockets or under the collector's belt, leaving the hands free. Though these cloth and plastic bags are interchangeable in use, in general it will be found better to place the amphibians in the plastic bags and the reptiles in the cloth ones. When a capture is made the bag itself may be knotted at the top, though I prefer to carry short lengths of bell wire with which to secure the openings. Except in the case of very small specimens, I adhere to the rule of one specimen to each bag. Often, in the case of active herptiles, the introduction of a second specimen will allow the escape of the first.

Bags containing specimens must be kept out of the direct sun at all times. If it is necessary to leave occupied bags, in order that the hands may be free to effect further captures, be sure that a shady place is selected and remember that the sun shifts. The place where bags are temporarily deposited should be well marked so there is no difficulty in finding them when one returns. Bags containing poison-ous specimens should be boldly labelled as such. Since a collector may often not wish to retrace his steps in a collecting area, it is perhaps better to carry all captives along as one proceeds. The temporary deposit of bags is useful mostly in areas where the going is rough, as on mountain ledges. Bags containing small reptiles can be tucked under the belt; those containing poisonous snakes should be carried well away from the body. I use a hook at the end of the noosing pole to transport venomous snakes out of the collecting area and back to the car.

Knowledge of an animal's habits combined with the experience of having actually captured specimens combine to enable a good collector to find specimens where they could be easily overlooked. Thorough collecting is not easy work; it involves much lifting of rocks and turning of logs, probing of crevices and investigation of holes. Harmless snakes often fight furiously when captured—this may be especially true of such kinds as the larger water snakes and whipsnakes. Nevertheless, the use of one's hands alone is preferred over a noosing stick with these species. There is far less chance of injuring specimens. The injuries they are able to inflict with their teeth are inconsequential. Water snakes may lie out on bushes overhanging ponds and rivers and dive quickly into the water when approached. With them, the use of a long noosing pole may be essential if they are to be captured during daylight hours. They are easily taken at night with the use of a strong flashlight or headlamp.

Night collecting equipment should include a source of light (carbide lanterns and battery operated lamps are both good) and a net for capturing aquatic forms. Photo by R. E. Watts.

Bullfrogs and related species are most easily captured at night. Photo courtesy American Museum of Natural History.

NIGHT COLLECTING

Many reptiles and amphibians are nocturnal. Such species may remain far underground during the day, and even the most diligent search will fail to reveal their whereabouts. At dusk and during the night, however, they prowl on the surface and are easily captured. During really warm weather periods many reptiles are most active at night. In places where poisonous snakes are found, night collecting is an activity which must be pursued with great caution. These animals are naturally most alert and active in times of dusk and darkness and the danger involved in collecting and bagging them at such times is great. I do not think it is advisable for a field collector to work alone at night where there are dangerous snakes. Relatively few bites occur at night, but this is only because collectors are not usually active during the hours of darkness in places where broken, brushy terrain can conceal coiled forms. In some areas, the larger rat snakes regularly ascend trees, and collectors should develop the habit of looking upward, as well as under foot.

COLLECTING POISONOUS SNAKES

The capture of poisonous snakes involves special techniques, varying somewhat with the species involved. As with everything else, practice leads to perfection in the bagging of venomous snakes. The procedure cannot be separated from a degree of danger, and the first attempt of an inexperienced collector to capture alive and unharmed a poisonous snake of large size can be a breath-holding experience for the onlooker. There is little standardization of the equipment used to capture poisonous snakes: I know of no two field men who use identical equipment. I use a slim but strong dowel with a screw eye attached to one end. The pole is about four feet long and perhaps half an inch in diameter. The other end of the pole has an L-hook attached to it. A seven-foot-length of bell wire is bent double and threaded through the screw-eye opening; the terminal portion is spread to form an opening about six inches in diameter while the loose strands are held in the hand against the pole. When slipped over a coiled reptile's head, the noose is brought back to a point at least a foot behind the snake's neck before the noose is drawn tight. This method allows the escape of some specimens that could easily have been taken if the noose were drawn tight immediately behind the head. The reason for securing a hold farther back is to prevent injury to the snake's spine during its violent efforts to free itself from the noose. Rattlers which have been noosed and allowed to dangle by the neck often will not feed in captivity.

An opened bag must have been prepared beforehand. In brushy country this is quickly and easily accomplished with the use of safety pins and wire. Three of the pins have been fastened at regular intervals about the opening of the bag. Each pin has a twelve-inch length of wire attached. The affair is quickly attached to bushes with its mouth open in a triangular form and the bottom barely touching the ground. This operation takes but a few moments and is done after the quarry is sighted. Poisonous snakes often "freeze" when they first sense possible danger, and few will escape during the few moments it takes to fasten the bag in place. The noose is drawn securely but not too tightly about the snake's body and the struggling reptile is placed in the waiting receptacle. This is freed of the bushes and twisted several times to close the mouth, which is then bound tightly with wire in two places. The bags are carried from the place of capture hanging from the hook-end of the pole. Freshly caught

Collect Snakes

Catch Frogs

Common collecting implements. Top, Pilstrom tongs; center, noose; bottom, snake stick fashioned from hoe. From Smith, *Snakes as Pets*.

snakes bite through the bags in their efforts to escape, and the droplets of venom trickling down the sides of a collecting bag give mute testimony to what would happen if they were allowed to dangle carelessly at one's side.

There are many other ways of catching poisonous snakes; each collector seems to have his own method. Snakes may be pinned to the ground and grasped behind the head—this method I emphatically do not recommend, especially to the novice. Aluminum tongs are available commercially and are useful. They have a hand grip which operates the jaws by means of a spring and are especially good for dealing with coral snakes and *Amphiuma* salamanders. The huge diamondbacks are best captured without the use of restraint; this can be accomplished because the snakes often hold their ground when encountered, scorning the flight of their smaller relatives. They can be lifted from the ground and placed in a bag with a long pole having an angle iron on the end. Or they may be gradually backed into an open-mouthed bag that is attached to the frame of a large landing net that fishermen use.

The eastern diamondback is often found in the burrows of the gopher tortoise. A twenty-five-foot length of garden hose is ferreted into the burrow as far as it will go, and it is often possible to tell whether a rattler is present in the burrow by listening at the end of the hose. The rustling caused by shifting of the coils of a large rattler is easily distinguishable from the more ordinary noises of the other inhabitants of such a retreat. Or a snake may hiss or sound its rattle when prodded by the end of the hose. If the indications point to there being a rattler present, a small quantity of gasoline can be poured into the hose and results awaited. The fumes will usually cause snakes to make a quick exit. Refinements such as the addition of a furniture caster to the end of the hose will make it easier to get it to the end of the gopher burrow. Several small cuts can be made near the end to allow the escape of gasoline and a plastic funnel may be used over the ear to help detect sounds within the hole. Often a rattler will emerge from a gopher hole if the entrance is simply covered. A whole book could be filled with accounts of how to capture poisonous snakes and the successes—and failures—that have accompanied this precarious pastime.

Except, perhaps, in open places where every footfall can be studied with care, snakebite-proof boots should be worn in areas where poisonous snakes are numerous. Manufacturers produce knee-high leather boots which cannot be penetrated by even the largest rattler. Aluminum leggings with strap fasteners also can be obtained; they cost much less than the heavy leather boots. Ordinary wire screening, sewn into the leg bottoms of dungarees, affords some protection. Rubber overshoes and ordinary hunting boots will prevent many bites. In ledgy country it is difficult and dangerous to climb with leather-soled footwear. Ordinary rubbers, slipped on over whatever other footwear is being worn, will help to prevent falls.

Persons who engage more or less regularly in the hunting of poisonous snakes, or those who keep specimens in captivity, should not be without a supply of the sera used to counteract the effects of bites, since it sometimes is not quickly available when needed. It is rather expensive to buy but will maintain its strength for a number of years and should be a part of the equipment of anyone who handles the venomous crotaline snakes. If exotic elapines are to be handled it should be determined in advance where sera effective against their bites can be obtained in a hurry. Often this will be the nearest large zoo.

The bite of a poisonous snake, if an appreciable amount of venom has been injected, constitutes a medical emergency of the first order. Rightly, the treatment from the very start should be in the hands of a doctor who is qualified to assume the responsibility. In some areas, where not many bites occur, most doctors will not see a case of snakebite during their entire years of practice. Two booklets should be kept on hand by those who study or collect venomous snakes. One is published by the Wyeth, Inc. firm of Philadelphia, Pennsylvania and is titled *Antivenin*. The other is titled *Venomous Snakes of the United States and Treatment of Their Bites*, written by W. H. Stickel and published as Wildlife Leaflet Number 339, available from the U.S. Fish and Wildlife Service, Washington, D.C. Both are free and can be had by mail request. They are informative and well-illustrated publications that conveniently capsule the information required by a doctor who is treating a snakebite victim. Neither presupposes a previous knowledge of tropical medicine—the heading under which snakebite is placed.

Snakebite kits consisting of suctioning devices, tourniquets, and incising instruments are available commercially, cost very little, and are accompanied by instructions for their use. So many factors enter the problem of snakebite that it is presumptuous of one not in the medical profession to offer remedial suggestions; there are enough of these in the assorted literature, and I believe that often they have done more harm than good. The only advice of the present author is this: before doing anything, make sure that it is a poisonous snake that has bitten you. Books commonly state that a poisonous snake will leave one or two prominent punctures in the skin, while the bite of a harmless snake leaves a U-shaped series of small cuts. This can be misleading. If a harmless snake has the opportunity to seize and chew it will leave a series of lacerations, but from a strike and immediate withdrawal the resulting wound may consist of two punctures which precisely resemble those of a poisonous snake. Pain and swelling will quickly follow the bite of most poisonous snakes of the United States. When you are sure you have been bitten by a venomous snake, get to a hospital as quickly as your means will permit, but without undue exertion—in other words, walk, don't run. If the bite has occurred on the hand, remove rings at once, or the swelling following a bite will make it difficult to cut them off. Keep as calm as possible and remember that only a small percentage of bites are fatal, regardless of treatment. Provide the doctor-in-charge with the aforementioned booklets and the sera.

There is much lack of agreement as to the proper treatment of snakebite, but there is one thing that is generally agreed upon throughout the papers dealing with the subject. This is that the ingestion of alcohol in any amount can do nothing but worsen the condition of the patient. Snake handlers sometimes boast of the number of times they have been bitten. This is curious reasoning. To be intimately associated with poisonous snakes over a long period of time without being bitten is an admirable accomplishment and one that attests to the skill of the herpetologist. The capturing of poisonous snakes has been gone into in some detail because potentially the venture is a dynamite-laden one. Most herpetologists find it more pleasurable and interesting to collect the many beautiful and harmless herptiles that are found in forest and desert.

CAPTURING LIZARDS

Lizards can be caught in a variety of ways. Some can be approached closely enough to permit a quick grasp. Others flee with great alacrity when the collector approaches to within a few feet. These kinds can be noosed with a slender pole or a fishing rod. Fine copper wire, sewing thread, and fishing line have all been used with success. The noose should be one which will stay open, yet have a loosely-sliding knot. It is slowly worked into position just behind the unsuspecting reptile's head, then tightened with a quick upward pull. Lizards should never be grasped by the tail, for most will readily divest themselves of this member and leave it writhing in the hand of their would-be captor while they scurry off to safety. More than any other reptile, perhaps, the lizards are, typically, creatures of the sun.

Species which may be very difficult to capture during the day can often be taken readily after the sun has gone down or in the early dawn. Collecting of nocturnal lizards requires a knowledge of their retreats. Some hide among rocks or under the bark of fallen trees, while a few are quite specific in their plant associations, especially in tropical regions. Dogs are sometimes used to find and run down the really large tropical lizards. Generally, the herptile collector will find little use for a dog in the field, but it is interesting to note that hunting types can be trained to locate and point reptiles as well as birds and mammals.

COLLECTING TURTLES

A long-handled net is an essential item of equipment for the turtle collector. A boat, too, is useful, but many kinds can be taken from the shore by hand or with a net, particularly during the spring and fall, when they may congregate in shallow water. The larger diving species are easily among the most difficult of all reptiles to capture, but that their capture can be successfully done on a wholesale scale is attested to by the large numbers which are offered for sale in markets. Skin and scuba diving have been successfully employed in the capture of certain rare freshwater turtles of the larger types. When under water turtles seem to lose much of their natural caution and can be easily approached in their hiding places. In muddy or silt-laden waters this method is not effective. Small turtles often frequent shallows in large numbers and can be netted or seined without much difficulty, especially at night. Another favorite abode of baby turtles are the offshore masses of lily pads or water hyacinths. These, incidentally, are the favorite habitat of the more aquatic snakes and salamanders. A mass of hyacinths that is raked ashore or scooped into a boat will often reveal small aquatic herptiles of many kinds. The diminutive water snakes *Liodytes* and *Seminatrix* often abound in company with salamanders like *Amphiuma, Siren,* and *Pseudobranchus,* and baby turtles of the larger species.

Turtles can be successfully trapped in places where they are abundant. Turtle traps of various designs have been invented. One consists of a barrel or large wooden box with a ramp that is pivoted with just the right weight distribution to permit a turtle to ascend it in quest of the bait fish or meat, but will give way under the animal's weight when a certain point is reached, dumping the hapless reptile into the enclosure. A trap of this type may be weighted down with heavy stones and the water level should be kept low, to prevent the drowning of the less-aquatic types that may enter it. Like all traps, it should be visited frequently. A lot of time and money can be spent in the making of traps and the results they produce are hardly worth it from the standpoint of a private collector who wishes to obtain only small numbers of animals. Snakes have been taken in enormous numbers with funnel-like arrangements leading from their den openings in the spring. Pits dug in lizard areas will sometimes trap a few individuals. For the more secretive snakes and lizards, as well as salamanders, one of the best traps is a board or flattened cardboard box, placed strategically in their known haunts. It is particularly useful where natural cover is not abundant. In favorable places, such a simple trap will reveal specimens nearly every time it is visited.

COLLECTING AMPHIBIANS

Frogs and toads can be netted or caught by hand during the day but the best method of taking them is at night, when they appear stupefied by the glow of a headlamp or flashlight. Wading boots or waterproof overshoes are useful adjuncts to collecting in swampy areas or the shores of ponds and streams. It is best to segregate the species in bags of their own. Some frogs exude a poison which will quickly kill frogs of other kinds. As already noted in Chapter X, one such American species is the pickerel frog, an animal that should never be allowed close contact with other amphibians.

A simple turtle trap. From Fish and Wildlife Service *Circular 35.*

A boat makes it possible to easily collect sleeping turtles at night and on overcast days. Photo by D. W. Tinkle.

Standard procedure for the hunting of salamanders consists of turning over rocks and pieces of wood along the course of streams, both in the water and along the shore. Some of the aquatic species are exceedingly slippery, and the roughened-surface rubber gloves that are available can be very useful in collecting hellbenders, mudpuppies, and the like. In good spots, during the spring, one may be able to catch, literally, as many frogs, toads, and salamanders as he desires by night collecting. Be conservation-minded and capture only what you actually need for study.

MISCELLANEOUS

Night driving over little-used roads in suitable areas can be very productive. Road surfaces tend to retain heat for a longer period than the surrounding soil and air. Many nocturnal snakes, lizards, frogs and salamanders will come to rest on a road. The best ones are bordered by fairly heavy vegetation and have a dark top. Driving should be at the rate of 12 to 18 miles an hour for best results. This improves the chance of sighting an animal and permits a quick stop to minimize the possibility of its crawling off after it has been sighted. The bagging of a venomous animal such as a Gila monster (where it is legal to capture them) or rattler is best accomplished under the illumination of the automobile headlamps.

Many of the methods of capturing herptiles described here are equally applicable to the collecting of exotic or tropical species. Because some of the latter may grow to huge size, two or three persons may be better than one. In the United States the spring and fall are the best seasons for collecting. In northern portions of the country herptile collecting comes to a halt in October and cannot be resumed until March, at least. In the South, collecting of some kinds of herptiles is possible throughout the year. All areas seem to produce a midsummer lull, when one may hunt for days without finding any individuals of even the commonest species. Some may actually aestivate at such times, while others may take to roaming mostly by night.

Collecting bags and jars for amphibians should be provided with moss to prevent the drying out of captured specimens. On a long automobile trip they may be stored in a styrofoam cooler to prevent losses from overheating. Bagged poisonous snakes should be enclosed in strong wooden boxes. Florida now has a law specifically governing the manner in which poisonous snakes may be transported and displayed.

Collecting reptiles in their natural haunts can be a rewarding and healthful pastime. A notebook should be used to record the names of specimens and the times and places of their capture. The information can then be transferred to a permanent record system which keeps a running account of the animals' activities in captivity, including such items as growth and feeding, breeding, etc. It is by such observations that we have acquired much of our knowledge about herptiles.

XII

Housing Herptiles

The housing of herptiles can be made as simple or as elaborate as one wishes. One often sees a beautiful and exquisitely detailed terrarium inhabited by herptiles in varying stages of decline, while the crudest of arrangements will often house a thriving colony. The amount of money and effort that one is willing to invest in a cage for herptiles is related only remotely to the ultimate welfare of the animals it will house. Often a simple cage which provides the correct degree of lighting, heat, and humidity will serve far more satisfactorily than an expensive one which fails to provide any of these important fundamentals.

The average herptile enthusiast starts off with a single cage. Others are added in time, and the end result is often a conglomeration of cages which vary much in size and design. There may be nothing basically wrong with such a display, but a much more appealing arrangement can be developed with careful thought beforehand. Different herptiles require quite different surroundings in captivity, but it is possible to maintain a certain uniformity that will not be disrupted by additions to the collection. Try to set aside a room, or a portion of one, and plan on paper how it will be developed into a small herpetarium. Think carefully about lighting and heating problems. Remember that cages have to be cleaned and their inmates fed, and make sure the cages you select provide for quick and easy accomplishment of these tasks.

CAGES

The most versatile of cages for herptiles is the ordinary aquarium that is equipped with a secure cover. Such a cage can comfortably house anything from a desert lizard to a thoroughly aquatic salamander. Aquariums are not expensive, and one or more can be arranged to enhance the decor of even the most tasteful living room. Try to settle on a size for your tanks, giving due thought to the

With the correct type of cover and substrate, an aquarium can be used as a cage for almost any type of herptile. Photo by M. F. Roberts.

cleaning problem. I do not believe that a size smaller than the standard ten-gallon aquarium is practical; the low silhouette twenty-gallon size is ideal for anything but the largest snakes, crocodilians, and lizards, for which special cages must be bought or built.

Despite their attractiveness and general usefulness, however, aquariums do have disadvantages. For the larger and less secretive snakes—those which do best without soil or plants in their cages—

aquariums are difficult to keep in sparkling-clean appearance because of the large amount of glass surface that is exposed. For the same reason they are not the perfect cages for such large lizards as tegus and Gila monsters. And I consider them totally unsuitable for the housing of any but the smallest poisonous snakes. Growing turtles and crocodilians, as well as newts and the larvae of salamanders and frogs, require frequent feedings and changes of water. Larger aquariums may present a problem in this respect unless the herptile keeper wants to go all out and install special plumbing that will permit the draining and refilling of aquariums without their being moved . . . or unless he's willing to purchase one of the power filters designed for effective filtration of large aquariums.

Theoretically, it might be thought that a captive herptile will prosper directly in proportion to the extent in which its natural environment is duplicated. This seems not to be the case with some species. First of all, it is next to impossible to completely duplicate a natural environment in a cage. The closest approach to this ideal would be to go into the field and select an area which encompasses the natural range of a group of herptiles, then erect an escape-proof barrier around the area. Even this plan would have many flaws, so intricate is the exchange between living organisms and their total environment. Many environmental factors are not critical ones for herptiles, and with each species it is our problem to determine just what the critical factors are; these factors can then be adjusted according to the requirements of the animals. Certain problems of light, heat, humidity, and food intake must be resolved. If any one of these is grossly distorted, the animal will certainly die. To successfully maintain herptiles, one must know something of their natural history. The present book and others fill this need.

BASIC VIVARIA TYPES

No matter how much thought is given to the subject, any indoor enclosure for herptiles will fall into one of five types. Even if the aquarium or other cage is very large it will tax one's skill to the utmost to successfully combine any two of these distinct types. Even zoos rarely attempt it. The word "terrarium" is, by definition, a place where land animals are kept. Some of our herptiles are completely aquatic and suitable homes for them would have to be called aquariums. The term "vivarium," though connoting, in its narrowest sense, an enclosure where there is at least a partial duplication of natural habitat, will be used in referring collectively to all of the enclosures used to house reptiles and amphibians. There follows a list of the five basic types of vivaria for herptiles, with mention of the animals that are commonly kept in them:

1. **The exhibition cage:** contains no furnishings other than a drinking dish or tree bough; papers or small rounded pebbles may be used as a floor covering. Used mainly for snakes of the larger, non-burrowing species but may be used also for tegus and other large lizards and some tortoises.

2. **The desert terrarium:** has several inches of fine sand on the bottom and is appropriately landscaped with potted cacti and other desert plants; may or may not have a water container. This type of vivarium is the only one in which certain desert animals will thrive. Included in this category are horned lizards and other desert species, some tortoises, and a few snakes.

3. **The woodland terrarium:** may represent a portion of a temperate forest or a piece of tropical jungle; humidity may be adjusted to the needs of its occupants and may range from quite low to very high; water pool is usually present; foliage may be dense or sparse. Useful for many of the smaller herptiles, particularly lizards, small snakes, and amphibians.

Herp cages can be as simple or complicated as desired, as long as the animal can adapt to it easily.

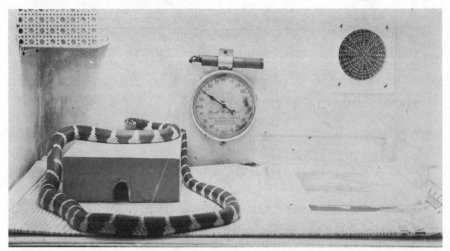

4. **The marsh-stream terrarium:** has approximately equal areas of land and water. Used extensively for semiaquatic reptiles and many amphibians.

5. **The aquarium:** may have a projecting rock or two but is used primarily for the thoroughly aquatic herptiles which seldom or never leave the water; may be fresh water, ocean water, or mildly saline. Used for the thoroughly aquatic herptiles, including such types as amphiumas, sirens, mudpuppies, mud and musk turtles, marine turtles, and snakes.

EXHIBITION CAGES

A series of exhibition cages, uniformly stacked or arranged in tiers, lighted from the inside or from without, can form an extremely attractive display of reptiles. A well-constructed wooden box can be converted into a suitable cage with a few tools and a little effort. The better method, however, is to plan on paper exactly what you want the finished product to look like, carefully note the measurements of the cage's components, then go to a lumber yard and select the wood. Ordinary commercial shelving is a little less than a foot wide and may be purchased in many grades. It is easily handled and will serve very well for the bottom, sides, and even top of the cage. Four pieces, cut to specified size, can be nailed together to form the framework. The back can consist of a section of pegboard, nailed securely to the four sides. In the front, two pieces of right-angle countertop binding strips can be fastened to accept a sliding pane of glass which will open from either side. The floor of the cage may be covered with a strip of paper toweling, a water dish added, and one has an acceptable display case in which the majority of snakes will thrive for years.

The above instructions cover the construction of the simplest kind of cage, yet one which suits very well the needs of most snakes. All sorts of refinements and modifications can be made. Do not be afraid to use your imagination. I have studied the construction of snake exhibition cages in dozens of institutions and private collections and have yet to find the perfect one. The dimensions of the cage described will often be about two feet in length and a foot high. It provides good ventilation and can be easily and thoroughly cleaned; food can be introduced from either end, and the occupant is perfectly visible. One may wish to have a hinged cover of hardware cloth, or glass which slides up and down rather than sideways and can be

Home-made cages of the same style and size present a very neat and attractive appearance.

locked in place with an overhanging cover that is provided with a hasp. Cages can be painted or stained in any desired color and thoroughly waterproofed with a coat of clear shellac or varnish or one of the newer clear plastic sprays. A hoodlike arrangement over the top can be constructed to provide concealed lighting and some heat as well. Screening should not be used anywhere in the construction of a snake cage, for there are only a few snakes which will not rub their snouts raw in attempting to nose their way through it. Hardware cloth of suitable mesh size is better, but even this can cause damage; I prefer pegboard to other means of ventilation.

Exhibition cages should have no openings through which it is possible for a snake to gain exit. And be aware that captive snakes often give birth to babies that are able to squeeze through the smallest holes. For instance, a baby brown snake (*Storeria*) could easily squeeze through a pegboard hole, but snakes of this size are not ordinarily kept in exhibition cages. They do better under moderately dry woodland terrarium conditions.

Cages for poisonous snakes should have sliding partitions to permit the locking of the inmates in one side while the other side is being cleaned. They should be handled as little as possible, both as a safety precaution and because of the fact that most of them are very temperamental and are likely to go off their feed if unduly disturbed. If it is necessary to remove a specimen from its cage, do so with a snake hook—an angle iron or shelf bracket fastened to the end of a stick. Many books give the impression that a snake will wind itself about the end of such an implement and not attempt to escape or fall off. This cannot be depended upon. Snakes, especially juveniles, will often lose their balance and fall to the floor when being transferred with a hook. Such a fall, particularly in the case of a heavy-bodied snake, is likely to result in an injury which may not be apparent at once but is ultimately fatal. Because of this I long ago formed the habit of placing every cage housing poisonous snakes at floor level before attempting a transfer of the occupants. Most venomous snakes can be gently guided from one container to another without any physical restraint. I always take pride in being able to guide a rattler in and out of its cage without having the snake sound its warning. Harmless snakes may be placed in a bag during cage-cleaning; if they are large, they may be allowed to crawl about and get some exercise.

Ground-dwelling herps can be kept warm by using a perforated false bottom. Light bulbs placed under this bottom will provide sufficient heat. Photo by G. Marcuse.

The exhibition type of cage may or may not be provided with a small box which allows the occupant to remain out of sight when it desires seclusion. It is almost a necessity for a few of the more nervous species, but most can do without it. Any snake which remains perpetually hidden makes a poor subject for observation.

Exhibition cages must be provided with a container for drinking water; some species drink often, others only rarely. I have experimented with every conceivable type of dish and have found that nearly all have serious drawbacks. Either they can be entered by the snake and the water thus tracked about the cage, or they tip easily—with the same result. The one exception is the small glass dish that is sold in stationery stores as a sponge cup. It comes in straight-sided designs and with convex sides. Either type is good and cannot be tipped by any ordinary snake. I prefer the dish with the rounded form.

A rock to assist in skin shedding may be placed in an exhibition cage, and a single tree branch may be added for snakes which climb, but I would not advise the use of any other accessories. Exhibition cages can be constructed in any size desired. One that is three feet long and half as wide and high will house comfortably the largest snakes found in the United States. Their glass fronts may be cleaned easily, inside and out, by simply reversing the surfaces.

It is possible to set up elaborate thermostatically-controlled heating units in exhibition cages, but this is not done even in the better zoos. Hot water pipes can be diverted to heat reptile cages, but this has its drawbacks. By far the best heating arrangements for a collection of reptiles is a central one which can be controlled with a thermostat. A range of 70 to 85 degrees is suitable for nearly all snakes; many tropical kinds do best at the upper limit of this range. A nightly drop is permissible, but I would regard 65 degrees as a point of danger for non-hibernating snakes in captivity. Snakes may regularly encounter much lower temperatures in the natural state, without ill effect, but captives seem to lack the ability to do so, although otherwise very healthy. In the absence of a better heating method, strategically placed light bulbs of the appropriate wattage can be used to maintain suitable cage temperatures. Do not attempt to maintain a collection of reptiles without a good means of controlling temperature; serious exotic fish fanciers would not attempt to maintain their animals in a cold environment, and most reptiles are no better able to withstand chills than tropical fishes.

A simple but efficient desert terrarium. Photo by R. J. Church.

DESERT TERRARIUM

The desert terrarium is perhaps the easiest to set up and keep in good condition. In its simplest form, the desert terrarium has two to three inches of fine sand, a few potted cacti and stones in the background, and perhaps a weathered piece of wood. There is no drainage problem, for the idea is to keep the desert terrarium as dry as possible. What little moisture the potted plants require can be supplied to them directly, at their roots, without dampening the remainder of the cage. The cacti used should be kept in the soil in which they were found or purchased. If they were bought unpotted, a sandy loam mixture with a little slaked lime added makes a good potting medium.

The sand selected should be of a fine grade, not the coarse type sold for use in aquariums. It should be rinsed repeatedly to remove the dust, then thoroughly dried out before use. This can be accomplished quickly by heating in an oven. The potted cacti should be sunk in the sand to conceal their individual pots, and the sand gently sloped toward the front of the cage. Desert animals will rarely find or use a drinking dish, even if it is sunk level with the surface of the sand.

Water should be provided by a spray over the background rocks, or a lettuce leaf may be wetted and placed in the cage from time to time. A constant dry heat is especially essential for the desert terrarium. An aquarium tank with a screen cover and a light reflector above makes a good desert terrarium. One with better ventilation can be made by fastening screening or hardware cloth to a wooden framework. Nearly all desert reptiles require natural sunlight or a substitute for it. Few thrive for any length of time in northern climates, though there are exceptions which do exceedingly well. Many desert reptiles will burrow into the sand at night.

WOODLAND TERRARIUM

The woodland terrarium, more than any other, will tax the artistry of the herptile enthusiast who contemplates it. Once again, an ordinary aquarium is probably the best container with which to start. Over the bottom, lay an inch-thick layer of charcoal and coarse gravel, well mixed. The charcoal and gravel will assist drainage and help keep the cage free of disagreeable odors caused by souring of the soil. Slope the floor covering from the rear to the front. The taller plants will be in the rear, and this is where the greatest depth will be required. Next, add about two inches of good soil—select this from a place where many and varied plants are growing in profusion. If you do not have the inclination to go out and dig in the woods, potting soil may be purchased in stores. An advantage to selecting the soil from a healthy natural woodland is that many of the plants and seedling trees may be picked up along with it and one can be sure that their soil will have the correct degree of acidity or alkalinity.

Aquarists have produced beautiful arrangements in the tanks of their exotic fishes, and it is no less possible to do the same with an artistic arrangement of forest plants. Try to visualize a piece of landscape with tall plants in the rear, shorter ones in front, a few moss-covered rocks and the decaying portion of a tree bark. Here we have all the ingredients of a beautiful design—it remains only to carefully pot the plants so as to appear natural, yet not hide the animal forms the vivarium will contain. A container of water should be sunk flush with the surrounding terrain near the front of the enclosure. Small stones imbedded in the soil about the perimeter of the pool will make easier the removal and occasional cleaning of it. If woodland plants are used they may be set directly into the soil of the

Toads and many small snakes and salamanders will survive in a simple woodland terrarium. A partial glass cover will help retain the high humidity required. Photo by M. F. Roberts.

terrarium. Potted plants that are bought in a store had best be left in their containers, which should be sunk flush with the surface of the surrounding soil. This type of terrarium should have at least a partial covering of glass and should be sprinkled frequently. Tree-climbing lizards will appreciate limbs over which to cavort—in fact, a terrarium of the woodland type can be heightened to provide a good home for arboreal as well as terrestrial and burrowing animals. Salamanders may peer from beneath pieces of bark while anoles chase each other over the branches. It is about the only kind of a set-up in which herptiles of very different types may be mixed—with due regard, of course, for the respective sizes of the animals.

Some care must be used in feeding terrarium inmates to make sure that a few do not get the entire food supply. If any small snakes are introduced, make sure they are of kinds which will not promptly devour the other animals in the cage. For instance, ringneck snakes (*Diadophis*) are handsome little creatures which do well in a moderately moist environment, like that of a woodland terrarium. Their drawback is that they will devour any of the equally attractive little salamanders that one may wish to keep. Brown snakes (*Storeria*), while not as beauitful as the ringnecks, will confine their diet to slugs, earthworms, and insects.' The growth or decline of the plants in a woodland terrarium is a good indication of whether the soil has a correct moisture content; spraying can be adjusted accordingly. In general, it is best to keep the bottom layer of gravel and charcoal quite wet. With the woodland terrarium it is possible to bring indoors for year-round enjoyment a small portion of the forest and its inhabitants.

MARSH-STREAM TERRARIUM

Many herptiles inhabit the shorelines of lakes, ponds, and streams. Some spend a portion of each day in the water and the rest of their time on land. Still others are aquatic at certain times of the year, but terrestrial for the remainder of the time. For most of these types, the marsh-stream terrarium is suitable. It is probably the type of terrarium that is used more frequently than any other, for the baby turtles and caimans that are sold in such large numbers find an ideal home in this type of cage. A terrarium of this type can be very simple in design. Starting with an aquarium which does not leak, we simply add a couple of inches of well-rinsed gravel and slope it at one end to form a land area. To reinforce the bank, we can add a row of small stones as a line of demarcation between water and shore. Water depth may be about two inches, and the dry area can rise another two inches above this. The whole set-up can be attractively lighted with an inexpensive aquarium reflector, which will also provide some heat. In a more elaborate form, the marsh-stream terrarium can be divided across the center, or diagonally, with a piece of glass or wood. The land area can be set up as in the woodland terrarium, but the plants chosen should be of kinds that can withstand a great deal of moisture. Bog plants are excellent for this purpose. The water area can have as its bottom a layer of gravel. The dividing wood or glass strip may be of any height desired, but the water level must be approximately equal, or the animals will not be able to go from one section to the other easily. An assist in this regard can be had by placing next to the shoreline a rock which slopes from the water to a level even with the bank of land area. Such a rock will also help to prevent the partition from shifting. In this connection, a diagonal dividing strip is better than one which goes from side to side, for it will be held in place by the corner angles of the aquarium. Still another variation of the marsh-stream terrarium can be made by using an island, sur-

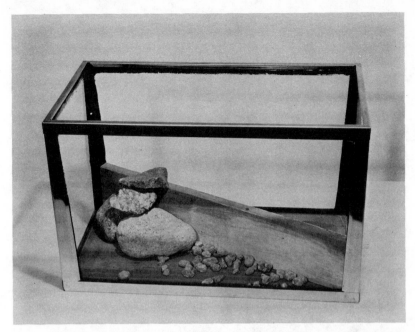

The marsh-stream terrarium is easily constructed and will house a great variety of amphibians and reptiles. Photos by M. F. Roberts.

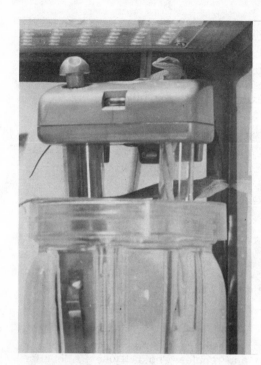

Small terraria or aquaria with shallow water may be heated by suspending an aquarium heater in a jar of water. Photo by M. F. Roberts.

rounded by water. This can be simply done by arranging a group of stones in the middle of the aquarium, or at its end, fitted together so as to allow no crevices between them. Turtles and small crocodilians are unappreciative of plant life and tend to trample the foliage in their cage. A plain rock shoreline fits their needs very well and permits the terrarium to be more easily cleaned than would be the case with a more elaborate set-up.

Another way of setting up a marsh-stream terrarium involves the use of a plastic basin, glass bowl, or metal tray. This is planted to simulate a small island, then placed in the aquarium while the water level is raised to a point just below the edge. When cleaning becomes necessary, the island is simply lifted out of the aquarium.

In any of these arrangements, an undergravel aquarium filter may be used to help keep the water clear and lessen the frequency with which it must be changed. In the water section, a few plants will add to the naturalness of the picture. These are useful chiefly where salamanders and frogs are concerned, for many turtles can be expected to devour aquatic plants. Generally speaking, the marsh-stream terrarium does not lend itself well to a company of mixed herptiles. Turtles tend to bite and harass other animals, while frogs will devour any salamanders that they can cram into their mouths. The woodland terrarium is by far the best if one desires a "happy family" grouping of herptiles, and even in this type of cage all of the inmates should be of approximately the same bulk.

AQUARIUM

The herpetologist finds a limited use for the true aquarium. Gilled amphibians, which derive their oxygen from the water, can be kept in an aquarium and if this is aerated, so much the better. Certain other herptiles, while finding it necessary to come to the surface for air, nevertheless spend most of their time underwater, either lying on the bottom or swimming about. The management of an aquarium for herptiles differs little from that in which fishes are kept. It can have a sand or gravel base, a filter, and an aerator, as well as an attractive arrangement of underwater plants. None of these is essential, however, and I am a great believer in simplicity of design when it comes to cages for animals. Often the presence of numerous accessories will have no bearing whatever upon the welfare of amphibians and reptiles. Or their effect may be deleterious if they interfere in any way with a state of total cleanliness in the tank. In most cases, the herptiles which can be kept in a shoreless aquarium will be comfortable in water of shallower depth than that which would be used for most fishes. Freshwater turtles should be able to reach the surface of the water without swimming, for even some of the very aquatic types will tire and drown, while others, like the soft-shells and marine turtles, find no inconvenience in periodically swimming to the surface for air.

MISCELLANEOUS EQUIPMENT

All containers for herptiles, even the true aquarium, should be kept covered with screening or glass. If the latter is used, provision must be made to allow a change of air within the cage. This can be accomplished by slightly elevating the glass at its corners, or using two pieces and separating them a bit in the middle. Condensation of moisture should not be allowed to become too great. If there is a dripping from the top or on the sides of the terrarium, the whole thing should be allowed to dry out for a day or so, during which time a screen cover may be used. Subsurface heating cables can be em-

Often a light bulb in a reflector unit is the simplest way to heat a terrarium or shallow aquarium. Photo by M. F. Roberts.

Some of the tools necessary to keep the marsh-stream terrarium or aquarium clean. Photo by M. F. Roberts.

ployed in terrariums, but I am not in favor of their use, for they do little to warm the air which the creatures breathe and thus only half-fulfill their purpose. Light bulbs in sufficient wattage will warm not only the air but the soil as well. In a cool room a good blanket will help to prevent too great a fall in temperature if the bulb is extinguished at night. A careful check with a thermometer should be maintained in all herptile vivaria.

In very large terrariums, an infrared lamp may be used for heating purposes. It may be alternated with one of the simpler sun lamps which screw into a regular socket. Spotlights, either within or outside large terrariums, can be used to create beautiful lighting effects. In addition to aquariums and wooden exhibition cages, many other containers can be utilized in the keeping of herptiles. In rearing large numbers of baby turtles or amphibian larvae, the plastic basins sold in department stores for household use are very good. They are light and can be cleaned frequently with a minimum of effort. Plastic baby baths and wading pools can be used with good results for some herptiles that are unable to climb a smooth wall.

OUTDOOR TERRARIUMS

The subject of outdoor pools is one upon which many books have dwelt at length. Details of their construction and maintenance are readily available. In warm climates, outdoor enclosures similar to the flight cages used by aviculturists are excellent for some of the larger reptiles. The present book is meant to stimulate the imagination and encourage the development of new ideas in the field of herptile husbandry. If the reader's experiments disclose a new or better way of keeping a certain species of herptile in health over long periods, the information will be gratefully received by herpetologists everywhere. I have long entertained the idea of turning an entire room into a sort of huge woodland or desert terrarium, where herptiles of suitable compatibility could lead their lives fairly naturally. It is a plan which requires considerable thought in advance, but has been accomplished successfully with birds—why not herptiles?

XIII

Feeding a Collection

Before any herptile is purchased, its food requirements should be given some consideration. When a specimen has been captured in the field and brought home, the problem becomes a ready-made one, if the creature is to be kept in health. Many herptiles can go without food for long periods—a year or more in some cases, if they have an abundant supply of water. The herptile menu is a very varied one; some species are extremely specialized in their requirements while others eat a wide variety of animal and vegetable substances. A good appetite is one of the surest signs that a reptile or amphibian is in good health. If there is anything radically wrong with the animal or its environment, it will generally refuse to eat. It will not always be possible to determine whether a snake, lizard, turtle, or salamander has been feeding before it is acquired. Some species lose weight rather quickly when they have been off-feed; others do so more gradually. Some can be brought back to a state of health after a very long fast, but others seem to reach a point of no return after fasting for a considerable time. If and when such kinds finally do start eating, the intake of food sometimes hastens their death. The herpetologist with a practiced eye can usually evaluate the condition of a specimen without trouble. The inexperienced person may find this more difficult. When the purchase of a specimen from a pet shop is contemplated, I do not think it is unreasonable to ask a dealer to demonstrate whether it will feed. Such a demonstration, if negative, cannot be accepted as conclusive, however, for some reptiles will feed in the dark when they will not do so under light, some require a minimum of disturbance while eating, and so forth. Personally, I would not own or keep in confinement any animal which refused to eat. When I acquire a herptile and find that it refuses to accept food when all conditions seem to be right, I persevere with numerous attempts with types of food that I believe approximate the natural diet of the animal. When signs of emaciation start to become manifest, I quickly dispose of the herptile—releasing it locally if it is a native species.

There are pros and cons to the subject of force-feeding. I would not force-feed any herptile unless it was extremely rare or valuable. With the smaller species, force-feeding will seldom meet with good results. It is the snakes and crocodilians which may benefit from force-feeding—the latter nearly always feed of their own accord when the temperature is right; snakes, on the other hand, sometimes refuse to feed under the most ideal conditions, though this is not usual if they are otherwise healthy.

Most herptiles in the adult stage are carnivorous animals; herbivorous species are to be found among lizards and chelonians, but among the former are rare and among the latter consist mainly of the land-dwelling tortoises. Few kinds exclude all animal matter from their diet. Terrestrial or semi-aquatic amphibians—the frogs and their relatives—generally recognize only live food, though individual specimens can be tempted with pieces of meat moved before them. Aquatic amphibians are a little less particular and will usually find and devour bits of meat placed in their aquarium. Snakes are entirely carnivorous; the rodent-eating kinds seem to prefer their food dead, but not decomposed. This greatly simplifies the matter of feeding them, for baby chicks and mice can be frozen and stored for later use. Lizards will accept both living and non-living food, though the smaller kinds are quite amphibian-like in their inability to see non-moving objects. Turtles and baby crocodilians present few problems in their feeding, but in the case of baby specimens, the food presented must be highly nutritive, which means that vitamins and minerals may have to be added.

Many herptiles can be provided for, in part at least, by the foods bought for human consumption, especially if these foods are enriched by the addition of powdered or liquid vitamins and minerals. With other species, the food must be purchased as needed, collected in the field at intervals, or raised in cages. The herpetologist who has only a few specimens may find it not worthwhile to raise their food, if it can be readily captured or purchased locally. Those having large collections may find it very necessary to raise their own herptile food, if a continuous supply is to be ensured at all times during the year.

Many of the snakes most favored for private collections live largely, if not exclusively, upon warm-blooded vertebrates. Most which feed upon mice and rats will also accept baby chickens; this may simplify the feeding problem, for chicks cost no more than mice, and those who would be averse to the storing of frozen mice in the home refrigerator may not offer the same objection to frozen chickens. Frozen animals should be thoroughly thawed before being offered to snakes or other reptiles. In the case of recalcitrant feeders, good results can often be had by slightly warming the preferred food. Once it was thought that snakes would accept only live food; curiously, this idea persisted for many years and was prevalent even among professional reptile keepers—those on the staffs of zoos, for instance. Experience has shown that snakes will often accept dead food more readily than that which is alive. Reptiles can be severely injured by the bites of rodents, and this possibility is eliminated with

Chickens, from chicks to adults, are useful foods for many constrictors and poisonous species. They are often easier to obtain than rats or mice. Photo by C. P. Fox.

Mice are an old standby for feeding snakes. Modern plastics make it possible to raise large numbers easily and with little of the smell associated with rodents. Photo by T. A. Mazzarello.

the use of dead food. Poisonous snakes will often approach and strike a dead animal just as they would a live one. It is a mistaken notion that poisonous snakes will strike only moving objects. The venom assists in the digestive process but is not essential to it. An animal that has been poisoned by a venomous snake can be fed to a harmless reptile without ill results. This is mentioned because sometimes a rattler or similar type of snake will envenom a live animal, then refuse to show further interest after it has expired.

RODENTS

Mice may be caught in large numbers in suitable places both in city and country. Ordinary snap traps may be used, or one may prefer to catch the mice alive with a simple box trap or one of the cage-like commercial products. Wild rodents are difficult to handle, and I can see little advantage to trapping them alive, particularly if ordinary snap traps can be set out in the evening and visited the next day. In hot weather an animal quickly decomposes and is attacked by hordes of carrion-eating insects. Wild reptiles have been seen feeding upon decomposed animals, but I do not recommend the feeding of such to captives. The mice and rats that are sold as pets can often be purchased at a special price if the herptile-owner will explain to the pet shop proprietor what they are needed for and how many will be bought each week. One of the quickest and least messy ways of killing one or several rodents that are to be used as reptile food is to enclose them in an airtight container of small size. I find a quart-size juice container with a screw top convenient for this purpose. Six adult mice will expire in a few minutes when confined together in a jar of this type. For a single mouse a smaller jar would be effective.

There is a wealth of information available in booklet form on the subject of raising mice, rats, hamsters, and other small mammals. If you wish to raise your own supply of mice or other rodents you can easily and inexpensively do so. I can offer a few suggestions on the raising of mice. To start your breeding colony, select mice which have a large average size and can be handled without biting. The progeny of such specimens are likely to inherit the disposition of their parents. White or albino mice may be the easiest to obtain for a start, but you may find that your breeding plant produces a surplus beyond what you need for your herptiles. If this happens you may wish to sell mice to local pet shops. White mice bring the minimal price; the so-called fancy varieties—blacks, blues, reds, tans, and so forth—can be sold at a higher price and the income from this source can help defray the cost of raising them. Standard wire cages with exercise wheels and watering bottles can be purchased in pet stores and are fairly satisfactory if they are protected from drafts. Perhaps better are simple wooden boxes of small size, equipped with hinged covers of hardware cloth. For the raising of mice on a wholesale scale, plastic basins of rectangular shape can be fitted with suitable covers and have the advantage of being easily washed from time to time. Nesting material may consist of wood shavings, shredded papers, or hay. In a cage which has only the top exposed to view, it is hardly necessary to provide nesting boxes. The female has a gestation period of twenty-one days and should be placed in a cage of her own when about to give birth. Mice of gentle, well-domesticated strains generally do not harm their babies, although nervous mice may eat them. Babies are weaned at three to five weeks and are mature at two months. Mice live up to four years, but their prolificacy diminishes long before this; in a breeding colony it is hardly worthwhile to maintain individuals over a year in age. An ideal temperature for breeding is 75 degrees. Sudden drops should be avoided, as with herptiles, and the temperature should never be allowed to go below 55 degrees. A wide variety of food is eaten. One very successful breeder uses a soft mash consisting of a mixture of dog food, chicken meal, bread, oats, and mixed grains. Sweet potatoes, apples, lettuce, nuts, and clean grass cuttings are offered sparingly. Rats and hamsters may be propagated with little more difficulty than mice, but they require larger quarters. If gently treated, rats can become extremely responsive pets, and the more tender-hearted herpetologist may find it difficult to feed them to his reptiles.

INSECTS

A collection of lizards or amphibians will require a steady supply of insects. These can often be netted or otherwise trapped during the summer, but such a supply is often abruptly terminated with the onset of cold weather. The meal worm (*Tenebrio*) has long been a stand-by of the vivarium keeper. A colony is easily started in a discarded aquarium or other smooth-sided, covered container. Wheat bran will form the burrowing and feeding medium for the "worms," which grow to about an inch in length, pupate, then become blackish beetles about half an inch in size. It should be about three inches in depth and covered with a piece or two of burlap that is kept moistened. Adult beetles will feed upon slices of apple or carrot. Worms

Mealworms are simple to maintain in many types of containers, as long as they are well fed and not allowed to become too moist. Photo by R. Gannon.

or larvae will tend to congregate in the folds of damp cloth from which they can be easily removed with forceps. A certain number of adult beetles may be removed from the colony, but enough should be left to ensure the deposit of large numbers of eggs. A temperature of 75 to 80 degrees is satisfactory, and breeding activity can be increased with the sparing addition of canned dog food. Before feeding them to one's herptiles, the worms may be allowed to crawl around in a saucer containing a few drops of a vitamin concentrate. Some of this will adhere to their bodies and the lizards will benefit from it. Mealworms should not be used continuously in the feeding of lizards or other small herptiles. They have a shell-like covering which gives rise to intestinal disturbances in animals which have been fed upon them exclusively. They should be varied with other kinds of insects and spiders.

A better insect food, particularly for the very small herptiles, will consist of newly-hatched praying mantids (*Mantis* and *Paratenodera*). The mantid's egg cases may be collected in large numbers in the autumn and if kept stored in a cool place will not hatch until needed. Normally, an egg case will contain more than a hundred small mantids, and hatching can be allowed to take place in the vivarium itself. The babies will emerge soon after the egg case is warmed and will for a time provide an abundant supply of food for small lizards. In the natural state, hatching does not occur until spring.

Although mealworms are a good occasional food, they are very hard-shelled, and continuous feeding may be harmful to herps. Photo by R. Gannon.

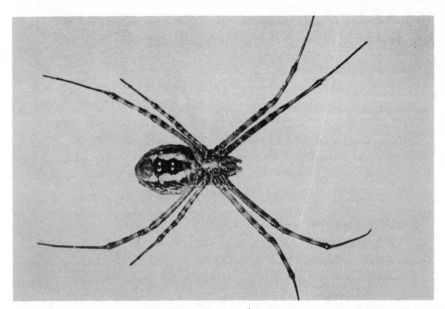

Spiders are good food for many amphibians and some lizards and snakes. They are easily collected in meadows by using a sweep net like that used in collecting insects. Photo by G. Marcuse.

Ants are good food for many lizards, but they are unfortunately difficult to raise in numbers. Dried pupae sold as "ant eggs" are not very nutritious. Photo courtesy American Museum of Natural History.

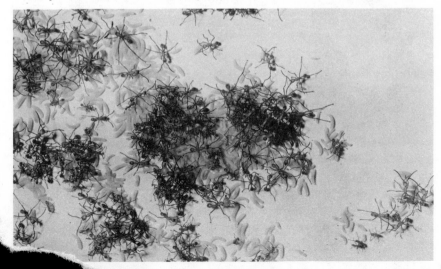

Crickets (*Gryllus*) are an excellent food for insect-eating herptiles. They may be raised in numbers in a terrarium-like set-up which provides an inch or two of loam spread over a base of gravel. Numerous hiding places in the form of pieces of cardboard should be provided. The colony may be started with a dozen or so adults. They will deposit their eggs in the soil, and soon the baby crickets will make their appearance. The adults should be removed at this time, to prevent the eating of the young, for crickets are cannibalistic. Food may consist of such items as oatmeal, lettuce leaves, raw apple, and dog biscuit. The colony should be lightly sprinkled from time to time; a temperature of about 75 degrees is adequate.

EARTHWORMS

The earthworm (*Lumbricus*) is particularly good for the feeding of many terrarium animals, though the majority of insect-eaters among the lizards will not touch them. Usually one may collect his own supply of worms by simply going out with a flashlight on a warm night when it is showering. They come to the surface at such a time

Earthworms are relished by many herptiles and are inexpensive; they can often be picked up after heavy rains. The smaller worms are usually taken more easily by many animals than are the larger ones. Photo by P. Imgrund.

and can be picked off lawns quite easily. If not overcrowded, worms can be stored in a cool place for long periods and will require little attention. Damp leaf mold, rather than soil, is preferred for the temporary storage of worms. If one wishes to carry a supply over the winter, a special box or other large container must be arranged to house them. Rich loam, mixed with rotted wood fragments and leaf mold, forms a good burrowing medium for the worms. Finely chopped raw potatoes and bread saturated with milk are good foods, but should be introduced in small quantities just below the surface; careful watch kept to make sure there is not excessive souring of the burrowing mixture. The mixture may be sprinkled from time to time to keep it moist, but not wet. A piece of burlap bag can be placed over the surface and the worms that are selected for food can be taken from under this, to avoid excessive spading or shovelling which will result in the injury and death of some worms, with consequent fouling of the soil mixture. The correct amount of moisture and a cool environment are the secrets of maintaining a good supply of worms over the winter months. Live bait dealers carry worms and these may be used to form the start of a colony, or they may be purchased in small quantities to meet actual weekly requirements of the herptiles. Unless, however, the vivarium keeper maintains a supply of his own, they will seldom be available in the winter.

WHITE WORMS

White worms, *Enchytraeus albidus*, are a nourishing food for newly-hatched turtles, the smaller salamanders and salamander larvae, and adults of the smaller kinds of frogs and toads. They remain alive and active for long periods in water, and this is an advantage to their use for aquatic herptiles. Inexpensive to buy, nearly any aquarium or pet store can provide a starting culture, along with a small amount of soil. To raise them in quantities, a well-constructed wooden box filled to a depth of six inches or more with garden soil and leaf mold or peat mixture will prove satisfactory. The worms should be separated into several groups and each buried under the soil at a depth of about two inches. Good foods for the worms are small portions of stale bread moistened with milk and cooked oatmeal. It is customary to lay a piece of glass over the soil to conserve moisture—it is necessary that the loam be kept damp but not actually wet. A temperature of 60 to 65 degrees gives best results.

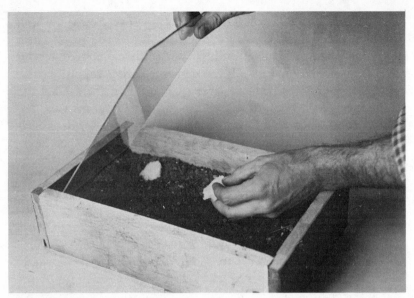

Although special raising containers are required, white worms are well worth the extra bother. Small amphibians love them. Photo by R. Gannon.

The worms will form masses, particularly where food has been introduced, and the required quantities can be picked out with forceps. If the soil should sour it will be necessary to start the colony anew with a fresh mixture of loam and dead leaves or leaf mold. The adult worms measure less than an inch in length and should be placed before the herptiles being fed in small masses, rather than individually.

TUBIFEX WORMS

Tubifex worms (*Tubifex, Limnodrilus*) are also useful in the rearing of some small herptiles and the feeding of adults of some larger species. They may be caught or purchased alive, or obtained in the freeze-dried form. The latter will serve most purposes as well as live worms. The worms themselves are tiny red creatures which inhabit muddy shallow waters. Their collection and storage presents some problems; for this reason the freeze-dried product is preferred over the natural one. The babies of the very small basking turtles—bog and spotted, for instance—are exceedingly difficult to bring to maturity without a highly nutritious diet that can be easily assimilated. Tubifex meet their requirements very well, but should be alternated with other nourishing items. They are not easily propagated under artificial conditions, but live worms can be stored over considerable periods in damp sand in a cool place.

OTHER FOODS

Various other small invertebrates can be raised with a degree of success as food for herptiles. Included are such forms as wax worms, flies, and fruit flies. Cockroaches make a fine food for many reptiles and amphibians, but most persons would find raising them for this purpose objectionable in the extreme. Be careful of feeding to

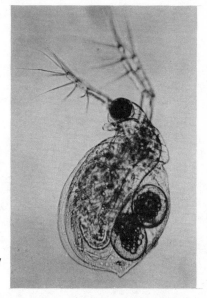

Daphnia and other small crustaceans are good as treats for salamanders, some frogs and some young water turtles. They are often difficult to culture, however. Photo by K. Lerch.

herptiles cockroaches captured in apartment houses and other places where measures for their control are being exercised. Some of the insects may be carrying poisonous substances.

Minnows of various kinds are among the best foods for small carnivorous turtles, crocodilians, certain lizards, and snakes, particularly garter and water types. One may seine them from ponds and streams, as well as saltwater inlets, but probably the easiest way to obtain a supply is from the dealer in live baits for fishermen. The latter often classify them according to type; such names as "shiners," "chubs," and "mummies" are common designations. The fish may be freshwater or saltwater kinds and will vary considerably in price. Saltwater types seem just as satisfactory as those from fresh water, from the standpoint of the vivarium keeper. They may be fed whole to animals like snakes and small monitors, or they may be finely chopped for feeding to turtles. They are so highly nutritious that it is possible to raise the commoner pet store turtles from infancy to adulthood on a diet of chopped fish alone. They can be kept frozen and used as needed during winter months when the live bait dealer may be out of them. Water snakes care little whether their fishes are alive or dead. Smelts, a fish-market item, will also prove useful in feeding herptiles. It is a good practice to rinse them thoroughly in fresh water before feeding them to terrarium animals.

Small fish, whether purchased goldfish or guppies, or collected minnows, are excellent food for many water turtles and water snakes. They will also be taken by some frogs and salamanders. Photo by L. E. Perkins.

An item used widely these days in the feeding of herptiles is canned dog food. Crocodilians, the larger aquatic salamanders, and many turtles will gustily devour spooned portions that are placed in their water. One of the better grades should be purchased and to each spoonful that is used a pinch of bone meal and vitamin concentrate may be added. On such a diet many captive herptiles will flourish for years. It is hardly necessary to list the many vegetables and fruits that are consumed by vegetarian herptiles. Specific food preferences are given in the accounts of the different species. In general, no vegetable substance that a reptile or amphibian will consume is likely to prove harmful to it. Some of the mushrooms which are very poisonous to humans are eaten by box turtles without ill effect. Tortoises and lizards may prefer vegetables which have been grated finely to those which are offered in larger pieces. With the former it is an easy matter to mix powdered vitamins and minerals when their use is indicated. Experiment with the foods bought for human consumption, both fresh and canned. Results will often surprise you—as when a favorite lizard that has been off its feed will perk up and show an interest in the white portion of a hard-boiled egg!

LACK OF APPETITE, FORCE-FEEDING

Herptiles occasionally stop eating for reasons that are not at once apparent. Species which are accustomed to hibernating may feed sparingly during the winter, even if kept warm. Prior to parturition, some reptiles fast and may continue to do so for a while after the eggs have been deposited or the young ones born. An incipient illness will cause a reptile or amphibian to stop eating. Severely chilled reptiles, in particular, often stop feeding before other symptoms of respiratory affliction are shown. Usually a snake stops eating for some days before shedding its skin. Some of the more nervous types of snakes will refuse to eat for long periods without apparent cause. A hiding box within their cage will often benefit such specimens. In fact, I think it is a good idea to provide all newly-captured reptiles with retreats in which they may feel themselves secure.

If all conditions of its environment seem correct and a herptile still shows no appetite after being tried with several kinds of natural foods over a period of a month or two, force-feeding may be considered, particularly if the specimen is a rare or exotic one. Force-feeding will not work well with amphibians or turtles; it can be

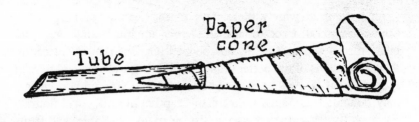

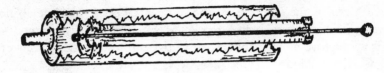

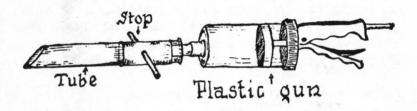

Various methods of force-feeding reptiles. From Smith, *Snakes as Pets*.

successfully used with crocodilians and the larger snakes and lizards. The force-feeding of a poisonous snake is not worth the risk involved.

In force-feeding a reptile an assistant should hold the animal still and in a straightened position while the operator administers the feeding. Slender and blunt-tipped forceps can be used to force some article of natural diet well into the throat of the reptile. The food should first have been lubricated with cod liver oil to facilitate its passage, at the same time lending additional nourishment to the meal. When the mouse, fish, or other item is pushed into the throat, the forceps should be carefully withdrawn. Often the meal will be swallowed at once, semi-voluntarily, one might say. In other cases,

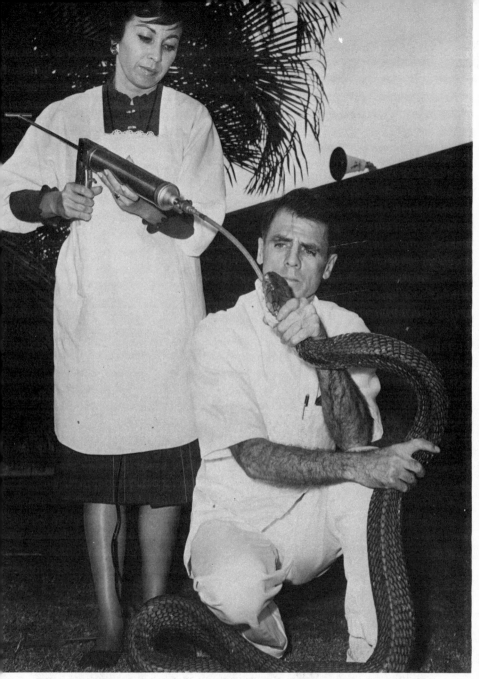

Force-feeding large or dangerous species, such as this king cobra, is a job which should be undertaken only by experts. Photo by B. Haast.

however, it will be necessary to hold the reptile's mouth closed and gently massage the throat area to induce passage of the meal. After force-feeding, or natural feeding, for that matter, a reptile should not be handled for a while. After one or more forced meals, many reptiles begin to show a natural interest in food.

Instead of using a whole animal in force-feeding, some herpetologists prepare a special mixture with the idea of getting as much concentrated nourishment as possible into the animal. The following is a sample preparation for the force-feeding of a six-foot snake:

3 tablespoons of finely ground liver or lean raw beef

1 raw egg

4 drops liquid multivitamin preparation

Enough milk or water to bring the mixture to the consistency of a thick liquid

To the above, an antibiotic medication may be added in appropriate dosage, if required. Depending on the size of the reptile being fed, one may use a caulking gun, battery hydrometer, or ordinary hypodermic syringe. A rubber or plastic tubing of suitable diameter can be attached. The tube is inserted into the animal's mouth and slowly forced well into the gullet. Then the food mixture is forced through the tube. The size of the meal should be determined by the size of the reptile. With small specimens, a single tablespoonful or less may be suitable. Between forcefeedings, natural food should be offered. When it is necessary to continue the forced administration of food over an extended period, it may be done at intervals of a week or ten days.

Snakes, particularly those which are not feeding voluntarily, should have a plentiful supply of fresh drinking water available at all times. Water which has been contaminated from any cause should be removed at once from the cage. The tendency of rodents to urinate or defecate in a dish of water is another strong point against their use in the live state as food for snakes. A reptile may die from the effect of drinking contaminated water. Snakes can seldom be induced to drink milk voluntarily.

The appearance of a reptile or amphibian will reflect the attention that has been given to its diet. In nature, few species feed entirely upon a single substance. Snakes are rather more specialized in their feeding habits than most herptiles. The majority appreciate and benefit from some variety in their diet.

XIV

Illnesses and Other Problems

If carefully managed, herptiles do not present their keeper with many health problems. Ill reptiles and amphibians are rarely found in the wild state; many of the afflictions of captive specimens are traceable to mishandling at time of capture or thereafter. It is an unfortunate circumstance that some of the more important ailments of captive herptiles are contagious and will quickly spread from one animal to another if they are in contact. If there is one most important rule that should be observed by those who keep herptiles, it is this: isolate all new specimens for at least two weeks to determine their true state of health before they are brought into contact with the rest of the collection. Herptiles which appear healthy will once in a while be carrying an incipient illness. New specimens should not only be caged apart from the others but also should be kept in another room, if possible, until they have started to feed regularly, appear to be free of parasites, and present a generally healthy appearance. The introduction of a sick animal can throw an entire collection of similar types into poor health almost at once.

The herptile illnesses with which we are familiar are not known to be directly transmissible to humans. In fact, they are often highly selective to the animals themselves. There are few diseases which can be transmitted from amphibians to reptiles or vice versa, red-leg being one of the exceptions, unfortunately common. It is much easier to use common sense precautions to prevent illness than to cure it after it has arisen. Once an illness takes hold, only rarely is there a spontaneous remission—generally the cure of the afflicted creature will rest with the know-how of its owner. It can be a

Well-meaning people sometimes buy a nearly-dead specimen with the hope of reviving it. It would probably be more humane to let such specimens die or to kill them instead of prolonging their agony. Photo by M. F. Roberts.

most gratifying experience to bring a really sick herptile back to a state of health. Like the breeding of herptiles and the successful rearing of their babies, the curing of a sick animal is demonstrative of an expertise of which the herptile enthusiast may be justifiably proud. The specific illnesses of reptiles and amphibians have been less studied than those of many other animals. They therefore present an excellent field for experimentation. It should be remembered that even among humans some of the most important cures for common illnesses have been discovered quite by accident and sometimes by persons not in the medical profession!

TURTLE DISORDERS

Tortoises, even those from relatively cool natural environments, often contract a pneumonia-like respiratory condition when they have been chilled. Aureomycin can be useful in combating this. The tablets or capsules sold for use on birds may be dissolved in the afflicted reptile's drinking water or sprinkled on its food. Some veterinarians are qualified to treat sick reptiles and will inject an antibiotic.

Swellings on or about a turtle's head, or elsewhere, may be found occasionally. A bot fly is often responsible for these; its technical name is *Sarcophaga cistudinis*. Each lump may contain several maggots which will eventually emerge and fall off their host, pupate, then become adult flies. The condition may be cleared up by incising the lump carefully with a sharp razor or scalpel, forcing out the contained matter, then swabbing the affected area with an antibiotic emulsion. This will prevent an infection, a condition which often occurs even when the maggots emerge naturally. Sometimes, if deeply burrowed into the tissues of the turtle, they will prove fatal. Our box turtles are common hosts of these parasitic flies.

Eye disorders in turtles often produce total blindness and are usually accompanied by loss of appetite and general debility. Gantrisin is a product of promise in the treatment of eye troubles. The affected animal's eyes should be swabbed with soft, dry cotton tips to remove as much pus as possible. Then a drop of Gantrisin is placed on each eye. The condition usually clears up quickly. Terramycin or any of the fungicide remedies sold for aquarium use may prove effective, applied in the same manner.

Fungus infections are among the most serious with which a turtle keeper may contend. Some fungus afflictions remain confined to a small area indefinitely. We might call them non-malignant. Other types will spread rapidly. Turtles with fungus should be isolated at once in an easily-cleaned container. A high state of general cleanliness must be maintained and the animal must have a means of leaving the water to dry out completely, from time to time, during the course of treatment. A 5% iodine solution may be applied to the affected area, but never around the eyes. This is allowed to dry before the turtle is permitted to enter water. The treatment may have to be continued daily over an extended period. Vinegar has long been considered a good fungus cure and a badly affected turtle may, as a last measure, be placed in a very strong bath—say 50% vinegar and 50% water, and allowed to remain for a couple of days. Some zoos use this method of treating fungus to the exclusion of all others. Table salt is useful in the prevention, as well as cure, of some types of fungus. About three ounces to each five gallons of water does well. An abundance of sunlight will prove very helpful.

Often a liquid vitamin compound like Poly-Vi-Sol will help promote healing of injured skin and shell areas. This can be applied freely, then covered with vaseline to prevent washing away. Cuts may be swabbed with a $2\frac{1}{2}\%$ solution of mercurochrome, which should be allowed to dry before placing the animal back in its aquarium. A timid turtle may stay withdrawn into its shell while one attempts to treat conditions of the head, neck, or limbs. Such a reluctant patient can be made to extend its head and limbs by a gentle rasping of its shell or by holding the reptile in an upside-down position.

A few kinds of turtles have a naturally soft shell. With most, however, a soft shell is indicative of poor health. An abundance of vitamins and sunshine are the requisites for treatment. It seldom occurs in turtles which are beyond babyhood. In far-advanced cases the shell may become as soft as tissue paper and in my experience has been incurable by any means. Baby turtles that are fed nutritiously and given adequate sunshine or a substitute do not develop soft shell. Fortunately, the practice of painting turtles' shells to increase the saleability of the little reptiles is no longer a common one. If a turtle is acquired in this condition, the paint must be removed as promptly and thoroughly as possible. This is best accomplished by careful chipping with a sharp knife. Paint removers should not be used.

RICKETS

Crocodilians and lizards are sometimes afflicted with rickets, a condition caused by a lack of vitamins and sunshine. In the slender-snouted crocodilians, the jaws may become grossly deformed. In lizards, a common manifestation of the condition is a paralysis of the rear legs or weakness of the jaws. The condition can be cleared up by providing a good diet and plenty of sunshine. Multivitamin preparations will prove useful; if natural sunlight is not available, the use of an ultraviolet lamp will help. Rachitic animals commonly do not survive their early years, but even if the condition is arrested with proper care, the bone deformities will remain.

SNAKE AILMENTS

Snakes sometimes have difficulty in the shedding of their skins. Normally, when this process is about to take place the reptile's eyes will turn bluish-white and its body will lose much of its natural luster. Gradually, the eyes become clear again and the snake is about ready to shed. If this does not take place within a week after the eyes have cleared, it is well to apply assistive measures. The best I know is to

An improper diet early in life caused the humped back in this caiman. Although the animal may live, it will always be deformed. Photo by M. F. Roberts.

place the snake in a damp linen bag for about twenty-four hours. The shedding starts at the snout and if the rostral shield of the reptile has been damaged it will often prevent an effective sloughing of the old epidermis. An assist with fine-tipped tweezers to get the process started will often help in such cases. A snake may sometimes fail to shed several times, then relinquish two, three, or more old skins at once. This is not usual, however. Most snakes rapidly decline when they are unable to slough. A snake in the best of condition will be able to shed its skin even when there is no rock or other rough surface in its cage. A complete skin-shedding without assistive measures is another indication of good health among serpents.

Probably most snakes would have little difficulty in shedding if they were supplied with a container of water in which to immerse themselves. With most species, however, a bathing tank will be used to the extent where the continual wetness gives rise to blisters of the skin. These blisters are believed to be fungoid in origin. They spread and ultimately cause the death of the reptile. Strangely, snakes which are semi-aquatic in the wild state are as susceptible as others to this

559

condition. Treatment consists of carefully slitting open the blisters, forcing out any liquid, and applying a solution of 50% ethyl alcohol. Sul-Met may be used instead of alcohol. Even the extremely aquatic snakes which spend nearly all of their time in the water can contract this condition. Its occurrence among them in an aquarium can be minimized by the use of water which is highly acid.

Respiratory illnesses among snakes seem to vary in their intensity, much as they do among humans. They run the gamut from simple colds which can be cleared up quickly by keeping the reptile warm and well fed to pneumonia-like conditions which are always fatal if broad-spectrum antibiotics are not applied. A snake with a cold will frequently cough or sneeze, much as a human does. When an infected snake is held in the hand, a peculiar rattling or disturbance of breathing will be noted. At the first sign of such trouble, isolate the affected reptile in a cage that is kept at a temperature of 80 degrees. Often the disturbance will clear up in a few days. More serious is the pneumonia-like condition brought about by severe chilling. A snake with this condition will refuse food and frequently raise its head and puff out its throat—an indication of labored breathing. The only cure for this condition is the injection of an antibiotic. It can reach epidemic proportions in a collection, either by direct contagion or the transference by mites, and can seldom be cured by home remedies. If the snake is highly valued, see a veterinarian. Otherwise, destroy the reptile when a puffing-out of the throat is first noted. If dissected, a snake with this pneumonia-like condition will show a bubbly congestion of the lung. I have had much personal experience with respiratory illnesses in snakes and can attest to the inadvisability of having reptiles shipped to cold climates by whatever means. Air transportation, even when the animals are picked up at the airport, does not solve the problem, for nearly always chills will occur. Perhaps the use of insulated shipping crates or styrofoam containers would minimize their incidence. If you insist upon receiving a snake in a cold climate during wintertime, keep the reptile isolated and in a warm situation until you are sure that it has not contracted a respiratory illness.

Mouth-rot is a disease about which much has been written. It occurs among snakes and lizards as well, but is perhaps most prevalent among the large constricting serpents. Its causes are obscure and among others have been suggested such things as long fasts, deprivation of drinking water, mouth injuries caused by biting or striking hard objects, and so forth. Most authorities agree that a bacillus is responsible for the onset of the condition. At first, the condition may manifest itself by only a small white spot in the mouth of the reptile. This rapidly enlarges and causes necrosis of tissues throughout the mouth. In extreme cases, the mouth itself may be much distorted by the masses of matter which develop. Mouthrot is very contagious, and a victim of it should be at once isolated from other reptiles. Fortunately, it is a curable condition. Any mild antiseptic, applied daily to the snake's mouth with a cotton swab, will prove beneficial; many severe cases have been cured in this way. Presently, the product of choice for the cure of mouth rot is Sul-Met, a $2\frac{1}{2}\%$ aqueous solution of sulfamethiazine, applied liberally and daily to the mouth of the affected reptile until the condition has cleared up. Snakes with mouth rot generally refuse to eat, and it may be necessary to force-feed them during the period of treatment. During this time loose teeth and decayed gum tissue should be removed from the reptile's mouth. Eventually, if the treatment is successful, the reptile will start eating of its own accord and may be considered cured when no evidences of oral lesions are present.

Ticks are a common malady of recently imported reptiles. The condition is easily cured and causes no lasting damage. Photo by G. Marcuse.

From the beginning of snake-keeping, parasites have been a problem. Serpents from the tropics and semi-tropics are often literally covered with parasites when captured. With such specimens they are often of little more discomfort than are fleas to a dog. But with captive snakes it is different. The smaller kinds spread quickly throughout a collection and may speedily prove fatal to the smaller snakes. There is evidence that they are able to transmit serious blood-poisoning among reptiles. Ticks are easily seen with the naked eye and can be pulled off the skin of a snake with tweezers. Perhaps a better method is to suffocate the parasite with a drop of oil or glycerin. It will then drop off and the danger of leaving its head imbedded in the skin of the reptile is eliminated. Mites pose a more difficult problem, for they are tiny and often multiply rapidly when conditions are favorable. A collector who has a large aggregation of specimens can be justifiably proud if no mites are present. To exclude them from a collection one must exercise the most meticulous quarantine measures for specimens coming in.

There are many ways of eliminating mites—nearly all are effective in some degree, but few seem to solve the problem completely once the pests have become firmly established. Snakes infested with mites may be placed in jars of water; this will drown most of the parasites in a short time. Those that crawl to the head may be eliminated with the application of olive oil. Cages must be thoroughly cleaned or a reinfestation of the reptiles will occur when they are placed back in them. Aquariums are easily cleaned with the use of ammonia and water. Wooden cages present more of a problem, for the tiny arach-nids may hide in crevices, and nothing short of a complete repainting of the cage will eliminate them. Gradually, specifics for the cure of reptile maladies are being developed. In the case of mites, Dri-Die is one of these, and perhaps the best. It has long been used to elimi-nate mites among birds and is readily available commercially. Unlike many parasite killers, it does not contain DDT and is harmless to reptiles. Every new snake should be placed in a bag which has been liberally dusted with Dri-Die and allowed to remain there for an hour or more. When a general infestation of cages has taken place, the powder may be sprinkled into all corners and crevices. Almost any flea powder will help to eliminate the mite problem, but none con-taining DDT should ever be used. Water containers should be re-moved from the cages of specimens being treated for mites, since some mite-killing powders are very injurious to reptiles if swallowed. The manufacturers of insecticides sometimes change the ingredients of their preparations without changing the brand names. For this reason always check the label of every container purchased. Dri-Die, for instance, sometimes comes premixed with insecticides.

One of the most important considerations to be taken into account in the construction or purchase of a snake cage is whether it has any interior surface which could cause bruises to the reptile's snout if rubbed against. Wire screening, unlacquered wooden surfaces, and corner constructions are a few of the cage conditions which may cause severe bruising to the snout of a reptile which is continuously nosing about its cage. Snakes seem unmindful of the injuries caused to their snouts and consequently the rostral shield is often destroyed. This is less likely to happen with boas and pythons and the poisonous snakes than with the more nervous colubrine serpents. Snout

Various medications for the treatment of common ailments of turtles maintained in captivity are available at pet shops. Additionally, preventives in the form of food additives, especially vitamin-fortified preparations, are available. There are, however, very few commercial remedies specifically compounded for the treatment of ailments of other herptiles.

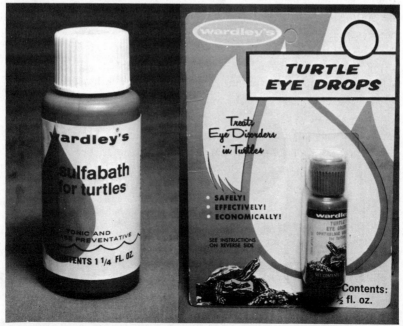

Turtles kept on concrete floors rub the plastron badly. This can be prevented by using smooth or soft flooring materials. Photo by M. F. Roberts.

destruction has been linked by some herpetologists to mouth rot. I have not seen evidence of this, but the destruction of a snake's snout may spoil an otherwise perfect specimen. Lizards can reproduce tails which have been lost, and among amphibians the replacement of lost limbs and other structures is commonplace. But I have not known of a snake to regrow the scalation on its snout when it had become damaged by abrasion against rough surfaces. Once a snake's snout has been damaged, if the nose shield has been completely destroyed, it will not be regenerated. A snake which has damaged its snout by probing can have the injured tissue swabbed with mercurochrome. It should be placed in a bag for several days to allow partial healing, then put into a cage where there is no possibility of further damage. The damaged area may heal over but will not assume its original coloration or surface tissue.

DISEASES OF AMPHIBIANS

Among amphibian diseases, the red-leg disease of frogs is one of the most commonly encountered. It is not only communicable from frog to frog, but may even be transmitted to salamanders and snakes. I have captured frogs which developed red-leg after a short period of confinement. The amphibian simply became badly bloated and a suffusion of red over the under-surface of the rear legs became apparent. These specimens ceased to feed but often lived for long periods. Their bodies appeared water-logged. Some references state that a protracted period of confinement at a low temperature will cure this ailment, but I have kept such specimens at temperatures of 40 to 50 degrees with no apparent improvement in their health. The disease is usually caused by the bacterium *Aeromonas hydrophila*, and should respond to antibiotics. The cure is so uncertain and the spread of the disease so swift that it is probably better to destroy infected specimens.

Fungus infections are not uncommon among captive newts and salamanders. Their development seems linked to overcrowding and temperatures which are too high. A lowered temperature will prolong the life of an amphibian which has fungus but, as with red leg, cure is evasive if possible at all and, once again, it is probably best to eliminate quickly diseased specimens, for fungus is very contagious. If one wishes to experiment in the matter of a cure, this had best be accomplished with the specimen in strict isolation from the rest of the collection. Some of the remedies used by aquarium fish hobbyists to combat fungus infections will benefit sick amphibians.

Unless every effort is made to prevent them, escapes are bound to occur in a collection of herptiles. Sometimes the animal is quickly recovered and seems none the worse for its experience. Rarely, its

With few exceptions, salamanders and frogs have very delicate skin, as shown by the exposed blood vessels of this newt. Desiccation leads to death; abrasion often leads to fungus. Photo by M. F. Roberts.

health may actually have improved during a period of freedom, even under seemingly adverse conditions. When an escaped specimen is caught, it is well to isolate it as one would a newly-received specimen, until it is certain that no ailment has been contracted. Amphibians particularly are likely to suffer skin abrasions after escape from their vivarium. These often form the planting ground for fungus infections.

When any reptile is placed in a bag, as during cage-cleaning, every care should be exercised to see that the animal does not fall from a table or chair. It is best to leave bagged animals on the floor, in a place where there is no danger that they will be stepped on. A fall from a height of several feet will almost never kill a reptile at once. However, spinal injuries are very frequent and these ultimately prove fatal. Often, after a fall, a specimen will stop eating and go into a slow decline. Reptiles have a delicate bone structure, and while the breaking or loss of the tail may be of little consequence, any injury, however slight, to the main portion of the spine will eventually cause the death of the animal.

Occasionally it may become necessary to destroy a sick animal. There are many ways of accomplishing this, for reptiles and amphibians are not as tenacious of life as commonly thought. I consider freezing the most humane method of killing a sick herptile. The specimen may be placed in a cloth or plastic bag and put into the household freezer. The struggles of animals so treated are half-hearted and quickly diminish, for cold takes an extremely rapid hold on reptiles particularly. Amphibians are a bit slower to succumb. It is doubtful whether any herptile suffers physically when this method of killing is employed.

SELECTED BIBLIOGRAPHY

Anyone interested in herptiles should belong to at least one of the international organizations devoted to their study. Each of these groups publishes a journal which contains articles of interest to all herpetologists, whether taxonomists, ecologists or behaviorists.

The quarterly journal *Copeia* is published by the American Society of Ichthyologists and Herpetologists and contains articles on both fish and herptiles (about half-and-half). Generally speaking, it has a larger content of long articles than the other journals. If interested in membership, apply to Dr. James A. Peters, Secretary, Division of Reptiles and Amphibians, U.S. National Museum, Washington, D.C. 20560.

The Herpetologists' League has published *Herpetologica* since 1936. This exclusively herpetological journal is smaller than *Copeia* and tends to have shorter articles; it is strong on taxonomic and North American subjects. Interested parties should contact Hobart E. Landreth, Okla. Zoo—U. of Okla., R.R. 1, Box 478, Oklahoma City, Okla. 73111.

The Society for the Study of Amphibians and Reptiles (formerly the Ohio Herpetological Society) publishes a journal which contains articles of varying size and content—both notes and monographic studies have been published. The Society also has a reprint program, providing reprints of major early herpetological work. Contact SSAR, c/o Zoology Department, Ohio State University, Athens, Ohio 45701.

Herpetologists with a strong interest in turtles and tortoises should consider joining the International Turtle and Tortoise Society. Their *Journal* contains articles of both a popular and semi-technical nature and is concerned principally with care of captive animals and conservation of wild populations. Prospective members should write to International Turtle and Tortoise Society, P.O. Box 45555, Los Angeles, Calif. 90045.

Two books of importance to keepers of amphibians and reptiles are mentioned here to emphasize their value to terrarium keepers. One is John Van Denburgh's *Reptiles of Western North America* (California Academy of Science, 1922). Although this two-volume work is somewhat outdated taxonomically, it still contains a great deal of useful description of western lizards and snakes. The photographs are clear and very useful. The book is usually easily available from second-hand book dealers.

The popular *Field Guide to Reptiles and Amphibians* (of eastern North America) by Conant now has a western companion. It is Robert Stebbins' *Field Guide to Western Reptiles and Amphibians* (Houghton Mifflin, 1966). This small volume contains information on all the salamanders, frogs, toads, turtles, lizards and snakes found west of the Great Plains area. The plates are beautifully done, and the text contains a great deal of information on natural history as well as identification. The two field guides should be in the library of every keeper of herptiles.

Articles of interest to amateur herpetologists also appear occasionally in other journals, such as *The American Midland Naturalist* and *Southwestern Naturalist*. Most college libraries receive most or all of the above journals, so they should be available to interested parties.

The following is a list of some of the more significant English-language works on reptiles and amphibians. No strictly juvenile books have been included, nor have any purely technical treatises. The books listed vary in depth of their treatment of the subject matter; all are thoroughly readable and useful to students at every level of learning. Many older books, particularly those of that master writer-herpetologist, Raymond L. Ditmars, have much to offer but are now obsolete in some ways. Some of the books are no longer in print but may be available in libraries or used book stores.

Allen, E. Ross and Wilfred T. Neill, 1950. *Keep them alive.* Ross Allen's Reptile Institute, Silver Springs, Florida.

Bellairs, Angus de'A., 1957. *Reptiles.* Anchor Press, Ltd., Tiptree, Essex, England.

Bishop, Sherman C., 1943 (and later reprints). *Handbook of salamanders of the U.S. and Canada.* Comstock Publishing Co., Ithaca, N.Y.

Breen, John F., 1967. *Reptiles and amphibians in your home.* T.F.H. Publications, Inc., Neptune City, N.J.

Carr, Archie, 1952. *Handbook of turtles.* Cornell University Press, Ithaca, N.Y.

Clyne, Densey, 1969. *Australian frogs.* Periwinkle Books, Lansdowne Press, Melbourne, Australia.

Cochran, Doris M., 1961. *Living amphibians of the world.* Doubleday & Co., Inc., Garden City, N.Y.

Cogger, Harold, 1967. *Australian reptiles in colour.* East-West Center Press, Honolulu, Hawaii.

Conant, Roger, 1958. *A field guide to reptiles and amphibians of the U.S. and Canada east of the 100th meridian.* Houghton Mifflin Co., Boston, Mass.

Curran, C. H. and Carl Kauffeld, 1937. *Snakes and their ways.* Harper Brothers, N.Y., N.Y.

Ditmars, Raymond L., 1908 (and later editions). *The reptile book.* Doubleday & Co., Inc., Garden City, N.Y.

——, 1931 (and later editions). *Snakes of the world.* Macmillan Co., N.Y., N.Y.

Fitzsimons, V. F. M., 1962. *Snakes of southern Africa.* Macdonald & Co., Ltd., London, England.

Isemonger, R. M., 1962. *Snakes of Africa.* Thos. Nelson & Sons, Johannesburg, South Africa.

Kauffeld, Carl, 1957. *Snakes and snake hunting.* Hanover House, Garden City, N.Y.

Klauber, L. M., 1956. *Rattlesnakes.* 2 vols. University of California Press, Berkeley, California.

Oliver, James A., 1955. *The natural history of North American amphibians and reptiles.* D. van Nostrand Co., Inc., Princeton, N.J.

Pope, Clifford H., 1939. *Turtles of the United States and Canada.* Alfred A. Knopf, N.Y., N.Y.

——, 1955. *The reptile world.* Alfred A. Knopf, N.Y., N.Y.

——, 1961. *Giant snakes.* Alfred A. Knopf, N.Y., N.Y.

Pritchard, Peter C. H., 1967. *Turtles of the world.* T.F.H. Publications, Inc., Neptune City, N.J.

Rose, Walter, 1950. *The reptiles and amphibians of southern Africa.* Maskew Miller, Ltd., Cape Town, Republic of South Africa.

Schmidt, Karl P. and Robert F. Inger, 1957. *Living reptiles of the world*. Hanover House, Garden City, N.Y.

Smith, Hobart M., 1946. *Handbook of lizards*. Comstock Publishing Co., Ithaca, N.Y.

——, 1965. *Snakes as pets*. T.F.H. Publications, Inc., Neptune City, N.J.

Stebbins, Robert C., 1954. *Amphibians and reptiles of western North America*. McGraw-Hill Book Co., Inc., N.Y., N.Y.

Worrell, Eric, 1963. *Reptiles of Australia*. Angus & Robertson, Ltd., Sidney, Australia.

Wright, A. H. and A. A. Wright, 1949. *Handbook of frogs and toads*. Comstock Publishing Co., Ithaca, N.Y.

——, 1957. *Handbook of snakes of the United States and Canada*. 2 vols. Cornell University Press, Ithaca, N.Y.

Zim, H. S. and H. M. Smith, 1953. *Reptiles and amphibians: A guide to familiar American species*. Simon & Schuster, N.Y., N.Y.

INDEX